EMDR Therapy and Adjunct Approaches
With Children

Ana M. Gomez, MC, LPC is a psychotherapist in private practice, a researcher, and a national and international speaker. She has presented extensively nationally and internationally, on the use of EMDR therapy and other adjunct approaches with children and adolescents with complex trauma, attachment injuries, and dissociation. She received her professional degree in psychology with a specialization in clinical psychology from the Catholic University of Colombia, and her master's degree in counseling psychology from Arizona State University. Ana has served as a practicum supervisor at the Educational Psychology Department at Northern Arizona University. She was the recipient of the 2011 distinguished service award from the Arizona Association for Play Therapy. She is a facilitator for the EMDR Institute, a specialty presenter on EMDR therapy with children, and an EMDR-HAP trainer. Ana is the author of several book chapters on the use of EMDR therapy with children, *The Thoughts Kit for Kids* and *Dark, Bad Day…Go Away*, a book for children about trauma and EMDR, which has been translated into four languages.

EMDR Therapy and Adjunct Approaches With Children

Complex Trauma, Attachment, and Dissociation

Ana M. Gomez, MC, LPC

SPRINGER PUBLISHING COMPANY
NEW YORK

Springer Publishing Company, LLC
11 West 42nd Street
New York, NY 10036
www.springerpub.com

Acquisitions Editor: Sheri W. Sussman
Production Editor: Joseph Stubenrauch
Composition: Newgen Imaging

ISBN: 978–0-8261–0697-1
E-book ISBN: 978–0-8261–0698-8

14 15/ 5

The author and the publisher of this Work have made every effort to use sources believed to be reliable to provide information that is accurate and compatible with the standards generally accepted at the time of publication. The author and publisher shall not be liable for any special, consequential, or exemplary damages resulting, in whole or in part, from the readers' use of, or reliance on, the information contained in this book. The publisher has no responsibility for the persistence or accuracy of URLs for external or third-party Internet Web sites referred to in this publication and does not guarantee that any content on such Web sites is, or will remain, accurate or appropriate.

Library of Congress Cataloging-in-Publication Data

Gomez, Ana M.
  EMDR therapy and adjunct approaches with children : complex trauma, attachment, and dissociation / Ana M. Gomez.
     p. ; cm.
  Includes bibliographical references and index.
  ISBN 978-0-8261-0697-1—ISBN 978-0-8261-0698-8 (e-book)
  I. Title.
  [DNLM: 1. Child. 2. Eye Movement Desensitization Reprocessing—methods. 3. Dissociative Disorders—therapy. 4. Object Attachment. 5. Stress, Psychological—therapy. WS 350.6]

  618.92'8523—dc23

                                                                                        2012006987

Printed in the United States of America by Gasch Printing

To my mother Elizabeth and my father Pedro
And to my husband and life partner Jim

Contents

Contributors

Emily Jernberg, PhD, a psychologist practicing in Ann Arbor and Rochester, MI, has provided treatment for over two decades and supervises other therapists. She has extensively presented both in the United States and abroad and published, most often on the subjects of adoption, attachment, and Theraplay. Emily serves on the advisory board of the Theraplay Institute. She is the daughter of the late Ann M. Jernberg, PhD, creator of Theraplay and founder of the Theraplay Institute (Chicago, IL).

Pamela K. Krause, LCSW, is a clinical social worker and a senior trainer for the Center for Self Leadership teaching the Internal Family Systems model of therapy. She has a subspecialty in adapting the IFS model for use in younger children. Pamela has a private practice near Harrisburg, PA. In addition, she has been on the Board of Directors of several nonprofit organizations where she helped develop programs for at-risk adolescents.

Pat Ogden, PhD, is a pioneer in somatic psychology and the founder/director of the Sensorimotor Psychotherapy Institute, an internationally recognized school specializing in somatic–cognitive approaches for the treatment of posttraumatic stress disorder and attachment disturbances. She is a clinician, consultant, international lecturer and trainer, and first author of *Trauma and the Body: A Sensorimotor Approach to Psychotherapy* and is currently working on her second book, *The Body as Resource: Sensorimotor Interventions for the Treatment of Trauma*.

Frances S. Waters, LMSW, DCSW, LMFT, is an internationally recognized trainer, consultant, filmmaker, and clinician in the area of childhood trauma and dissociation. She is the past president of the International Society for the Study of Trauma & Dissociation, contributing editor of *The Journal of Child & Adolescent Trauma*, and serves on the advisory board of the Leadership Council on Child Abuse & Interpersonal Violence.

Foreword

It is an honor to be invited to write the Foreword for this book by Ana Gomez, who is well known to the eye movement desensitization and reprocessing (EMDR) community for her many contributions, including her dramatic DVD demonstrating EMDR treatment with a young client, her dynamic advanced EMDR workshops, and her presentations at conferences around the world. Within the pages of this book, Gomez artfully brings together her many years of lecturing, clinical experience, EMDR skills, and creative strategies. The primary intention of this book is to inform the reader about developmentally appropriate strategies and protocols to assist in treating children with complex trauma, including dissociative symptoms, attachment issues, and inappropriate social behaviors. However, it is my belief that the contents are relevant to the understanding and implementation of EMDR with clients of all ages and diverse backgrounds.

The relational aspect is a key ingredient when providing treatment to children and families; however, sometimes it can be extremely challenging to create a therapeutically positive and trusting relationship with highly reactive and traumatized children. Most often, children do not elect to be in therapy and are resistant to input from teachers, parents, principals, therapists, and so on. According to Perry, "Recognizing the power of relationships and relational cues is essential to effective therapeutic work and, indeed, to effective parenting, caregiving, teaching, and just about any other human endeavor" (Perry & Szalavitz, 2006). Most child therapists are adept at establishing rapport with children; however, the standardized EMDR treatment protocols require specific modifications when applied to young clients. How does the clinician explain EMDR to a child and the caregiver and get consensus from both to engage in the process? This book is filled with valuable resources for establishing a therapeutic bond and helping children and their caregivers to build a stable and trusting relationship not only with the therapist but also with one another. In addition, joyful, concrete, "hands-on" activities are included to engage even the most oppositional child and naïve parent. Most importantly, client-centered treatment is emphasized, and Gomez is sensitive to and mindful of the cultural background, religious beliefs, and values of her clients.

Knowing how to prepare and when a client is ready for EMDR treatment can be a challenge and significantly more difficult when working with highly traumatized children and adolescents. In Chapter 3, "Phase Two: Preparation," Gomez introduces the work of Perry, Panksepp, Porges, Siegel, and Schore as foundational theories of brain physiology to support the comprehensive treatment protocols she has developed to prepare the avoidant, dysregulated child and to give caregivers opportunities to positively interact with their children. Throughout the book, the importance of attunement, emotional resonance, and mindfulness is underscored. According to Dworkin (2005), "The concept of attunement embodies both alignment and resonance. Attunement occurs when one person tunes in to another; that is, a person nonverbally perceives and feels the other's experience. When this occurs, the other person feels 'felt.' Attunement is very close to empathy. It creates an attachment bond between the two people involved. In practice, attunement is what happens when the clinician really 'gets' what the client is feeling in the moment and the client realizes it. Attunement is a requirement for successful EMDR" (Dworkin, 2005). To explain the steps of the EMDR methodology, to prepare the child for possible negative affect, and to help the child construct a safe place while simultaneously establishing attunement, developmentally appropriate metaphors and interactive activities are described in detail and illustrated with heartwarming case examples.

Often I have encountered clinicians who are confounded by how to introduce and implement EMDR treatment with children and adolescents. Some clinicians feel that many of the steps of the standard protocol should be eliminated with the rationale that children do not have the cognitive ability to engage in the full process. My experience applying EMDR with children is that they can do all the steps successfully if modifications appropriate to the child's age and developmental level are incorporated. This book methodically takes the reader through the standard EMDR protocol inclusive of all eight phases, engaging the child's participation in each phase through playful activities and creative, often, nonverbal exercises. In addition, Gomez adheres to the adaptive information processing (AIP) model as the theoretical basis for case conceptualization and treatment planning with young clients. The AIP model as described by Shapiro (2001), "Regards most pathologies as derived from earlier life experiences that set in motion a continued pattern of affect, behavior, cognitions, and consequent identity structures. The pathological structure is inherent within the static, insufficiently processed information stored at the time of the disturbing event. In a wide variety of cases... pathology is viewed as configured by the impact of earlier experiences that are held in the nervous system in state-specific form" (Shapiro, 2001). Gomez embraces Shapiro's theory by introducing the concept of AIP and the basics of the EMDR steps to children through concrete language and innovative, nonthreatening activities that appeal to their imagination, cognitive ability, and right-brain functioning while simultaneously building a trusting relationship. Throughout the book, employing playfulness and creating safety are the underlining elements utilized to help children understand and become involved in the process of healing.

Bravos to those practitioners who are compassionate about treating children and have the placidity to work with highly dysfunctional families. The child specialists I have met over the years are creative, inventive, and enthusiastic individuals. Most of these clinicians are eclectic in their approach to guiding children and family members to positive outcomes and stable relationships, relying on a myriad of techniques and methodologies. In this book, Gomez ingeniously illustrates how she builds rapport and engages family members in the therapeutic process through poignant case examples; in addition, she describes in detail how she integrates music, art, sandtray, and play therapies with EMDR as well as the therapeutic approaches of sensorimotor psychotherapy, theraplay, and internal family systems (see Chapters 11–13).

"Traumatized children tend to have overactive stress responses and... these can make them aggressive, impulsive, and needy. These children are difficult, they are easy to upset and hard to calm, they may overreact to the slightest novelty or change, and they often don't know how to think before they act. Before they can make any kind of lasting change at all in their behavior, they need to feel safe and loved. Troubled children are in some kind of pain—and pain makes people irritable, anxious, and aggressive. Only patient, loving, consistent care works; there are no short-term miracle cures" (Perry & Szalavitz, 2006). Honoring the pain of the child while helping him or her feel accomplished and normalized (see Chapter 9) is one of the important tenets of this book. According to Gomez, this goal can be accomplished through "the use of play—the natural language of children." She employs laughter, colorful metaphors, and age-appropriate cognitive interweaves, musical instruments, fine and large muscle activities, and humor to help children and their caregivers explore alternative behaviors and build relationships based on love, safety, and trust.

"A child's sense of self is engendered by accumulated interactions with his parents and provides the core filter which other life experiences are viewed. It is vital to remember that interpersonal interactions are the product of inner worlds converging….The problematic relationship is simply another symptom of a wounded inner world" (Shapiro, Kaslow, & Maxfield, 2007). As much as the title of this book indicates, the contents are specific to the integration of EMDR with children, I encourage all therapists who encounter clients with problematic relationships, complex trauma, attachment issues, and dissociative symptoms to read *EMDR Therapy and Adjunct Approaches With Children: Complex Trauma, Attachment, and Dissociation*. Many of the activities and protocols can be adapted to the adult perspective and give the adult client an opportunity to tap into his playful and creative right brain. Reading this book is a pleasant, effortless journey well worth the time.

Robbie Dunton, MS
EMDR Institute Coordinator

Preface

This book was inspired by the journey of the many children, adolescents, and adults who have allowed me to witness their pain, courage, and strength, as well as the incredible moments of healing they experienced during our therapeutic work. Many parts of this book also contain elements of my own journey to find integration and completeness within myself. Through my own therapeutic work with eye movement desensitization and reprocessing (EMDR) and other adjunct approaches, as I visit the many corners of myself, I have been able to mindfully experience how healing takes place within. Dr. Francine Shapiro has helped us understand that what keeps us apart are the wounds that remain written in memory and that continue to influence how we write the stories of our present and future. The belief of not being enough, the lack of self-acceptance, the shame, and the unsettled pain perpetuate for many; an existence of judgment, separateness, and suffering that is then passed on to the new generations.

Through the many years of clinical work with severely traumatized individuals, I have been moved and inspired by their stories to investigate, try, and even create new ways to assist them and be an active participant of their healing journeys through the use of EMDR therapy and other adjunct approaches. The main goal of this book is to provide tangible and doable strategies that make EMDR therapy developmentally appropriate and effective with children who hold the greatest wounds, and as a result, their treatment requires greater levels of complexity. It contains useful, practical, and in-depth information about the use of EMDR therapy with children with complex trauma, which is an area that has not been addressed before in the EMDR literature. This book is not intended to provide information on the basic EMDR procedures, but instead to provide to the EMDR clinician advanced tools to treat children with complex trauma, attachment wounds, and dissociative tendencies.

It is my belief and clinical experience that EMDR therapy is best used when the EMDR clinician possesses excellent knowledge of the procedures and technical aspects of EMDR therapy, and at the same time, the EMDR clinician has done his or her own therapeutic work to achieve some level of integration and assimilation of his or her own memory systems. When the first aspect is present, in the absence of the second, we may have good EMDR technicians who are able to follow procedures, but have difficulty resonating and attuning with their clients at a deeper, more profound level. The capacity to mentalize (Fonagy & Target, 1997) and the skills that are part of mindsight (Siegel, 2010), are not only important for parents and caregivers but also for clinicians working with wounded children. Without resolution and integration of our own maladaptive memory systems, our capacity to "hold the other in mind" (Fonagy & Target, 1997) may be limited. On the other hand, the second aspect without the first may result in EMDR clinicians that, despite their capacity to mentalize, resonate, and attune with their clients, lack the skills to use EMDR theory and procedures appropriately and effectively. All of these aspects may affect the overall therapeutic gains that clients with complex trauma histories may achieve during EMDR therapy.

Despite the current findings in the field of neuroscience that have enlightened our understanding of human nature and the functioning of the brain and nervous system, clinicians and practitioners still lack the "how to" to apply these concepts in their clinical practices. This book is written with the goal in mind of offering a "step-by-step" and a "how-to" approach to clinicians working with children with complex trauma. Throughout the book, the eight phases of EMDR therapy are thoroughly explored, offering in each a rich and wide variety of techniques and strategies that are clear, tangible, concrete, and creative for difficult-to-treat children.

This book provides the theoretical framework and the conceptual underpinnings for case conceptualization and EMDR clinical practice for children with dysregulation of the affective system. It covers key elements to develop case conceptualization skills and treatment plans based on the adaptive information processing (AIP) model. A broader perspective is presented by integrating concepts from attachment theory, affect regulation theory, affective neuroscience, and interpersonal neurobiology. These concepts and theories not only support the AIP model, but they expand clinicians' understanding and effectiveness when working with dissociative, insecurely attached, and dysregulated children.

This book presents aspects of our current understanding of how our biological apparatus is orchestrated, how its appropriate development is thwarted when early, chronic, and pervasive trauma and adversity are present in our lives, and how healing can be promoted through the use of EMDR therapy. In addition, it provides a practical guide to the use of EMDR within a systemic framework. It illustrates how EMDR therapy can be used to help caregivers develop psychobiological attunement and synchrony as well as to enhance their mentalizing capacities.

Many cases are presented throughout the book to illustrate the appropriate use of the strategies offered in this volume. However , it is important to highlight that they each embody a compilation of the many clients I have treated over the years and for the most part, represent hypothetical cases.

Another important goal of this book is to bring strategies from other therapeutic approaches, such as play therapy, sandtray therapy, Sensorimotor Psychotherapy, Theraplay, and Internal Family Systems (IFS) into a comprehensive EMDR treatment, while maintaining appropriate adherence to the AIP model and EMDR methodology. This is done with the goal of enriching the work that often times is necessary with complexly traumatized children and their families.

The strategies presented in this book have been effective in my clinical practice. I have received numerous anecdotal reports from the many clinicians who have attended my trainings and presentations and who have used such strategies effectively, obtaining very positive results in their own agencies and practices. In addition, research therapists participating in an ongoing study using EMDR therapy with children and adolescents suffering from depression have also been able to utilize these techniques successfully and efficaciously. This book offers all EMDR clinicians working with difficult to treat clients creative tools and strategies that can facilitate their healing process.

Acknowledgments

I would like to honor and recognize all the people who have inspired me and supported me through the journey of writing this book. I will begin with all the children and their families who have crossed my path as my clients. Their wisdom, strength, and endurance have inspired me in so many ways to create new paths, to walk through existing ones, and to be part of their life's adventures and passages.

I want to express a deep gratitude to Francine Shapiro, who has given us the gift of EMDR therapy and who has been a mentor throughout the process of writing this book. Thank you for the numerous hours you dedicated to reading this book and providing expert advice and guidance. I want to express my incredible appreciation to Robbie Dunton for her continued loving professional and personal support. It has been a great gift to have you in my life. I want to thank all of the dear friends from the EMDR community who believed in me and gave me their caring support from the beginning of my work with EMDR therapy: Karen Forte, John Hartung, Farnsworth Lobenstine, Sue Evans, Karen Alter-Reid, Robin Gibbs, Donald de Graffenried, Barbara Parrett, Jocelyn Shiromoto, Esly Carvalho in Brazil, Carmen Casado Ducos in Chile, Santiago Jacome in Ecuador, and Kathleen Reay and Tara Morrison in Canada. Thanks to Michael Scheeringa from Tulane University, who gave me his unconditional support in doing research on the effectiveness of EMDR therapy for children with depression. The knowledge I have acquired through this process has been invaluable for this book.

Many thanks to the wonderful clinicians who contributed to my book: Frances Waters, for your incredible knowledge in the work with dissociative children and a wonderful chapter on this subject. Thanks to Emily Jernberg for the many gifts you bring to clinicians working with children and especially for all the beautiful work you put into the chapter on EMDR therapy and Theraplay. Thanks to Pamela Krause for the many hours you dedicated to stimulating my mind, so I could arrive at a greater understanding of IFS and for your incredible contributions as we wrote a truly amazing chapter on EMDR therapy and IFS psychotherapy. Thanks to Pat Ogden for all the work you put into coauthoring an inspiring chapter on the integration of EMDR therapy and Sensorimotor Psychotherapy with children.

I could not have completed this book without the incredible support of my editors, Sheri Sussman and Joseph Stubenrauch. It was a delight to work with you. Thank you for your expert advice and for being the arm and hand that held me as I embraced the difficult task of writing this book.

Special thanks to all the neuroscientists that provided expert advice on various parts of chapter one: Jaak Panksepp, Stephen Porges, and Onno van der Hart. I also would like to highlight the significant influence my trainings with Daniel Siegel have had in my clinical work and my personal life.

Thanks to Richard Schwartz for the feedback offered on the integration of IFS strategies into EMDR therapy. Thanks to Phyllis Booth, David Myrow, and Sandra Lindaman, for the expert advice on the integration of Theraplay strategies into EMDR therapy.

Finally, I want to convey a deep sense of gratitude to my husband and life partner Jim Mason who has truly been the wind beneath my wings. Thank you for walking with me through light and darkness and through highs and lows and for your sensible advice as I wrote this book. Thank you for pre-editing the book and guiding me with your wisdom that goes beyond intellectual knowledge. To my beautiful Colombian family, especially my mother Elizabeth and my sister Oderay for your unconditional love, which I have been so honored to receive throughout my life and have held me high, especially as I embrace new challenges. In memory of my father Pedro for your hard work, love, and for giving me all you were, and all you had.

To all the clinicians who have attended my trainings and presentations in more than 40 cities in 10 countries, who have stimulated my mind with questions and stories of your own journeys in the clinical use of EMDR therapy. You all have been a true inspiration. To my beautiful furry companions that have given me through the years so much unconditional love: Churrusco, Blaze, Nugget, Amber, and Lady. Finally, I want to express a deep appreciation to my "helpers," whose wise and loving presence was felt in every word I wrote in this book.

EMDR Therapy, the Adaptive Information Processing Model, and Complex Trauma

*I*t has been a journey of over 20 years since Dr. Francine Shapiro developed what is now known as eye movement desensitization and reprocessing (EMDR) therapy. EMDR therapy is now validated as an evidence-based approach and included in the Substance Abuse and Mental Health Services Administration's National Registry of Evidence-based Programs and Practices. In addition, EMDR therapy has been independently designated as a psychotherapy approach (Prochaska & Nocross, 2010), and has been validated by approximately 20 randomized controlled clinical trials (see www.emdrhap.org/emdr_info/researchandresources.php). Results of recent meta-analyses show EMDR as an effective and efficacious treatment for posttraumatic stress disorder (PTSD) in adults (Bisson & Andrew, 2007; Bradley, Greene, Russ, Dutra, & Westen, 2005; Seidler & Wagner, 2006) and children (Rodenburg, Benjamin, de Roos, Meijer, & Stams, 2009). Approximately seven controlled randomized studies (e.g., Ahmad, Larsson, & Sundelin-Wahlsten, 2007; Jaberghaderi, Greenwald, Rubin, Dolatabadim, & Zand, 2004; Kemp, Drummond, & McDermott, 2010), and ten non-randomized studies with children found that EMDR therapy is effective in reducing PTSD symptoms (e.g., Fernandez, 2007; Hensel, 2009; Ribchester, Yule, & Duncan, 2010; Wadaa, Zaharim, & Alqashan, 2010), and behavioral and self-esteem problems (Soberman, Greenwald, & Rule, 2002; Wanders, Serra, & de Jongh, 2008). In a recent randomized study conducted by de Roos et al. (2011), EMDR treatment was found to be as effective as CBT with children experiencing disaster-related posttraumatic stress symptoms. In addition, the California Evidence-Based Clearinghouse for Child Welfare has now accepted EMDR therapy as an evidence-based approach for children. These are promising results that bring hope to the millions of children suffering as a result of having experienced trauma and adversity in their lives. This book is dedicated to the treatment of children with early, chronic and complex trauma.

DEFINING COMPLEX TRAUMA

Childhood complex trauma refers to the exposure of early chronic and multiple traumatic events. Oftentimes, these injuries and traumas are inflicted within the parent-child or adult-child relationship. As a result, the child is placed in an inescapable situation *on what the person's survival depends on* is the same person inflicting the pain. Abuse, neglect, family violence, traumatic loss and war experienced when important neurobiological structures are developing can have long lasting and detrimental effects in how children develop. According to Ford and Courtois (2009), complex trauma results from the exposure to repetitive and prolonged severe stressors that involve harm or abandonment by caregivers, and that occur at critical *developmentally* stages when fundamental biological systems are developing. As a result of exposure to complex trauma, children may exhibit dysfunctional regulatory mechanisms, insecure attachment, dissociative symptoms, compromised sense of self, behavioral problems, and impaired cognitive and social functioning among others.

According to Cozolino (2006), early interpersonal trauma in the form of emotional and physical abuse, sexual abuse, and neglect shape the structure and functioning of the brain in ways that negatively affect all stages of social, emotional and intellectual development. Early trauma, especially at the hands of caretakers, begins a cascade of effects that result in a complex posttraumatic reaction. (p. 230)

CHILDHOOD COMPLEX TRAUMA AND THE ADAPTIVE INFORMATION PROCESSING MODEL

The adaptive information processing (AIP) model constitutes the central piece and foundation of EMDR therapy (Shapiro, 2001). As EMDR therapy evolves, so is our understanding of the AIP model. The inclusion of principles and findings from the Polyvagal Theory (Porges, 2011), affective neuroscience (Panksepp, 1998, 2009), attachment theory (Bowlby, 1973, 1980; Ainsworth, 1978; Main, 1995; Liotti, 1992, 2006), interpersonal neurobiology (IPNB) (Siegel, 1999, 2010) and the structural dissociation theory (van der Hart, Nijenhuis, & Steele, 2006), can greatly support and expand our understanding of the AIP model and complex trauma.

According to the AIP model, a central aspect of health and pathology is memory (Shapiro, 1995, 2001). When children encounter maltreatment, abandonment, rejection, neglect and abuse, these experiences leave their footprints in the brain in the form of neural nets. Since important structures in charge of integrating and adaptively binding information and locating it in time and space, such as the hippocampus, do not mature until the age of 18 to 24 months (Siegel, 1999), this information is encoded in the young developing brain, following a path into implicit nonconscious, nonverbal memory. As a result, early attachment traumas and injuries will remain below awareness while still shaping how these children respond to present environmental demands. According to Shapiro (2001), the present symptoms are manifestations of past experiences encoded implicitly in the brain. The implicit encoding transpired either because these experiences occurred prior to the development of brain structures capable of moving information into explicit autobiographical memory, or because trauma and its accompanying dysregulated arousal inhibited the appropriate functioning of such structures. (Cozolino, 2011; Siegel, 1999; van der Kolk, 1999)

Along the same lines, Cozolino (2011) states: If everything we experience is represented by instantiations within neural networks, then by definition, psychopathology of all kinds—from the mildest neurotic symptoms to the most severe psychosis—must be represented within and among neural networks.... psychopathology would be a reflection of suboptimal development, integration, and coordination of neural networks. (p. 24)

Focal points in EMDR therapy are the memory network and the experiential contributors to pathology (Shapiro, 1995/2001). So far, research has shown the effectiveness of EMDR therapy when working with the memories of trauma and adversity and their neurobiological footprints. However, organic deficits are not considered to be the target of EMDR therapy, only its potential experiential legacy and sequelae.

As stated before, memory systems containing representations of the self and other in the child's brain are formed and reinforced by patterns of parent-child interaction. The caregiving system, and with it, the parent's internal working models, are closely and intimately connected to the developing attachment system of the infant. The parent already holds complex and intricate memory systems containing representation of the self and other that will closely influence how they respond to the demands and needs of the infant. Later on, once the child has also developed memory networks containing mental representations of the self and the parent, a mutual activation and reinforcement of memory systems takes place.

John, a 7-year-old boy, was brought to therapy by his mother who complained of John's oppositional and aggressive behaviors. After a thorough exploration of John's history and specific family dynamics, the mother reported feeling frustrated and desperate when John was acting out. She also identified "I am a bad mother" and "I am not valuable" as her negative beliefs. In addition, she identified a strong pressure on her chest and difficulty breathing when she was triggered by her child's behaviors. The mother stated that she either yelled or at times completely detached from John when he was exhibiting the activating behaviors. When the mother engaged in a float back, she connected with similar feelings, thoughts and bodily states she experienced in her past romantic relationships where she experienced emotional and verbal abuse at the hands of her partners. She also recalled images of herself crying as she looked from the window at her mother leaving. She remembered a mother that was socially active, but emotionally absent from home, a mother that never gave any physical or verbal affection to her. A closer look at John's responses yielded information about his cognitive, emotional and somatic responses as well. John stated that he felt angry, sad and very lonely after coming home from school and feeling like he had failed and was a bad kid for not performing well at school. When his mother asked him to clean up his room, he responded with anger and opposition, and as his mother yelled or left the room, leaving him to feel emotionally abandoned, a greater sense of loneliness took place. John identified the negative belief "there is nothing good about me," a sense of restlessness (jumpy inside) and a strong desire to run or hit someone or something once his mother yelled or left his room. These interactions happened on a daily basis, however, moments of connection and love where very much absent. This case clearly illustrates the mutual activation of memory systems containing maladaptive material and negative representations of the self and other that take place in the child as well as the parent. (See Figures 1.1 and 1.2). The activation of the parent's memory networks containing unresolved trauma and loss inhibited her capacity to "hold the child's mind in mind" (Fonagy & Target, 1997), and respond contingently to the needs of the child. These dysregulated maladaptive interactions preserve and enhance maladaptive memory systems. The intergenerational transmission of unintegrated, unassimilated and unresolved information encoded in memory perpetuates the development of pathology, trauma, and human suffering.

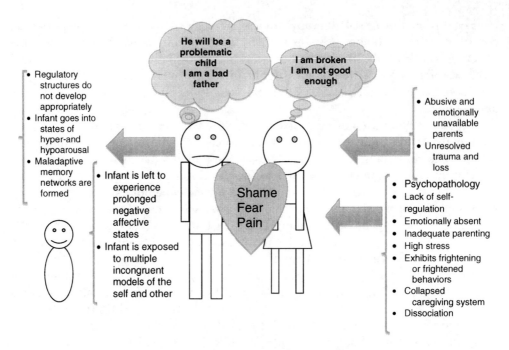

Figure 1.1 The shaping of memory systems.

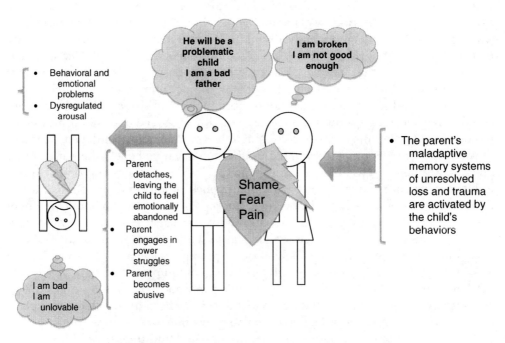

Figure 1.2 Mutual activation of maladaptive memory networks.

AFFECTIVE NEUROSCIENCE, AIP, AND EMDR THERAPY

Panksepp (1998) has demonstrated the existence of seven emotional systems present at birth. The SEEKING, FEAR, RAGE, LUST, separation-distress PANIC-GRIEF, maternal CARE and PLAY systems are subcortically concentrated and are gradually linked to cognitive autobiographical experiences (Panksepp, 2009). These raw emotional systems are not created environmentally, but they get shaped later on by lived experiences. *Panksepp advocates for bringing affects and cognitions into harmony with the reconsolidation of affective-cognitive memories as the primary goal of therapy.* This primary objective goes along with the AIP model and EMDR therapy, whose main goal is the assimilation and integration of memories containing cognitive, affective and somatic information. According to Panksepp (2009), the emotional circuits that are in the subcortical areas of the brain at birth constitute the raw emotions that in turn are shaped by environmental occurrences that then become socially constructed feelings. At birth, we possess inborn biological systems, however, how these systems function is shaped by the environmental experiences encountered by the organism. The brain's inborn systems and the neuronal connections are programmed and molded by experience. "How these raw emotional tools, provided by Mother Nature, link up to world events is of momentous importance for lived lives, sometimes proceeding smoothly and efficiently, promoting mental health, sometimes chaotically and inefficiently, promoting mental turmoil" (Panksepp, 2009, p. 6).

How we organize our perception of reality in the present and how we anticipate to the future is dependant on past experiences that have shaped the genetically dictated inborn biological systems (Panksepp, 2009). Repetitive experiences can shape biological and emotional systems as well as arousal regulating circuitry in the brain (Panksepp, 1998/2009; Porges, 2011; Siegel, 1999/2010; Schore, 2009). How early negative and traumatic experiences shape our implicit memory system is described by Siegel (1999), "Repeated experiences of terror and fear can be ingrained within the circuits of the brain as states of mind. With chronic occurrence, these states can become more readily activated in the future, such that they become characteristic traits of the individual" (p. 33). According to the AIP model, the memory networks developed as a result of the interactions between the active organism of the child and the environment become the lens by which reality is perceived and organized in the present. Children could be looking through lenses of fear and shame or, on the contrary, through the eyes of excitement and acceptance.

An especially important system for the child therapist is the play system. According to Panksepp (2009), play may actually help develop "fine-tuned" social brains that can respond optimally to environmental demands. "... play seems to be one of the most advanced methods nature has invented to allow a complex brain to create itself" (Brown, 2009, p.40). However, "...playfulness is inhibited by motivations such as hunger and negative emotions, including loneliness, anger, and fear" (Panksepp, 1998, p. 18). An animal study conducted by the same author focuses on the effect of fear on play. After rats were exposed to a single exposure to cat odor, animals displayed inhibition of play not for one hour or two but for up to five days. According to Brown (2009), when cats are completely deprived from play-fighting they can function in many areas well, but the only area where they have difficulty is in their social lives. Cats growing in impoverished play environments cannot discriminate friend from foe and they miscue on social signals, becoming either aggressive or socially isolated. Brown (2009) studied murderers in Texas prisons and he found the absence of play in their childhoods. When children play, new neuronal connections are being formed. "The very rich connections among brain's maps are reciprocal and may involve millions of fibers. My sense of these interconnecting and dynamic maps is that they are most effectively enriched and shaped by the 'state' of play" (Brown, 2009, p. 36). In animal studies, when rats are deprived from play, the urge to play is amplified. Children growing up in relationally impoverished, chaotic, and traumatizing environments experience heightened fear states, which in turn affects the play system and the child's ability to play. These play-deprived children, as stated by Panksepp (2009), may develop a heightened motivation to play when they are placed in the classroom. These children oftentimes get diagnosed and labeled with attention deficit hyperactivity disorder (ADHD) and treated with Psychostimulants, which according to Panksepp is an inhibitor of physical, play urges. In addition, long standing deprivation of play as a result of living in dysregulating, traumatizing and neglectful environments compromises the development of the social brain, resulting in children that are unable to connect and engage socially with others; either isolating or becoming extremely aggressive.

Another important system for the child therapist is the PANIC/GRIEF system that mediates separation-distress responses. According to Panksepp and Watt (2011), continued and persistent overactivity of the separation-distress PANIC system promotes the genesis of depression. Enduring activation of the separation-distress PANIC system leads to reactions similar to the children's responses to loss proposed by Bowlby (1980). The initial response, according to Panksepp, leads to agitation resulting from separation and an increased activation of SEEKING behaviors. This phase has been called by Bowlby, protest (see more detailed information further in this chapter). During the later phases, "despair" and "disengagement," there is increased hopelessness and withdrawal, leading to a significant decreased in SEEKING behaviors (Panksepp & Watt, 2011). In conclusion, the loss of an attachment bond, whether perceived or real, has the potential of overactivating the PANIC/GRIEF brain networks mediating separation-distress, resulting in the initial increase and later decrease in SEEKING behaviors. This is congruent with the AIP model, as the resulting responses and symptoms of depression are seen as consequential from the activation of memory systems containing information of events related to trauma, loss and adversity that remain unprocessed and unintegrated in the brain. An important contribution from affective neuroscience is the empirical support of the connections between the development of depression, experiences of loss and separation, and the overactivation and underactivation of two important emotional systems: The PANIC and the SEEKING systems. In addition, affective neuroscience brings up once again the importance of PLAY as a healing agent. According to Panksepp and Watt (2011), "social CARE and PLAY systems may substantially improve therapeutic outcomes" (p. 9). Shapiro (2001/2012) has brought up the importance of enhancing existing neural nets containing positive affective states as well as promoting the development of new patterns of neural firing resulting from exposing clients to positive affective experiences. The therapeutic relationship (Shapiro, 2001; Dworkin, 2005) as well as the importance of including play and playful strategies (Gomez, 2006, 2007b, 2008b, 2009b, 2010a, 2011) have been emphasized in EMDR therapy. Throughout this book a wide range of strategies geared toward stimulating both the PLAY and the CARE system during all phases of EMDR therapy will be thoroughly covered.

POLYVAGAL THEORY, AIP, AND EMDR THERAPY

The polyvagal theory emerged out of the work of Stephen Porges on the evolution of the autonomic nervous system (ANS). According to Porges (2009), our emotional difficulties and, ultimately, disorders become "hardwired" into the nervous system. Before Porges, the function of the ANS was seen as a system of balance: The sympathetic nervous system (SNS) constituted the accelerator and the parasympathetic nervous system (PNS) the brakes. However, Porges brought up the complexities of the functioning of the ANS and how it is actually a hierarchical system that responds to environmental challenges. This model describes three different subsystems that are associated with specific behavioral and physiological responses that allow the organism to respond adaptively to danger and stressful circumstances: The parasympathetic ventral vagal system, called the social engagement system; the sympathetic system, in charge of the mobilization of fight-flight responses; and the parasympathetic dorsal vagal, that activates immobilization-shutdown responses and promotes dissociative states. According to Porges (2011), through evolution, mammals developed the two vagal, systems, which are programmed to respond with very different sets of strategies. The Dorsal vagal system and the ventral vagal system, both branches of the PNS, respond to world's demands in very different ways. The ventral vagal system stimulates physiological states that support social behavior, social communication, visceral homeostasis and the formation of social bonds. This system also allows us to respond flexibly and adaptively to environmental demands. Trauma, especially chronic, early and complex trauma, can inhibit the long-term availability of this system, constricting the child's capacity to respond adaptively to stress, self-regulate and form healthy attachment and social bonds. The dorsal vagal system, on the other hand, is connected to other behavioral strategies such as immobilization and behavioral shut down (Porges, 2009). When the memories of trauma and adversity are activated by environmental stimuli, children will see their environment through the lenses of these memory networks and as a result will provide an inaccurate assessment of the situation in terms of danger and safety. This "faulty neuroception" (Porges, 2011), may activate the defense system in situations that may be in fact safe, or on the contrary inhibit defense responses in environments that are actually risky. Children with histories of chronic and complex trauma oftentimes have social engagement systems that are unavailable and underdeveloped. These children did not have the appropriate experiences that allowed for the stimulation and development of the smart vagus system, resulting in a limited capacity to relate to others and respond to environmental demands adaptively.

EMDR therapy, throughout its eight phases, works initially during the preparation phase on stimulating the emergence of the ventral vagal branch of the ANS by promoting the creation of safe environments, enhancing and developing neural nets containing adaptive and positive material and stimulating the development of self and interactive regulatory strategies that allow individuals to modulate internal physiological states. Later on, during the reprocessing phases of EMDR therapy, the memories containing traumatic material are assimilated and integrated, resetting this "faulty neuroception" and promoting the availability of the social engagement system.

According to Porges (2011), neural circuits connecting the cortex to the brain stem control the regulation of facial and head muscles, which are directly affecting the social engagement system. The infant's ability to interact with caregivers and the world through the use of vocalization, eye contact and facial expressions, as well as the capacity to distinguish the human voice is dependent upon the social engagement system. However, a neuroception of danger can change the muscle tone, awareness of sounds, facial expressions, ability to have eye contact and general social engagement behaviors. The concept of neuroception has been coined by Porges to refer to how the nervous system can detect and discern whether the environment is safe or dangerous. Neuroception can be activated externally by environmental stimuli, or internally as it happens when experiencing physical pain. How the infant or the child perceives the social engagement system of the caregiver is of crucial importance in how internal representations of the self, the other, and the world are formed. In addition, the facial expressions of the caregiver, voice and gaze have the potential to activate a neuroception of safety or danger. By the same token, the child's facial expressions can have the same outcome in the caregiver's system. According to Porges (2011), "the flat affect of a depressed parent or the flat affect of an ill child may trigger a transactional spiral that results in compromised emotional regulation and limited spontaneous social engagement" (p. 15). Children with attachment trauma are oftentimes cued by the tone of voice, eye contact and facial expression of their caregivers. Britney, a 7-year-old child living with a mother diagnosed with borderline personality disorder, presented with highly dysregulated emotions and self-destructive behaviors. During the clinical interview with the child, she reported having the urge to cut and scratch her arms when her mother was frustrated with her. A thorough exploration of Britney's triggers yielded a clear picture of her interactions with her mother. When her mother was either angry or frustrated with Britney, she became extremely agitated and had the urge to run and escape from the house or to cut or scratch herself. Britney stated that she could almost feel how her mother was feeling and she "could see it in her face and feel it in her mother's voice." This, in turn, activated metaperceptions such as "I am a bad kid" and emotional reactions that Britney was not consciously aware of at the moment, as this information remained implicitly and nonconsciously encoded in the brain. Britney's history revealed a mother with multiple hospitalizations resulting from suicidal ideations. Throughout Britney's life, the mother had multiple and repetitive episodes of rage and deep depression. Role reversing was identified as one of Britney's mechanisms of adaptation to not having her attachment needs met. Britney's history did not include any physical or sexual abuse, and outside her relationship with her mother, no other early traumatic events were reported. Not only did the mother's dysregulated emotional responses and lack of social engagement activate Britney's agitated states and the urge to hurt herself, but her teacher and other authority figures' emotional reactions and facial expressions also activated a neuroception of danger. Britney also presented at such a young age with panic attacks, which were activated by fear of abandonment and loss. When Britney witnessed her mother's dysregulated emotional states, she experienced a rupture in the attachment bond with her mother. Her first panic attack, a few months before her first therapy session, was actually precipitated by the loss of her dog. Experiences of misattunement, abandonment and loss activated memory networks containing information related to her past attachment experiences with primary caregivers, and resulted in the activation of a neuroception of danger and the resulting panic attack. After the first panic attack, Britney also became cued by her own physiological responses and even her heart palpitations activated a neuroception of danger.

As stated by Porges, "a neuroception of safety is necessary before social engagement behaviors can occur" (p. 17). Parent-child dysregulated interactions concurrently activate the defense system and the attachment system (Liotti, 1992/2006). When the defense system is activated, the creation of social bonds is thwarted. In addition, it results in a "faulty neuroception" of safety and danger. According to Porges, when there is a neuroception of safety, it results in the activation of brain circuitry that inhibits defense responses, which in turn activate prosocial behaviors. The core and crux that the polyvagal theory has helped us understand is how "autonomic states are linked to social behavior" (Porges, 2011, p. 120).

An important contribution of the Polyvagal theory is the view of visceral organs as strongly connected and anchored in brain structures through the bidirectional connection the ANS offers. In other words, peripheral organs and the central nervous system maintain an intimate and close bidirectional communication through the ANS. The polyvagal theory helps us understand how the activation of memory networks containing traumatogenic material is experienced viscerally as well as how the environmental stimuli received by peripheral organs also has the potential to activate latent memory systems. "It is no longer appropriate to treat the ANS as functionally distinct from the central nervous system. We start to recognize that peripheral organs do not 'float in a visceral sea.' Rather, they are anchored to central structures by means of afferent pathways that are continuously signaling central regulatory structures..." (Porges, 2011, p. 21). This bidirectional connection between central nervous system structures and the body through the afferent and efferent fibers of the ANS expands our view of the intricate relationship between memory networks and the body. EMDR therapy, throughout the eight phases of treatment and especially during the reprocessing phases, promotes different levels of information processing: cognitive, affective and sensorimotor. According to the AIP model, the sensations and bodily states experienced during trauma and adversity become ingrained in patterns of neuro firing. It is important to highlight that an important aspect of EMDR therapy is the accessing and binding of affective and bodily states along with cognitions and meta-perceptions. Resetting a "faulty neuroception" is accomplished in EMDR therapy by promoting the assimilation, binding and integration of memory systems containing implicit information of early thwarted social engagement experiences.

The new understanding of the ANS brought up by the Polyvagal theory enriches and supports the work EMDR clinicians do to promote healing. An important aspect of EMDR therapy and the reprocessing of memories of trauma and adversity is the presence of dual awareness. When individuals can maintain dual awareness during the reprocessing of traumatogenic material, the social engagement system is participating. In addition, the preparation phase of EMDR therapy can be clearly seen as a phase where various activities, strategies and techniques are used to promote social engagement and the stimulation of the smart vagus system. The EMDR clinician is also aware of how his or her tone of voice, eye contact, facial expressions, and ability to attune to the child have a fundamental effect in supporting a neuroception of safety in the child's system as well as maintaining social engagement. When social engagement is reduced during reprocessing, the integration of memory systems stops and dual awareness is compromised. Recognizing the physiological changes occurring when social engagement is reduced is of extreme importance for EMDR clinicians. If the child is unable to maintain eye contact, his or her voice loses inflection, positive facial expressions diminish, awareness of the human voice is less acute and social engagement with others decreases, a neuroception of danger has been activated, resulting in a limited participation of the smart vagus system and a reduction in the child's integrative capacity.

The polyvagal theory also helps us understand how in children with attachment injuries and traumas, triggers may be found in the current parent-child interactions. The parent's voice, facial expressions, gaze and social engagement or lack thereof with the child can be very powerful triggers that may promote a neuroception of danger. Moreover, the polyvagal theory enhances our understanding of the important relationship between the neural circuits between higher brain structures, the brainstem and between the brainstem and the visceral organs (Porges, 2009).

THE WINDOWS OF TOLERANCE AND THE AROUSAL ZONES

The concept of the windows of tolerance was brought up by Dan Siegel (1999). This model highlights individual differences related to the capacity to tolerate various intensities of arousal (see Chapter 11). While some children may have a high threshold for comfortably managing and responding adaptively to various degrees of arousal, others may present with a limited and constricted capacity to tolerate them. The concept of the windows of tolerance is in fact congruent with the notion of "dual awareness" brought up by Shapiro (1995/2001). When clients are within appropriate windows of affect tolerance and in an optimal arousal zone, children are able to maintain mindful awareness of the present. The reprocessing of maladaptive information encoded in the brain in the form of neural networks occurs when the child can maintain present and mindful awareness while accessing the memories of trauma and adversity. When children move out of windows of tolerance, because they are experiencing either "too high" or "too low" levels of arousal, the integration and binding of these networks halts. Keeping children within optimal arousal states where dual awareness can take place is pivotal to the assimilation of memory systems (Shapiro, 2001, 2011).

IPNB, AIP, AND EMDR THERAPY

IPNB brings a viewpoint that integrates objective realms of scientific findings and subjective realms of human knowing (Siegel, 2010). According to IPNB, the mind is embodied and relational and "a process that regulates the flow of energy and information." Mindsight is a core concept of IPNB that refers to the process that allows human beings to monitor and modify the flow of energy and information within relationships, the mind and the brain (Siegel, 2010). Key aspects of health and well-being, according to IPNB, are the eight domains of integration: integration of consciousness, vertical integration, bilateral integration, integration of memory, narrative integration, state integration, temporal integration, interpersonal integration, the mirror neuron system and transpirational integration. As we achieve wholeness, different levels of integration take place. According to Siegel (2010), unresolved trauma, neglect, and other thwarted early experiences may block integration. This can result in impaired differentiation and ability to link and relate to others.

EMDR therapy is geared toward promoting the client's ability to embrace more freely present experience and acknowledge internal and external realities while remaining contained and regulated. It also promotes the development of a renewed and coherent sense of self that cannot be achieved without the equal and balanced participation of the two brains: the left and the right or the harmonious work of the subcortical and cortical areas of the brain. Shapiro (2001) has emphasized the trait and state change that takes place during the different phases of EMDR therapy and the increased integration among different levels of information processing: Cognitive, emotional and somatic. An important aspect of EMDR therapy is dual awareness, and a mindful presence while accessing the memories of trauma and adversity. Mindful attention to the different elements of the current experience as unprocessed memories are activated while remaining aware of the present reality is a core element highlighted during the different phases of EMDR therapy. "One of the key practical lessons of modern neuroscience is that the power to direct our attention has within the power to shape our brain's firing patterns, as well as the power to shape the architecture of the brain itself" (Siegel, 2010, p. 39). A great contribution of IPNB is the understanding and compelling evidence of how social and interpersonal relationships shape and sculpt neural circuits and how the capacity for mindfulness and mindsight play an important and integrative role that promotes the healing of human suffering. As IPNB helps us elucidate and come to a more solid understanding of the neurobiological underpinnings of human experience, based on scientific findings but not constricted by them (Siegel, 2011), our understanding of the AIP model also continues to expand.

ATTACHMENT THEORY, AIP, AND EMDR THERAPY

John Bowlby (1969/1982) pioneered the development of attachment theory and with Ainsworth (1967) brought up awareness into the biological predispositions of infants to seek proximity and safety from primary caregivers and attach while still exploring their environments. This is what they called "secure base." Bowlby also brought up the concept of the "attachment behavioral system" of the child and the "caregiving system" of the caregiver, both geared toward promoting parent-child proximity and the ultimate protection and survival of the child (Cassidy, 1999/2008). According to Bowlby and recent attachment researchers, the relationship with the attachment figure serves as an external regulator of the internal affective states of the infant (Schore, 2009). According to Bowlby, the child, through the repetitive interactions with the attachment figure, develops mental representations of the environment, the attachment figure and the self. This is what Bowlby called: internal working models. According to Schore (2009), "for the rest of the lifespan, internal working models of the attachment relationships with the primary caregiver, stored in the right brain, encode strategies of affect regulation that nonconciously guide the individual through interpersonal contexts" (p. 118). These working models in the AIP model are seen as memory networks emerging from the repetitive parent-child interactions that ultimately constitute the foundation for the development of the self. These memory systems in the brain become the lenses through which the individual will see, interpret and experience other relationships. Even though Bowlby views these internal working models as primarily cognitive, in the AIP model, these patterns or neural firing, instigated by the interactions with the caregiver, contain the affective and somatic experience of the child as well as the meta-perceptions that correspond to how the child made sense of the whole experience.

In 1978, Ainsworth et al. designed a laboratory procedure to evaluate the different forms of infant attachment, which is known as the Strange Situation (SS). In the SS, the infant stays with the mother, then with the mother and a stranger, and then just with the stranger. The infant's behaviors are observed at separation and reunion. Out of this laboratory procedure, three infant classifications of attachment arose: Secure, avoidant and ambivalent (Figure 1.3). The most relevant information that yielded the different classifications came from the behaviors exhibited by the infant at the reunion with the mother. Infants that exhibit a secure attachment seek proximity with their mothers, are regulated and soothed by the mother's presence and go back to playful states quickly. Infants with avoidant strategies do not not seek proximity with their mothers; in fact, they avoid and ignore the mother. The infant with ambivalent strategies is highly distressed by the absence of the mother, shows high preoccupation with the attachment figure and the presence of the mother does not soothe or regulate the infant.

Main and Salomon (1986) included a fourth category, which they named disorganized/disoriented (see Figure 1.3). In this category, the infants exhibit disorganized and disoriented behaviors that, in recent literature, has been suggestive of the parent activating the attachment system as well as the defense system of the infant (Liotti, 1992/2009). This is the category of attachment more closely associated with the development of dissociative strategies, behavioral collapses and the presence of trance-like-states (Liotti, 2009). Using the AIP model as a lens, this clearly shows how infants have already developed neural nets containing information related to the parent, the self and the environment. These neural pathways that remain in implicit memory are activated by the separation from the caregiver, setting in motion a series of strategies used to adapt and modulate internal arousal and optimize the experience so attachment needs are met. Research using the Adult Attachment Interview (AAI) has suggested that the parent's state of mind with regards to attachment experiences and the resulting attachment category is highly correlated with the kind of attachment their children will form with them.

Avoidant	Ambivalent	Disorganized
• Caregiver emotionally unavailable, rejecting, and unresponsive • Minimizes and limits opportunities for connection and interaction • There is a "deactivation" of the attachment system and the need for connection • In older children, denial. Strong reliance on self-regulation • Biased toward parasympathetic dorsal vagal states	• Caregiver is intermittently available and responsive • Caregiver is intrusive and has difficulty differentiating • Caregiver does not respond contingently to the needs of the child • Caregiving responses are geared to meet caregiver's needs, not the child's needs • There is an "overactivation" of the attachment system • Strong reliance on interactive regulation. Needy and clingy child who is not soothed by the caregiver's presence • Biased toward sympathetic states	• Caregivers exhibit frightened, dissociated, incongruent, and frightening behaviors • Physical, sexual, and emotional abuse • Caregiver has difficulty regulating affect and regulating the child • Presence of dissociation • Controlling style of interaction in relationships • Social engagement system underdeveloped and unavailable • Great difficulty creating social bonds • Experience "too high" or "too low" arousal states

Figure 1.3 Insecure Attachment Categories.

Data adapted from Main, 1995; Cassidy, 1999; Siegel, 1999, 2010.

Dissociation

When studying the etiology and genesis of dissociation, several models have been proposed. (Also see Chapter 6 of this book). Some models view dissociation as an intrapsychic process developed as a defense against trauma and pain (Putnam, 1997). On the other hand, dissociation is also seen as the result of the parent-child interactions that involve frightened or frightening parental behaviors. These responses are usually seen in disorganized-disoriented attachment. The cornerstone for the development of dissociation is the internalization of multiple and reciprocally incompatible models of the self and the parent (Liotti, 2009).

Within this model, two prominent etiological variables have been linked to the development of dissociation: First, the repetitive parental frightening or frightened interactions (Liotti, 1992, 2009; Main, 1995; Main & Solomon, 1986) and, second, the repetitive dyadic interactions between the child and the caregiver where the parent is emotionally unavailable.

Bowlby and Robertson classified young children's responses to the loss or separation from the mother figure in three phases (Bowlby, 1980; Figure 1.4). The initial phase was called "protest" where the child showed indicators of distress: crying, anger and fear. Throughout the second phase, "despair," the child exhibited increased hopelessness, disengagement and withdrawal. During the final phase, termed "detachment," the child showed absence of attachment behaviors when reunified with the mother. The infant also shows blank and emotionless faces.

Barach (1991) has brought up the connection between the terms detachment (Bowlby, 1973/1980) and dissociation. According to Liotti (1992), detachment is the result of the caregiver's prolonged physical or emotional unavailability.

If these dyadic parent-child interactions become pervasive without the caregiver providing opportunity for repair, dissociative states may become sensitized. According to Perry et al. (2009), children's brains are undergoing crucial periods of organization and development. As a result, if the child enters dissociative states frequently, these neural networks become sensitized and a lesser stimulus is required to elicit dissociative states.

According to Main (1995), a frightening parent creates an irresoluble conflict for the child or the infant. The child concurrently wants to seek the parent for security and contentment while at the same time is wanting to getaway from the caregiver, who represents a source of danger. As a result of this quandary, disorganized incongruent

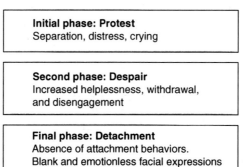

Figure 1.4 Children's responses to loss and separation.

attachment behaviors are generated. Consequently, the child develops internal working models of the self that become fragmented and incoherent (Main, 1995). According to Liotti (1992), these incoherent and contradictory models of the self and the attachment figure cannot be integrated due to their contradictory nature. Most recently, Schore (2009) brought up how the primary caregiver induces extreme and prolonged levels of arousal without interactive repair. The caregiver becomes the source of danger, activating both the attachment system and the defense system at the same time. Unable to escape, the infant becomes helpless and hopeless and the only option at this point is to disengage and withdraw from the outside world. This state of hypoarousal submission and immobilization appears to be responsible for the early forming dissociative states. According to Schore (2009), "the infant's psychobiological reactions to traumatic stress is comprised of two separate response patterns: Hyperarousal and dissociation.... The maternal haven of safety suddenly becomes a source of threat.... This maternal stressor activates the infant's hypothalamic–pituitary–adrenal (HPA) stress axis, thereby eliciting a sudden increase of the energy-expending sympathetic component of the infant's ANS" (p. 120). Along the same lines, Schore speaks of a second reaction to relational trauma: Dissociation. "This later-forming response is dominated by a parasympathetic system in which the infant becomes hopeless and helpless and moves into a metabolic shutdown." (p. 120). As it is seen through the AIP model, these dysregulated interactions that activate sympathetic and dorsal vagal parasympathetic responses are ingrained and imprinted in patterns of neural activity in the brain, which remain unprocessed, unintegrated and isolated from other later forming memory systems containing adaptive information.

On the other hand, Barach (1991) brought up the etiological implications of having parent-child interactions where the caregiver is unresponsive. These experiences might set the stage for reliance on dissociative responses. According to Dutra, Bianchi, Lyons-Ruth, & Siegel (2009), in a longitudinal study, they found that maternal hostility and or frightening behaviors may not be the strongest predictors of further development of dissociation. "Instead, lack of positive maternal affective involvement, maternal flatness of affect, and overall disrupted maternal communication were the strongest predictors of dissociation in young adulthood" (p. 87).

The intergenerational transmission of attachment trauma has been described by a number of authors (Hesse & Main, 2006; Liotti, 2009). According to Hesse and Main (2006), when the attachment figure exhibits dissociative states, it activates the alarm system of the infant. "During these episodes of intergenerational transmission of attachment trauma the infant is matching the rhythmic structures of the mother's dysregulated arousal states ...... The massive ongoing psychobiological stress associated with dysregulated attachment trauma sets the stage for the characterological use of right-brain unconscious pathological dissociation over all subsequent periods of human development" (p. 123).

According to the AIP model, asynchronic dysregulated parent-child interactions create patterns of neural firing that become reinforced as they are activated over and over again through the moments of traumatic attachment interactions with caregivers. Later on, when facing eliciting stimuli, these patterns of neural activity are ignited as well as its accompanying autonomic activation. In addition, neglectful environments do not provide the raw materials needed for the construction of the self, making us "vulnerable to creating a fragile, poorly symbolized, unmoderated sense of subjectivity..." (Sleed & Fonagy, 2010, p. 156). Experiences of remaining unseen, unknown, unheard, unfelt and unrecognized by the parent are woven into the quilt of the brain's neuronal nets forming the base and foundation of our identity. "The most profound trauma comes when a neglectful environment gives nothing for the child to work with and when the material for constructing an image of oneself is oneself alone" (Sleed & Fonagy, 2010, p. 156).

Liotti's Etiological Model of Dissociation—Multiplicity of Ego States

According to Liotti (2009), "parental communications that are frightened or confused, but not obviously maltreatment of the infant may set dissociative mental processes into motion. Pathological dissociation, in infancy, is a primary failure in organizing multiple and incongruent models of the self and other into unitary mental states and coherent behavioral states rather than an intrapsychic defense against unbearable pain of severely traumatic experiences" (p. 56). These confusing, incongruent, and disorganizing parental behaviors may be the result of behaviors that are set in motion by the activation of neural networks containing information about the unresolved trauma and loss of the caregiver. According to Shapiro (1995/2001), when memories of trauma and adversity are activated, they remain in isolation, unable to link up to other memory systems containing adaptive information. Due to these memories not being assimilated into a larger adaptive memory system, the individual remains trapped, experiencing the present as if the past was still occurring. Consequently, children will perceive present environmental stressors and demands through the lenses of the past.

According to Liotti (2006/2009), the development of mild to severe forms of dissociation begins with disorganized attachment (DA). However, depending on the presence of other risk factors and the integration of the parent's memories of unresolved trauma and loss, the child with DA may follow three different paths into either developing full mental health or a dissociative disorder (Figure 1.5).

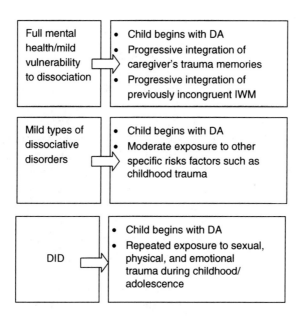

Figure 1.5 Liotti's etiological model of dissociation.
Note: DA, disorganized attachment; DID, dissociative identity disorder; IWM, internal working models.

As long as the caregiver's memory systems remain unprocessed and unintegrated, the child may continue to be exposed to the same experiences that laid the foundation for the development of dissociative mechanisms. The following case exemplifies how the caregiver's activation of maladaptive neural systems perpetuates the child's exposure to multiple and incongruent models of the self and other. An 8-year-old girl adopted at age 2 was brought to therapy by his two adoptive parents. She had extreme anger outbursts, mostly directed toward her mother. She engaged in name-calling and even threats of death toward her mother. The child reported no memories of the moments of rage and the resulting behaviors. The crisis lines were called multiple times and frequent hospitalizations were necessary. A variety of medications were used unsuccessfully and, at times, the frequent change of medication made things worse for this child and the entire family. The parents received extensive psychoeducation in therapy and specific strategies to manage the child's outbursts. After investigating step by step the parent-child interactions, the mother stated that she had an extensive history of abuse by her father and mother. When the child became agitated and called her names, no longer was she in her adult state, she felt once again victimized, and her child was perceived as a perpetrator. As a result, the mother was unable to respond as the adult mother she was while utilizing the strategies provided in therapy. The father of the child stated that the mother completely changed during the confrontations with her daughter. Sometimes the mother became extremely fearful and acted like a "younger person." Other times, she became agitated and yelled and threatened the child with abandonment. After these confrontations, the mother felt extremely guilty. To compensate, she allowed the child to get and do anything she wanted, including eating extra candy or breaking important house rules. In addition, as a result of the mother's inability to manage the child's affect, she felt highly incompetent when this child was threatening her, so she called the crisis lines endlessly, even when there was not an imminent danger. The child reported that the frequent calls to crisis lines, doctors and mental health professionals made her feel "bad," "abnormal," and "sick." The child stated that she had to constantly hear her mother on the phone repeating all the "bad" behaviors she had and how problematic she was. On the other hand, when the child was agitated, the father remained highly detached and peripheral. Sometimes, the father also became agitated and restrained the child by using physical force. Despite all the efforts of many different therapists that worked with this family over the years, no improvement was made. In fact, things continued to escalate and get worse.

When looking at this clinical picture, it is clear how the parents' own past trauma and attachment experiences inhibit their mentalizing capacities (Fonagy & Target, 1997; Sleed & Fonagy, 2010) exposing this child, as a result, to numerous contradicting and incongruent models of the self and other. Unless the parents can appropriately assimilate, integrate and resolve their past trauma, their responses will only continue to further dysregulate this child, promoting internal disorganization and dissociative states. If the mother continues to experience and respond to her child as if she was at times a perpetrator, a victim and a rescuer, this child most likely will not have the opportunity to develop memory systems containing appropriate and healthy representations of the self and other. According to Liotti (2009), the metaphor of the drama triangle can help portray the core nature of multiple and incongruent models of the self, as the child at times may experience himself or herself as a victim and the parent as the perpetrator. At the same time, the parent may be represented as a rescuer (Figure 1.6). These, according to Liotti, are the three main types of self-representations.

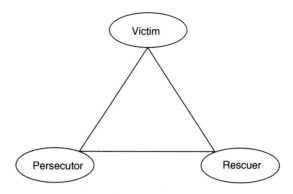

The Structural Dissociation Model

Figure 1.6 Types of self and other representations in disorganized internal working models.
Source: Adapted from Liotti (2009).

As stated by Liotti (2009), "pathological dissociation from childhood to adult age is the coexistence of reciprocally segregated contradictory ego states" (p. 56).

THE STRUCTURAL DISSOCIATION THEORY, EMDR THERAPY, AND AIP MODEL

The theory of structural dissociation of the personality (van der Hart et al., 2006) is based on Pierre Janet's view of dissociation as a division among systems that constitute the personality of an individual. According to this theory, personality is seen as a system "comprised of various psychobiological states or subsystems that function in a cohesive and coordinated manner" (van der Hart et al., 2006, p. 2), also described by them as a "dynamic, biopsychosocial system as a whole that determines [the individual's] characteristic mental and behavioral actions" (Nijenhuis & van der Hart, 2011, p. 418). According to the structural dissociation theory, two basic types of action systems make up, to a large degree, the personality of an individual: Action systems that support adaptation and action systems that defend the individual against major danger or threat. The lack of cohesion and integration of these systems, as a result of trauma, constitutes the core of the structural dissociation theory. As a result of this division of the personality, we see the presence of dissociative parts that are mediated by action (sub)systems such as the flight, fight and submission/shut-down systems. Dissociation entails the co-existence of dissociative parts of the personality, each with its own sense of self and first-person perspective: The Apparently Normal Part of the Personality (ANP) is guided by action systems of adaptation and daily life and at the same time is fixated on avoiding the traumatic memories. On the other hand, the so called Emotional Part of the Personality (EP) is guided by an action subsystem of defense and the action systems activated when the traumatizing event occurred. According to the structural dissociation theory, early and chronic trauma activates psychobiological action systems that as a result of the high levels of stress and activation remain unintegrated.

Shapiro's AIP model also posits that high levels of disturbance resulting from experiencing trauma inhibit and prevent the information processing system from properly assimilating and integrating the experience into adaptive comprehensive memory networks. This results in unprocessed memories that remain unintegrated and prone to becoming activated in the presence of trauma-related environmental stimulus.

Structural dissociation extends from mild and simple to severe with a more complex division of the personality (van der Hart et al., 2006).

1. **Primary dissociation of the personality.** Considered the simplest form of dissociation with the presence of a single ANP and a single EP. This is observed in simple cases of Acute Stress Disorder, simple PTSD and simple types of dissociative disorders.
2. **Secondary dissociation of the personality.** This type of dissociation occurs in the presence of persistent and/or increasingly devastating traumatizing events. The integration of various animal defense subsystems is thwarted. This is observed in cases of complex PTSD, also known as Disorders of Extreme Stress Not Otherwise Specified (DESNOS), Dissociative Disorder Not Otherwise Specified (DDNOS), and trauma-related Borderline Personality Disorder.
3. **Tertiary dissociation of the personality.** In this type of dissociation, in addition to the division of the EP, there is also a division of the ANP. This type of dissociation, according to van der Hart et al. (2006), is observed in cases of dissociative identity disorder (DID).

According to van der Hart et al. (2006), a major goal of the therapeutic process with individuals with structural dissociation is the synthesis, realization, presentification and personification that corresponds not only to the integration and assimilation of the traumatic experience, but also to the further growth of the personality. "Synthesis includes binding and differentiating sensory perceptions, movements, thoughts, affects and a sense of self" (p. 11). Realization involves the mental action of fully accepting and developing awareness of reality so the individual can reflect and adapt to this present reality. Oftentimes, trauma survivors are either fixated on avoiding such memories and lack the complete realization that it actually happened to them, or they completely live enmeshed in the past, not realizing that it is over. Integration of the trauma memories involves personification, which refers to "integrating the experience with an explicit, personal sense of ownership" (van der Hart et al., 2006, p. 12) and presentification, which implies "being firmly grounded in the present and integrating one's past, present, and future" (p. 12). All these are important aspects of the full integration of trauma memories according to this theory.

The AIP model as well as the structural dissociation theory has as a primary goal of treatment; the binding, assimilation and ultimate integration of traumatic memories that have been physiologically encoded in the brain (Shapiro, 1995, 2001). Based on the AIP model, the brain and biological systems are shaped by experience. These experiences are encoded in different forms of memory, implicit and explicit. Memories of trauma will follow a path into implicit encoding and isolation from other adaptive and positive information. The EP in the AIP model represents memory networks containing the emotions, thoughts, sensations and meta-perceptions of traumatizing and adverse events that have not been integrated into a coherent autobiographical memory. (The structural dissociation theory adds that EPs, like any other dissociative part, have their own first-person perspective.) The EP in the AIP model also represents thwarted animal defenses fight, flight, freeze and immobilization-shutdown responses taking place during the traumatizing event. In addition, they contain the potentially self-destructive coping mechanisms used to protect and modulate affect resulting from the activation of such memory systems holding traumatogenic material. Based on the structural dissociation theory, EP and ANP have various biological and psychological responses, with the EP exhibiting the activation of episodic memory systems and the ANP the activation of semantic memory systems (Nijenhuis & van der Hart, 2011).

In my opinion, the ANP is represented in the AIP model by memory systems that contain the mechanisms of adaptation that have been utilized by the individual to suppress, manage and avoid the existing memories of trauma. This is accomplished by using avoidance and keeping the memories of trauma and adversity away, compartmentalized and isolated. In the structural dissociation theory, avoidance is conceptualized as mental actions associated with the phobia of the trauma memory and phobia of the dissociative parts of the personality (Nijenhuis & van der Hart, 2011; van der Hart et al., 2006). An important goal of EMDR therapy is to promote and facilitate the linkage, connection and ultimate assimilation of such memory systems so they can be integrated into a healthy sense of self. This entitles, as van der Hart et al. (2006) state, the synthesis, personification, presentification and realization of the traumatic experiences. The structural dissociation theory proposes a phase-oriented treatment that involves the integration of mental actions and contents feared and avoided by the individual. During the initial phase of treatment, the clinician works on assisting the client in overcoming the phobia of mental actions and contents, phobia of EPs, phobia of ANPs for each other, phobia of attachment, as well as improving the level of functioning of ANPs, for example, through skills-training (van der Hart et al., 2006). In addition, the accessing and direct trauma work, in phase 2, is only done when the individual's integrative capacity has been adequately improved. The latest phase of treatment involves the integration of the personality. EMDR therapy is also a phased treatment approach that in its initial phases aims for the enhancement of the individual's regulatory and integrative capacities. The EMDR clinician works diligently on developing a therapeutic relationship based on attunement, resonance and security as well as in assisting the client in overcoming the "phobia of the trauma" by assisting the client in enhancing existing and developing new resources. Advanced strategies are also used to assist the client in exploring, accessing, processing and ultimately integrating memory systems containing traumatic material. The ultimate goal of both the structural dissociation theory and EMDR therapy may be seen as integration: Integration of the personality and integration of its memory systems.

EMDR THERAPY AND THE NEUROSEQUENTIAL MODEL OF THERAPEUTICS

The neurosequential model of therapeutics (NMT) developed by Dr. Bruce Perry and colleagues provides valuable insights into appropriate therapeutic interventions that follow fundamental principles of neurodevelopment. These principles are extremely relevant and can enrich the work that needs to be done during the different phases of EMDR therapy, but especially during the preparation phase. According to the NMT model, a critical element of therapeutic success is to provide activities that match and correspond to the developmental stages and physiological needs of traumatized children. According to McLean (1985/1990) when trauma responses are activated, the more primitive reptilian brain hijacks the higher parts of the brain. With this in mind, before adverse and traumatic memories can be accessed and processed, lower parts of the brain need to be regulated (Perry, 2006). According to Perry (2006), since trauma responses originate in the brainstem and diencephalon, when these lower parts are poorly regulated, they also disrupt and dysregulate higher parts. The activation of memory systems containing traumatogenic material in children with history of early and chronic trauma will be accompanied by the activation of brain structures intimately connected with regulatory processes. If trauma occurred when brain circuits in charge of regulation and survival were developing, the long term appropriate function of such systems may be compromised. Brainstem regulation should be initiated early in EMDR therapy and it should continue throughout its eight phases. However, the sequence of therapeutic activities will have a greater impact on the outcome of therapy if they closely mirror normal brain development (Perry, 2006). As a result, Perry suggests initiating therapy with brainstem-modulating activities. He actually considers EMDR therapy one of the forms of therapy that helps modulate lower parts of the brain. According to Perry, treatments and activities such as dancing, music, EMDR therapy, and massage, among others, can help regulate the brainstem. With this in mind, before a highly traumatized child can respond to more cognitive resources, the utilization of activities and strategies directed to regulating and working with the lower parts of the brain may be necessary.

A TYPOLOGY FOR EMDR THERAPY: CASE CONCEPTUALIZATION

After finishing my early training in EMDR therapy and using it with numerous cases, I started to notice that some children responded very well and fairly fast to EMDR therapy, while others either refused treatment or had symptoms that worsened after an EMDR reprocessing session. I also noticed that I was using a "cookie cutter" approach to the clinical practice of EMDR therapy with children. As a result, I was moving many children with complex trauma with limited and constricted capacities to tolerate affect into trauma processing when they were not yet ready. I started to create categories that could help me better understand the needs of each child, organize more effectively treatment plans and conceptualize each case more efficiently. I developed a typology that helped me organize the clinical landscape of each client and have appropriate expectations in terms of the work and time needed to walk through the eight phases of EMDR therapy.

Type 1 Cases

The children that fall into this clinical category come into therapy with a single or few traumatic events. Overall, they present with positive attachment experiences and external as well as internal resources that they can access during moments of activation. Despite the experiences of trauma and or adversity and how symptomatic they may be in the present, they exhibit appropriate levels of stabilization and ability to use approach and self-regulatory strategies. Neural nets containing information associated with a healthy sense of safety and congruent representations of the self and other are present in the child's system. These children tend to be successful at finding a safe place and, as a result, the calm-safe place EMDR protocol is usually used without any difficulties. The child is able to find a safe place, access it and use it efficiently as a state change strategy. These children are usually able to move fairly quickly into the reprocessing of the memories of trauma and adversity. The preparation phase is usually short and the reprocessing of disturbing material tends to be straightforward, as the child is able to reprocess several memories one after the other. These children possess the capacity to tolerate positive and negative affect and their windows of tolerance permits them the early accessing of traumatogenic material.

According to Shapiro (2001), during EMDR reprocessing, synthesis and linkages of memory systems happen with the resulting assimilation and integration of such neural networks into other adaptive memory systems in the brain. Considering how these children possess memory networks containing adaptive information, the assimilation of trauma memories tends to occur spontaneously, rapidly and efficiently during EMDR reprocessing sessions.

In addition, the parent(s) of these children may possess the qualities that allow them to promote attachment security and, as a result, the time the clinician will need to dedicate to working with the family system may be minimal. Having parents with the capacity to attune, mentalize, and synchronize with their children will significantly reduce the amount of time dedicated during the preparation phase of EMDR therapy to working directly with caregivers. In addition, in these cases, oftentimes the parent or caregiver has not been the wounding agent. However, if the parent has somehow contributed to the current clinical presentation of the child, parents in this category tend to participate more actively.

Overall, in this category, the time needed for preparation tends to be minimal, with the child responding well to safe place and resource protocols. Since the children in this category possess neural nets with positive and adaptive information, the reprocessing of disturbing events does not tend to encounter much "turbulence."

Type 2 Cases

These children portray more complex clinical presentations, such as: multiple experiences of trauma and a family system with identified areas of dysfunction. These are children that, despite the trauma they have suffered, present with great resiliency or with some positive early experiences of attachment with at least one caregiver. Despite the family dysfunctional patterns, both caregivers, or at least one is open and willing to actively participate in therapy. These children may have some difficulty identifying resources and a safe place. When using the calm-safe place or resource development protocols, these resources may become contaminated, as the child rapidly accesses negative elements and the associated dysregulated affect. A more extensive preparation phase may be needed to expand the child's capacity to modulate and tolerate affect. In addition, the preparation phase may include some level of work with the caregivers and, in general, with the family system. Other clinicians may need to be involved to appropriately meet the needs of the child and the family. However, some of these children, due to their resilient capacities, may be able to move fairly fast into the reprocessing of disturbing memories. Some others may require the titrated exposure, the fractionation or layering of the memories of hardship and trauma during the reprocessing phases of EMDR therapy.

Type 3 Cases

These children tend to be the hardest to treat and engage in EMDR therapy. They may present with chronic and severe early trauma. Most likely they present with disorganized attachment strategies and moderate to severe dissociative symptoms. The presence of co-morbidity is high, as well as the occurrence of self-destructive behaviors and regulatory strategies. The family system is oftentimes chaotic, highly dysregulated or absent. The presence of child protective service agencies as the custodial agents of these children make the clinical presentations more convoluted. Oftentimes, the presence of reactive attachment disorder, mood disorders and dissociate disorders and the misdiagnosis of the underlying trauma make these children linger in the mental health system for years without any real therapeutic gains. Fragmentation, pervasive emotion and physiological dysregulation accompanied by the existence of very narrow windows of affect tolerance are usually prevalent in these children. The presence of internal resources and neural nets containing adaptive and congruent information about the self and other are not present or are scarce. As a result of these clinical presentations, the use of EMDR treatment tends to be more multifaceted and intricate. Frequently, treatment is not a linear process going from resourcing to reprocessing. Instead, the clinician may have to go from resourcing to reprocessing and back to resourcing. Their dissociative symptoms can make it challenging for these children to stay present and maintain mindful present awareness. As a result, the preparation phase and reprocessing phases may require the utilization of advanced strategies to maintain these children's dual awareness and keep them within appropriate windows of affect tolerance.

I use the analogy of the "teeth" and the "steak" to assist clinicians in conceptualizing and understanding the level of participation and length of treatment for each of the typologies described above. The teeth represent the resources and the steak represents the amount of trauma. Children with type 1 clinical presentations come in with all their teeth in good condition. If you give them a piece of steak, they will be able to chew it up without choking and without too much assistance form the clinician. Children with type 2 clinical presentations come into therapy with several teeth missing and fairly large pieces of steak that need to be digested. They will be required to get "dentures" in order to be able to chew up the steak. They may even need to have the clinician cut or layer the steak for them, otherwise, they may choke while attempting to chew up the steak. Children that present with type 3 clinical landscapes come to therapy with very few teeth or none at all. They may also present with extreme fear of the steak. As a result, extensive preparation to help them overcome the fear of the steak while "putting in" dentures will be necessary. The clinician may have to use distancing strategies or start with minimal amounts of steak in order to help these children be successful in their EMDR treatment. The fractionation, layering and titration of the traumatic material may be necessary as well as sufficient amount of work to achieve appropriate levels of stabilization prior to the reprocessing of trauma memories.

This typology is not intended to be rigid and to limit all children to just only these three categories. Instead, it is intended to bring light into the effective use of EMDR therapy with various and diverse types of clients and families as well as to assist clinicians in using appropriate case conceptualization skills. Honoring the rhythm and speed each child needs for effectively moving through the eight phases of EMDR therapy is critical. The clinicians' ability to be flexible and adjust to different therapeutic rhythms, to go fast with some children while taking a very slow pace with others will highly enhance the effectiveness of EMDR child clinicians. This typology is intended to honor the rhythm and pace of the child, not the pace of the clinician. Some clinicians may have the need to go really fast and attain results as fast as possible, even when this rhythm does not necessarily honor the rhythm of the child. Others may always want to go very slow not because the child needs this pace, but because the clinician may fear the affect of the child during the work with EMDR therapy.

In addition, it is important to highlight that some children presenting with cases that resemble a type 3 presentation are incredibly resilient and, as a result, are able to move fairly quickly into the reprocessing of target memories. It is of extreme importance to see each child as a unique individual with very distinctive qualities and characteristics and not to box them into stereotypical prototypes. Keeping an open mind and the ability to understand the uniqueness and the rhythm of each child and the clinical picture while attending to best clinical practice guidelines is foremost encouraged.

This book is dedicated to providing a thorough review of how to use EMDR therapy effectively and efficiently with type 2 and type 3 cases. A wide range of strategies that can enhance treatment outcome with difficult to treat children, will be thoroughly presented.

SUMMARY AND CONCLUSIONS

Complex trauma includes the experiencing of early and chronic trauma and adversity. It oftentimes involves asynchronic dysregulated interactions between the infant and the caregiver. Latest neuroscience research and theory supports the idea of the development of the self as highly and intimately connected to the repetitive experiences with caregivers. Our understanding of the AIP model that supports and gives meaning to the work done with EMDR therapy has been expanded by principles and findings from the polyvagal theory (Porges, 2011), affective neurobiology (Panksepp, 1998, 2009), attachment theory (Bowlby, 1973/1980; Ainsworth, 1967; Main, 1978) and interpersonal neurobiology (Siegel, 1999, 2010). Understanding the intricate connection between early attachment experiences, development of biological systems as well as brain circuits is pivotal when working with complex trauma cases. Even though the human organism comes into the world with similar biological systems, they are shaped by the environment and experiences by which they are surrounded especially early in life. As a result, how these systems work later on and respond to environmental demands may be different for each individual. The AIP model gives us a view of health and pathology that is rooted in memory systems. These memory networks become the basis and foundation for the development of the self. Moreover, the polyvagal theory gives us light into the intimate and intricate connection between the central nervous system, brain structures and the body. Through the afferent and efferent branches of the ANS, the brain and the body are closely connected. When memory systems containing traumatogenic material are in a state of activation, so is the body. EMDR therapy accesses cognitive, affective and somatic aspects of the memories of trauma stimulating simultaneously cognitive, emotional and somatic information processing. As a result, EMDR clinicians should be well versed in how to be witnesses and at times active participants as they assist children in accessing the different levels and modes of information processing. EMDR clinicians need to be proficient in accurately understanding the AIP model and the current theories and research that support and enhance our appreciation of the AIP model.

2

Phase One: Client History and Treatment Planning

DEVELOPING THE CLINICAL LANDSCAPE

The basic goals of phase one are to:

- Develop a working relationship and a therapeutic alliance
- Determine if the client is appropriate for eye movement desensitization and reprocessing (EMDR) therapy
- Determine if the level of expertise of the EMDR clinician is adequate for the complexity of the case
- Collect a thorough developmental as well as medical and psychosocial history
- Develop a comprehensive treatment plan and case formulation

The goals listed above represent just the basic foundation of what constitutes the creation of a sound clinical landscape. When working with complex cases, a solid foundation is essential. This initial plan is founded on solid information gathering about the client and the family system. Not only the adverse and traumatic events, but also the developmental deficits and unattained milestones are identified. In addition, the presence of resources, positive and adaptive experiences, and areas of appropriate functioning should be included.

Who Is Appropriate for EMDR Therapy?

In its origins, EMDR therapy was developed as a form of treatment to ameliorate and heal trauma. According to the *DSM-IV*, trauma is defined as "an event that involves actual or threatened death or serious injury, or other threat to one's physical integrity; or witnessing an event that involves death, injury, or a threat to the physical integrity of another person; or learning about unexpected or violent death, serious harm, or threat of death or injury experienced by a family member or other close associate. The person's response to the event must involve intense fear, helplessness, or horror" (American Psychiatric Association, 2000). Under this definition, trauma involves activated freeze and immobilization-shutdown responses. However, many children who have adverse experiences that do not meet the above definition of trauma could develop emotional and behavioral problems.

Attachment wounds and injuries that develop as a result of repetitive maladaptive parent–child interactions are imprinted in the brain in the form of memory networks. These memory networks also become the lenses through which children organize their present view of the self, the other, and the future. EMDR therapy targets not only traumatic memories but also the experiential contributors to current malfunction and maladaptation (Shapiro, 2007). With this being said, EMDR therapy can be effective in treating children with symptoms deriving from adverse, traumatic, or maladaptive experiences. However, if the current pathology originates in organic deficits, EMDR therapy will only help with the potential adverse or traumatic experiences that result from it. For instance, if a child has a neurological impairment or an appropriately diagnosed attention deficit hyperactivity disorder (ADHD), these disorders could create adverse social, family, or school experiences for the child. Experiences of humiliation, rejection, and school failure, among others, may also create a separate set of symptoms or may exacerbate the existing ones. EMDR therapy, then, could be an adjunctive treatment to deal with the adverse emotional sequelae of organic deficits.

LEVEL OF EXPERTISE OF THE CLINICIAN

Clinicians working with complex trauma must have substantial understanding of the AIP model and the EMDR methodology. Such clinicians should have the EMDR therapy principles and procedures clearly integrated and consolidated. Expertise in working with attachment and dissociation is indispensable. Newly trained EMDR clinicians and clinicians without expertise in the areas mentioned above should seek consultation and receive advanced training before attempting to work with complex trauma cases. Information coming from neuroscience research strongly emphasizes the importance of attunement and synchrony in the therapist–client relationship. Clinicians that lack a well-integrated sense of self may have difficulty synchronizing and truly attuning to the child's internal world. This may be due to the clinician's unprocessed memory networks getting activated by the child's reactions or symptomathology. Working with dissociated and insecurely attached children can potentially activate the therapist's implicit maladaptive material. Clinicians undergoing EMDR treatment and exploration of early attachment experiences may potentially enhance their capacity to provide effective treatment. If the state of mind of caregivers with regards to their own early attachment experiences affect how they perceive and understand the mind of their children, how would the state of mind of clinicians with regards to attachment affect the perception of their child clients? Unfortunately, research in this area is almost nonexistent. Based on my own professional and clinical experience, I believe that the level of integration achieved by the clinician has the potential to directly affect the outcome of therapy. Clinicians who have achieved greater integration and self-awareness, resulting in a well-developed ability to connect while remaining differentiated, will be far more effective in providing therapeutic assistance to children and families compared to their counterparts.

CONDUCTING THE INTAKE INTERVIEW WITH THE CAREGIVER

During phase one, the clinician works on creating an atmosphere of trust and safety so a therapeutic alliance can be formed with the child and the caregivers. The clinician also gathers information from different sources to create a comprehensive treatment plan, a clear map, and a clinical landscape founded on the principles of the AIP model. How we conceptualize and formulate cases will directly influence the effectiveness of the treatment we provide.

The initial intake interview involves a wide range of areas that need exploration. The following tasks should be performed in each of these areas:

Presenting problem. Identify how the caregivers understand and define the problem. Find out the hypothesis they have formulated and how they have attempted to resolve and cope with the presenting problem.

Resources. The child's and the parent's resources and the areas in which they are functioning well should be explored. Identify situations and/or moments where the problem is not present. Get a clear picture of these moments by asking the sequence of events and who and how each person is involved. What was said and done by both the child and the parent that resulted in a positive interaction will yield information on their potential resources. This information is critical as it becomes part of a larger clinical landscape that will lay the foundation for how EMDR therapy will be administered.

Developmental history. Obtain a year-by-year history of the child's life, concentrating on attachment experiences and relationships, starting with prenatal records. The following introduction and questions exemplify how to begin this exploration:

> *"Now that you have clearly formulated the problem you are having with your child, I would like to get to know you and your child better. The more I know and the better I can understand your child's journey, the better helper I can be for both of you. I am going to start by asking questions that cover your child's life from the moment you found out you were pregnant:*
>
> *I wonder, how were your and your partner's emotional responses when you found out you were expecting a baby? What kind of thoughts did you have about yourself or your partner as a result of finding out that you were pregnant? What positive or negative beliefs, expectations, or thoughts did you have about your baby and his or her future? Could you describe the emotional climate that surrounded your pregnancy?"*

Information about the delivery and any medical issues that the mother or the infant may have experienced is of extreme importance. Health factors can interfere with the development of attuned, synchronized, and regulated interactions between the caregiver and the infant. The following is an example of how medical issues can affect the quality of the parent–child communications:

Emily's mother, after delivering her baby, had to have surgery due to an extremely large uterine fibroid. After the surgery, Emily's mother developed a serious infection, forcing her to have a series of surgeries. Emily's mother experienced severe pain and was hospitalized several times during the first two years of Emily's life. Emily used to extend her arms to her mother, but due to her physical limitations her mother could not bear any weight and had to refuse Emily's requests for closeness. Emily later on developed severe separation anxiety and exhibited frequent temper tantrums and self-injurious behaviors.

This case exemplifies how the mother's medical problems affected her ability to meet Emily's needs for connection and closeness. It is my hypothesis that the mother's inability to have attuned, regulated, and contingent interactions due to her medical condition during the first two years of Emily's life may have been a strong contributing factor to the development of Emily's current symptomathology.

The infant's responsiveness to the caregiver should also be explored. Colicky babies or infants dealing with pain and/or painful medical procedures tend to experience prolonged states of enduring negative affect. Ask questions such as, "How did you soothe your baby when he or she was upset or in pain? How easy was it for you to calm him or her down? What did you do when your baby did not calm down despite trying everything possible to soothe him or her?" Children who are premature are born with an underdeveloped parasympathetic ventral vegal system. According to Porges (2011), the social engagement system develops during the last trimester of pregnancy. This system allows human beings to connect and engage with others. If this system is immature at birth, the infant's capacity to engage and connect may be affected.

Moreover, data about the nature of family stressors throughout the child's life, details of the living environment, and a detailed list of significant relationships in the child's life, including any changes, long separations, and/or disruptions in these relationships should be included. Experiences with other caregivers should be explored. Who took care of the child while the caregiver was absent, and how the infant or child responded to the separation, needs to be addressed. This information will help you understand the internal working models of the self and other and the memory networks developed by the child as a result of his/her attachment experiences. We are also looking at the experiences that were conducive to attachment security or experiences that may have created disoriented, disorganized, or dissociated states.

Developmental milestones attained or lost, methods of toilet training, as well as parental expectations about personal hygiene and cleanliness, will provide information about the parent's teaching and discipline style.

Gather data from other sources. Case managers, teachers, and any other people that participate in the treatment of the child can provide valuable information that parents may not have. Child protective services records should be obtained in cases of children with multiple placements. Highly convoluted cases may require longer intakes that include the case manager, family support specialists and behavioral coaches that have worked or are currently working with the family. In theses cases, the development of the targeting sequence may require arduous work, as it requires that the clinician can put together all the information in chronological order.

Parent's discipline style and ability to set boundaries. The ability of the parent to create healthy boundaries needs extensive exploration. Very often, parents violate the child's boundaries by being too intrusive or, on the contrary, by being too distant. They either have very rigid walls that the child cannot enter or have very porous and even absent boundaries that can create enmeshment. With a well-developed sense of self comes a healthy sense of boundaries. Since attachment experiences affect how we come to develop a sense of self and other, they also affect how we develop our sense of boundaries. Most insecurely attached children and their parents have not developed a healthy sense of physical, emotional, mental, and spiritual boundaries.

Parent's attachment history. Attachment theory has emphasized that the central and instrumental role that early attachment experiences and the relationships we cultivate throughout our lives play important roles in our development. Research findings using the adult attachment interview (AAI) (e.g., Main et al., 2008; Main, 1995) have shed light into the connection between the parents' current states of mind in regard to their own attachment experiences and the child's attachment pattern. What appears to matter the most in terms of transmitting patterns of attachment from parents to children is the parent's ability to provide in the present a coherent and organized account of his or her own attachment experiences (Bretherton & Munholland, 1999).

In other words, it is not the content of the childhood attachment experiences, but how the caregiver has come to organize these attachment experiences in a coherent narrative. How the parent has come to organize these early experiences appear to, affect in turn, the parent's perception of the child and the resulting caregiving behaviors. Considering these important findings, gathering information on the parent's childhood attachment experiences, the presence of unresolved trauma and/or loss is imperative. Caregivers' unresolved trauma can interfere with their ability to have regulated, attuned dyadic interactions with the child, keeping the child in a constant state of alarm. Moreover, if the parent has been highly affected by the trauma experienced by the child or has experienced a similar traumatic event, the processing of the trauma memories using EMDR therapy with the child could be hindered. In this case, the caregiver may continue to enhance these maladaptive neuronal networks due to the level of disturbance held by the parent in association to the child's memories being reprocessed with EMDR therapy.

A good way to introduce this topic is by helping the caregivers understand the benefit and importance of getting a thorough picture of the child and the parent–child interactions. Let them know how it will contribute to identifying the best course of treatment for their child. In addition, provide some information about how attachment experiences directly affect the development of the self and our capacity to manage and regulate ourselves. In addition, offer information about how the unresolved traumas of the caregiver may influence how the parent interacts with the child in ways that are usually not conscious and occur below awareness. Considering that the parents who bring their children to therapy might carry shame and a sense of incompetence, we have to use caution when addressing this topic. Some parents may want to avoid or may question the need for providing information about their own attachment experiences. Be aware that this refusal to go along with your request could be related to the parent's attachment style or the fear of addressing unresolved trauma and loss. It is important that the clinician is able to provide an attuned, empathic communication and maintain a regulated internal state. The internal, nonverbal exchanges with the child and the caregiver will greatly impact the level of trust and safety they will experience in the therapeutic relationship. Establishing a relationship based on acceptance, empathy, and safety sets the foundation for connection. As Siegel (2010) has beautifully stated, it sets the foundation for mindsight where "the brain of each person comes to resonate with the nervous system's signal of another." I cannot emphasize enough how important it is for clinicians to work toward developing autonomous mental states, the ability for mindfulness, reflective thinking, and mindsight. In my clinical experience, EMDR therapy strategies and procedures nested in a well-developed ability to connect and nourish the client–therapist relationship will result in growth, healing, and integration. These qualities in the clinician are pivotal, especially with children injured by their attachment experiences. Before doing a more thorough exploration of the parent's history, some preparation may be necessary. Consider the type of parent you are working with. A type 1 parent (see Chapter 1 for a description of each type) may respond differently from a type 3 parent who shows higher levels of fragmentation and history of more severe and chronic trauma. Chapter 5 will address specific strategies that can be used with caregivers within EMDR therapy. In addition, the inclusion of other mental health professionals that can directly work with caregivers may be necessary.

The following are questions that can be helpful in identifying the caregiver's attachment experiences and his or her ability to promote attachment security. For parents who are highly dysregulated with extensive trauma histories, clinicians need to proceed with caution or possibly postpone this exploration until some preparation and stabilization has been attained.

Collecting the parent's as well as the child's attachment history is critical for the development of effective treatment plans. The use of the AAI interview protocol could be extremely helpful. As we collect this information, we are looking at how these experiences have shaped the parents caregiving system. We are also looking at the presence of attachment experiences that helped the caregiver to later develop the ability to connect, love, and have attuned interactions with their children. We look at the deficits and the potential difficulties in helping the child feel regulated through the interactions with the caregiver. We are also looking at the presence of unresolved trauma and loss in the caregiver's life. However, the most important aspect we are trying to assess is the coherence and organization in the narratives provided by the parent.

Use of the adult attachment interview. The AAI, developed in 1984 by Carol George, Nancy Kaplan, and Mary Main, is a semistructured protocol for adults about the overall current state of mind with respect to attachment experiences. In other words, the AAI evaluates how the adult organizes these experiences and the meanings that are assigned to these early attachment experiences in the present. Specific training geared toward mastering the administration and scoring of the AAI should be attained before formally attempting to use this instrument. The 20 questions and scales used in the AAI bring into light the "states of mind" of the adult in the different attachment categories: Secure/autonomous, dismissing, preoccupied, and unresolved/disorganized. One of the most important features of the AAI is its capacity to predict the infant's behavior toward the parent during the Ainsworth strange situation (Hesse, 1999). According to Main, Hesse, & Goldwyn (2008), the test analysis of the AAI is done in several stages. During the first reading, the coder examines the inferred experiences with each attachment figure. During this stage, five scales are examined that by themselves yield important information on the parental behaviors present in childhood. Rejecting, role reversing and involving, neglecting, pressure to achieve, and loving are thoroughly examined. The second reading examines the current state of mind with respect to attachment. The final step is related to the examination of AAI classifications and subclassifications and determination of the descriptors that best represent the state of mind of the adult.

The AAI classification categories are based on how the adult narrates childhood attachment experiences during the semistructured interview. The following is a summary of the descriptors of each category.

Secure autonomous. The adults with states of mind that are secure autonomous tend to be open and free to explore thoughts and feelings associated with their attachment experiences and appear to value them as influential in their lives. These adults tend to show a steady and coherent flow of ideas and can provide specific examples and evidence that can support the statement about attachment experiences with caregivers. The descriptions offered tend to be reflective and thoughtful (Hesse, 1999). Their narratives may contain descriptions of problematic and negative parenting experiences; however, they are able to provide a coherent and objective narrative of their experiences (Hesse, 2008). The term "attention flexibility" has been brought up to describe securely attached babies in the strange situation and secure-autonomous parents in the AAI. This important aspect of attachment-security can be interpreted as the capacity of the baby to attend to attachment and exploratory behaviors alternately. The same phenomenon is seen in adults classified as secure autonomous, as they are able to respond alternately to attachment-related experiences and evaluate the influence of such experiences in the AAI (Main et al., 2008). On the contrary, the other organized categories, dismissing and preoccupied, according to Main et al. (2008), show attention inflexibility. This means that the adult showing dismissing states of mind will be fixated on avoiding and diminishing

the importance and influence of attachment relationships, whereas the adult with preoccupied states of mind will be entangled and fixated with early attachment experiences.
An important quality of autonomous adults is the capacity to reflect and actively monitor their own thinking when recounting attachment experiences (Hesse, 2008). This is
what Fonagy and Target (1997) have called reflective capacity and mentalization and
has been proposed as a characteristic of adults categorized as secure autonomous. We
can conclude that the capacity to freely, collaboratively, and flexibly explore attachment
experiences while creating a coherent narrative of attachment experiences is closely connected to secure states of mind (Hesse, 1999, 2008). At the same time, attachment research
supports the notion that the parent's secure state of mind with regards to attachment
experiences creates the foundation for the development of security in the parent–child
attachment bond.

The adult dismissing of attachment. The responses of these adults tend to minimize the influence of early attachment experiences. They are also inclined to idealize and
present a very positive image of the primary attachment figure (Hesse, 2008). However,
when asked for examples that support their statements, they are unable to recall specific
events. "Well, my childhood was great, I had excellent parents that taught me how to
succeed in life. I do not remember anything in particular, but they were really good parents." According to Siegel (2010), these responses show a lack of access to explicit autobiographical memory. Their answers also tend to be contradictive when talking about their
caregivers. Despite describing their caregivers as wonderful, they may also report severe
rejection and neglect by the caregivers. According to Main (1995), these adults tend to
present a state of mind that maintains the attachment system deactivated. Adults placed
in this category may have a short conversation that will be extremely concise and to the
point. They may frequently say that they do not remember or cannot remember much of
their early years. In addition, they tend to show derogation and dismissal of experiences
linked to attachment relationships. According to Crowell, Treboux, and Waters (1999),
adults classified as dismissing use strategies to deny and minimize the impact of negative
attachment experiences. In addition, they have a propensity to include in their narratives
the PRODUCT of what their parent gave them not the QUALITY of their relationship,
connection or communication (Siegel, 1999). They may stress the importance of activities
and material things received from the parents. Their discourse will contain few expressions associated with their affective experiences while minimizing the presence of painful
or hurtful events. Adults that restrict attention to attachment-related experiences may
also insist upon their inability to recall childhood memories. They may derogate loss,
trauma, and separation by making them look foolish or ridiculous (Main et al., 2008).

The adult preoccupied with attachment-related experience. Adults placed in this
category will be likely to provide narratives that appear to maximize the influence of
attachment experiences. While the adult with a dismissing state of mind will focus and
orient AWAY from past attachment experiences, the adult with a preoccupied state of
mind will strongly focus TOWARD attachment experiences (Main et al., 2008). Their
accounts tend to be lengthy, oftentimes appearing fearful, passive, critical, or angry. They
may move into the present or present relationships, providing vague descriptions of early
relationships (Hesse, 1999). The narratives they provide lack clarity and do not address
directly the interviewer's question (Siegel, 1999). The expression of involving and preoc-
cupying anger, such as angrily talking about a parent as if the parent were present, is
an aspect of the discourse seen in this category (Main et al., 2008). Another important
characteristic of adults in this category is the presence of passivity and vagueness in discourse. Vague expressions, incomplete sentences, wandering away into other topics, use

of nonsense terms to end sentences or adding them to an already completed sentence are some examples of the discourses of adults placed in this category (Main et al., 2008).

The adult with unresolved/disorganized states of mind. Adults classified in this category present with lapses in discourse or reasoning when discussing issues of loss or abuse. This may be indicative of changes in their state of consciousness or dissociative states (Hesse & Main, 1999). These adults also show signs of disorientation in their narratives, such as prolonged pauses and incomplete sentences, and fail to maintain an organized discourse throughout the interview (Hesse, 1999). Lyons-Ruth and Jacobvitz (1999) report that during the administration of the AAI, traumatic memories arise associated with attachment figures. These memories are presented in incoherent narratives, suggesting their unresolved status. Several researchers have suggested that the incoherence exhibited by adults when narrating attachment experiences might be associated with dissociative processes occurring while the adult is attempting to provide accounts of his or her attachment history (Hesse & Main, 2000; Siegel, 1999; Hesse & Van IJzendoor, 1999; Liotti, 2009). This category of attachment has been linked to the development of infant disorganized patterns of attachment. If the parent has an AAI classification of unresolved, the infant of this parent will very likely form a disorganized attachment with this caregiver. This attachment category has also been connected to the genesis of pathological forms of dissociation (Liotti, 2009).

When working with insecurely attached children, the use of the AAI offers a wealth of information with respect to the state of mind of the parent with regards to early attachment experiences. Oftentimes, parents will need to receive EMDR therapy for best treatment outcome for the child. In this case, the use of the AAI will provide information that the clinician working with the parent can use to develop the targeting sequence. There is robust evidence that the pattern of attachment the child will develop with any given parent is highly determined by the parent's state of mind with regards to attachment experiences. This has been evidenced by the correlation between the responses of a parent to the AAI and the responses of the infant to the strange situation.

THE USE OF THE AAI IN EMDR THERAPY WITH CHILDREN AND THEIR PARENTS

When using EMDR therapy with insecurely attached dyads, much better results may be achieved when the parent is also involved. Promoting attachment security with a child who is in constant interaction with a parent with insecure status may affect the outcome of treatment. Thoroughly assessing the parent–child attachment patterns and interactions can provide a clearer view of the child's clinical landscape and treatment direction. The current symptoms may be directly or indirectly associated with these parent–child transactions and attachment patterns. Due to the implicit nature of attachment-related memories, these targets are not easily available during a regular intake. A majority of parents in my clinical experience are not even aware of how attachment behaviors and experiences may be participating in the symptoms currently exhibited by their children. However, during administration, scoring, and analysis of the AAI, EMDR clinicians can learn valuable information that can more effectively guide treatment. The use of the AAI can help identify: (1) The deeply ingrained strategies used to manage affective responses associated with the discussion of attachment-related experiences. (2) The state of mind and coherence of the parent with respect to his or her own attachment experiences and the presence of unresolved trauma and loss. In addition, how the state of mind of the caregiver affects the way in which he or she "hold[s] the child's mind in mind" (Fonagy & Target, 1997) and the resulting caregiving behavior. (3) Potential targets for EMDR processing. (4) Effective therapeutic strategies for parents that fall into the different attachment categories. For example, EMDR therapy preparation tools may be different, depending on the parent's state of mind reflected in the AAI interview. A parent with a preoccupied state of mind with respect to attachment may have different needs in contrast to the parent with a dismissing stand. In addition, besides the overall attachment classification offered by the AAI, scales for inferred experiences with attachment figures as well as scales designed to capture the current state of mind and the overall coherence of the parent are provided. The identification of targets associated with implicit memories of attachment as well as the mechanisms used to modulate affective responses associated with the recall of such experiences may not be accessible to the conscious mind of the caregiver. Direct questioning, float back, and affect scan strategies used in EMDR therapy may assist with the identification of such memories. However, in many instances, parents may deny or block any experiences associated with attachment injuries and traumas that could be directly affecting their ability to promote attachment security in their children. On the other hand, facing these traumas and injuries could be too painful, and uncovering such experiences too soon too fast could create greater dysregulation in the parent and the child.

During treatment, identifying early overt as well as covert dysfunctional and maladaptive parent–child interactions is critical, but this could be arduous. In many cases, rejecting, neglecting, pressure to achieve, and role reversing interactions are not initially visible to the clinician. The AAI gives us the first view of the presence of these experiences in the parent's life. Later on, an exploration of the presence of similar experiences in the child's life should be followed.

Parent–child quality of current interactions. Assessing how the parent and the child spend their time will give you information about problematic areas in the parent–child relationship and where therapeutic interventions are necessary. The following exercise can be used with both the parent and the child. However, for younger children use it only with the caregiver.

You may say, "*Please take some time to look at the interactions that you had with your child for the last two weeks. Using the circle provided below, please divide it as many times as needed, showing how you and your child spend your time together each day. Using the menu provided below, please indicate the percentage of time that you and your child have engaged in each activity during the last two weeks. Please include only the activities that are part of your life and discard the ones from the menu that are not.*

1. Physical activities
2. Nurturing play
3. Play
4. Nurturing touch
5. Arguments
6. Fights
7. Advice giving
8. No interaction
9. Talking
10. Doing homework
11. Separate activities in the same place
12. Giving instructions and orders

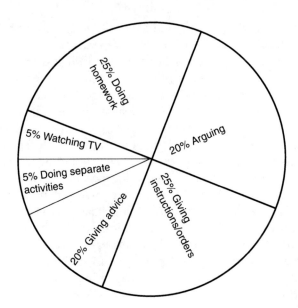

Figure 2.1 Parenting sample.

Figure 2.1 is an example of a "Parenting sample" provided by the caregiver of an 8-year-old girl presenting with oppositional behaviors and frequent anger outbursts.

When we look at this "Parenting sample" we can see how the caregiver spends 70% of the time giving the child instructions and advice, and doing homework. Play and connection between this child and her caregiver is completely absent. The inclusion in this dyad of playful and nurturing activities will be an important part of the work that needs to be accomplished during the preparation phase of EMDR therapy. Restoring the connection between the child and her caregiver will most likely provide stability and internal regulation to the child. Depending on the child's attachment style, these activities will need to be introduced progressively as the child can tolerate them (See Appendix).

Once we have the responses from the caregiver, a map can be created of the areas where the caregiver reports being successful or the areas where deficits are present. This information then becomes part of the clinical picture that will guide the work needed with caregivers for improving their ability to promote stability, security, and regulated states in their children's system.

Assessing the parent's ability to be playful. According to Brown (2009), when survival is not threatened, play appears to be the driving force that shapes and sculpts how the brain grows and develops. Play is essential for the emergence of well-modulated social abilities. The construction of the social brain may be best accomplished by utilizing play. Play has remarkable effects on the cortex, programming it to become fully social (Panksepp, 2009). Play appears to be indispensable when the brain is going through rapid development. Since the adult brain is not developing as rapidly, the driving force of play may not be as strong. Play can become the doorway to a new self, one that is much more in tune with the world (Brown, 2009). Looking at play from the AIP model, we could say that when the parent and the child experience mutual moments of joyful play, it creates new neural networks. If these networks continue to be activated and stimulated, the probability of these firing patterns becoming activated in the future is increased. Considering the neuronal connections in the brain develop in an "experience-dependent" way (Siegel, 1999), repetitive dyadic playful interactions can shape the structure of the child's social brain, allowing the child to have built-in networks associated with the ability for connection and social interactions.

When treating children with complex trauma, assessing the caregiver's ability to be playful is an important aspect of the initial phase of EMDR therapy.

The following are questions that can be included during the history taking and treatment planning phase: What do you do to have fun and be playful in your life now? Could you tell me about the last time you shared a playful moment with your child? How often do these moments happen now? When did the ability to be playful fade away? Ask the parent for his or her play history as they were growing up. Once you have established a baseline in terms of the parent's ability and current disposition to be playful, ask about the child's play history with others. Is the child having time in the present for playful activities? Chapters 5 and 12 will provide specific strategies that can be used during the preparation phase to improve the parent's disposition to be playful and reconnect with his or her ability to enjoy play.

Assessing parent's capacity for self-regulation. The emotional stability, the caretakers' ability to provide a safe and secure environment, and their capacity for affect regulation need to be addressed and explored. Allan Schore (2009), among others, has emphasized the role of the caregiver as a psychobiological external regulator of the child. The dysregulated parent is unable to modulate the child's internal states of arousal. Parents' presence may actually activate both the attachment system and the defense system (Liotti, 2009). These parent–child interactions generate disorganized internal states in the child's system. Having playful, attuned, synchronic parent–child interactions can foster the formation of new neuronal networks and reshape biological systems that lay at the core of the child's ability for emotion regulation.

Questions about the parent's coping style will shed information that can be used to create a treatment plan that will include goals to assist the caregiver in attaining more effective ways to cope and modulate affective states: *"How do you handle stress? What do you do to take care of yourself? How do you cope with difficult emotions? How effective are these coping mechanisms in helping you reach a positive emotional state? What emotion(s) do you find more difficult to manage? How is your support system?"* Assessing the amount of stress in the caregiver's life is important. *"What stressors do you have in your life now? What areas of your life create the majority of stress for you? How is your relationship with your spouse now?"* Some standardized instruments such as The Parenting Stress Index (PSI) (Abidin, 1995) can be used to assess the amount of stress present in the parent–child relationship.

Inquiring information about the mental health history of the family, especially of that of the caregivers, is critical. Considering how depression and, in general, parental psychopathology and unresolved trauma are important contributors to the development of insecure patterns of attachment in infants and children, a thorough exploration of the parent's mental health history is granted. Creating a timeline of the child's life with the parent's mental health history will be helpful in understanding the impact of the parent's pathology at different developmental stages (see Figure 2.2). Look at hospitalizations, suicidality, periods where the parent was stable and symptom-free, and periods of chronicity and acuity. The following is the time line of a 7-year-old female brought to therapy because the child was experiencing depression and self-injurious behaviors. During the intake, the mother

Figure 2.2 Time line of child's life and parent's emotional and mental health.
Note: DE, depressive episode; ME, manic episode; ML, memory loss; SA, suicide attempt.

reported having a diagnosis of bipolar disorder, a history of suicide attempts, and hospitalizations.

Based on this information, a picture of the environment that surrounded this child during the first years of her life and the attachment experiences that she was exposed to due to her mother's illness became evident.

ASSESSING THE STRENGTHS AND RESOURCES

The presence of adaptive and positive memory networks is indispensable before attempting the reprocessing of disturbing memories. A thorough evaluation of the internal and external resources that the child and the caregiver possess should be part of the clinical landscape. The ability to utilize these resources in the presence of triggering environmental stimulus should be included. A list or time line of all the mastery experiences, as well as the child's and parent's assets, should be identified during the initial interview. Discovering times when the parent felt successful as a parent and a sense of connection with the child is an important goal. In order to accomplish this objective, ask the parent to describe the best moments with the child and the elements that made this moment victorious in the parent's eyes.

DEVELOPING THE TARGETING SEQUENCE PLAN

As we develop the targeting sequence, we look at the emergence of symptoms, along with careful descriptions of the present triggers, including precipitating and ameliorating factors. Follow the next steps:

1. Identify the current symptom. This could be a behavior, a negative belief, a somatic response, or an emotion.
2. Identify the situations, events, and/or people that trigger the symptom.
3. Identify the earliest time the child has experienced this symptom or problem.
4. Create a time line of events where the symptom has been present.
5. Ask about the future goals or desired outcome and identify a future goal for each trigger.

TARGETING SEQUENCE TREATMENT PLAN FORM

1. **Presenting problem.** *What are the problems, symptoms, or issues your child is having right now?*
2. Incident that represents the problem or symptom. *What is the incident that best represents this problem or issue? Could you describe a time when your child had this problem or issue?*

3. Touchstone event and other past events. *What is the earliest time that you remember your child having the problem or issue you are reporting? Do you recall any other times in the past where this problem or issue was present?*

   Create a time line of events where this problem, symptom, or issue has been present.

   a. Touchstone Event (earliest)
   b. Worst Event (according to the parents)
   c. Other Past Events:

4. Present Triggers. *What situations, events, or people trigger this problem or issue? What usually happens before the problematic behavior, or what usually makes your child have these symptoms or problems?*

   Trigger 1 _____
   Trigger 2 _____
   Trigger 3 _____

5. Future Template. *How would you like your child to behave, feel, or think in the future when your child is in the presence of trigger 1, trigger 2, and trigger 3?*

   Identify a future goal for each trigger.

   Future template for trigger 1_____
   Future template for trigger 2_____
   Future template for trigger 3_____

CONDUCTING THE INTAKE INTERVIEW WITH THE CHILD

During the interview with the child, we are working on establishing a therapeutic alliance and on creating the foundation of safety and trust. Remember that you and your ability to foster a sense of trust and safety are the best tools. Your facial expressions, tone of voice, physical proximity, gestures, and eye contact and the quality of interactions with the child are the best containers and ways to help the child feel regulated as you explore current problems and traumatic memories. Incorporating play is crucial when working with children. According to Brown (2009), play represents a paramount way of keeping children feeling contained, regulated, and engaged in therapy. EMDR therapy needs to be presented in a way that is appealing, concrete, and playful. Playful activities keep the social engagement system active, allowing the child to safely explore events and situations that might be disturbing.

Be mindful of what the child can tolerate in terms of closeness. For a child who has not been provided with appropriate experiences of connection and affection, and who has learned to cope by shutting down the need for intimacy and closeness, a clinician showing too much closeness and affection could actually create internal discomfort. In these cases, closeness and nurturance need to be developed in a regulated titrated way. It should be introduced progressively as the child can tolerate it. However, the boundaries of the windows of tolerance need to be expanded and challenged as the child increases the capacity to accept closeness.

Meeting the child for the first time. The first meeting with the child is critical and sets the foundation for the formation of the therapeutic alliance. It should be a positive experience for the child. In my professional experience, scheduling an intake just with the caregivers, a session with the caregivers and the child and then a session just with the child has produced best results. With this, full and undivided attention can be provided to the child when meeting with the child alone. I usually introduce myself as a "helper" for children and families. The following is an example that can be used as an introduction:

"Hi Melanie, my name is Ana and I am so excited to meet you. I met with your parents last week and learned a few things about you and your family. I am really looking forward to getting to know you, and I hope you give me the opportunity to learn more about you. I have the wonderful job of helping kids, teens, and their families." Emphasize safety by saying, *"This is a very safe place for children and their families. As one of your helpers, my job is to make sure that you are safe here. This is a place where you can be you. Your opinions and your feelings are welcomed here. This is a place where you can say 'yes' and a place where you can say 'no'."* Clarify your role by saying, *"As a helper, I will listen to you and together we will find ways to help you with difficult feelings, thoughts, and worries. I will not hurt you in any way. I may teach you things even though I am not a school teacher. I am friendly and trustworthy, but I am not like one of your friends. I am on your side and will work on making sure that you are safe here and will work with your parents to help them keep you safe and take care of you. However, I am not like your mother or your father or a grandmother . . . I am a helper. Even though I am not like your parents, your teacher, or your friend, I am so excited to be in your life as your helper. I hope you can help me be the best helper I can be for you."*

It is pivotal to get information during the intake about the relationships formed between the child and other therapists. Oftentimes, corrective experiences need to be provided. A child whose prior therapist became her potential adoptive mother was extremely confused about my role during the initial sessions. The prior therapist for personal reasons did not end up adopting this child. However, this child thought that every therapist after this experience could be her potential "mommy." At the time I started working with her, this child had a new potential adoptive mother with whom she felt comfortable and safe. During the initial sessions, she showed extreme emotional dysregulation and oppositional behaviors toward the mother and me, the therapist. This child thought that if she formed a relationship with me, she would be leaving her current adoptive mother. In this case, the clarification of my role was fundamental, and it had to be done in the initial stages of treatment for almost every session.

Issues associated with confidentiality, especially with the caregivers, need to be addressed with the child and the caregivers. Making the process predictable will foster safety within the therapeutic relationship.

Notice how comfortable or uncomfortable the child is with respect to physical closeness and eye contact. A special handshake and a way to say hello can be developed with the child at the end of the first session. Notice if the child withdraws when asking for a handshake, or, on the opposite side, if the child gives a very aggressive strong handshake or high five. Notice the child's body posture, tone of voice, and activity level. Does the presence of the caregiver increase or reduce the child's activity level? How does the child respond to the separation from the caregiver and how does the child respond to the reunification with the caregiver? Does the child show difficulty separating from the parent? Does the child become really clingy or, on the contrary, does not engage much with the parent? When the parent joins the session, does the child engage with the caregiver or ignores the parent? Are there any differences in how the child interacts with the mother or the father? Once again, we are looking for responses and behaviors that provide data on the level of security in the child's attachment bond with each caregiver or the presence of anxiety, avoidance, or disorganization in these interactions.

CREATING THE COMPLETE CLINICAL LANDSCAPE

Once all the information has been gathered, the development of a comprehensive treatment plan and clinical landscape that can guide treatment is indispensable. Clinicians may be compelled to initiate treatment and use strategies too soon after meeting with the caregivers. It is true that oftentimes crisis intervention strategies and stabilization work needs to be initiated almost immediately. However, when treatment is initiated without a comprehensive and cohesive treatment outline, the treatment strategies will lack intentionality and direction. This has the potential to make EMDR therapy fragmented and ineffective. In addition, many new EMDR clinicians may see EMDR therapy as too mechanical and in pieces or fragments. Failing to see the whole and only seeing the parts may lead EMDR clinicians to provide a treatment that lacks cohesiveness and direction. This could compromise the outcome of therapy and may lengthen the overall time of treatment. How the preparation phase and all the reprocessing phases are organized and tailored to each specific case is ultimately based on the information gathered during the initial phase of EMDR therapy. This is not to say that, as EMDR therapy moves forward, adaptations and changes are made as new information arrives. A thorough clinical landscape should include the following information:

1. The child's targeting sequence: The current symptoms, triggers, past events, and future template should be developed thoroughly and clearly. There are two main approaches clinicians can take when developing a targeting sequence for children. The first one is the symptom-informed treatment planning oftentimes used with adults. When using this approach, the clinician is only interested in identifying past adverse or traumatic experiences that are associated with the current symptoms. The second approach uses a more developmental perspective and is concerned with all the negative experiences in the entire life span of the child. The clinician may create time lines and work on singling out all the experiences of adversity in each developmental stage. Oftentimes, these two ways of approaching treatment planning with children may not yield a big difference in the targeting sequence as may be the case with adults. This is due to the potentially greater number of adverse and traumatic experiences that adults may have as compared to children. This is only logical, considering the number of years children have lived in comparison to adults. Oftentimes, the information may not be much different in children when using a symptom-informed versus a developmental-focused treatment plan.
2. Whether a symptom-informed treatment plan has been selected or not, the clinician should have a thorough developmental history of the child.
3. The clinician should create a clear map of the present dysfunctional dysregulated parent–child interactions that need to be corrected and repaired. In addition, the child's unmet developmental needs should be identified along with parental deficits.
4. The clinician needs to pinpoint existing internal and external strengths and resources of the child, the parent, and the family system. Extended family members, mentors, peers, and teachers, among others, constitute other important relationships and attachment figures. The quality of these relationships, should also be thoroughly assessed and explored.

5. In addition, the clinician should create a map of parent–child interactions that are regulating to the child and the parent and the ones that are mutually activating. This will yield the specific interactions that continue to enhance memory networks containing positive and negative representations of the self, the other, and the world.

Once the clinical landscape has been delineated, the organization and planning of the eight phases of EMDR therapy begins. Even though each phase has specific procedural steps, each child will come with specific needs, talents, and deficits that should be honored in each step of EMDR therapy. Some phases offer more flexibility than others. The preparation phase is especially flexible and is completely organized, depending on the needs of each child and family. How much time is allotted to correcting and repairing maladaptive parent–child interactions, working individually with the child and or the caregiver, providing psychoeducation and working on affect regulation will vary and depend on the treatment plan and clinical landscape laid out for each child. The reprocessing phases also have room for flexibility. The use of interweaves of different kinds will also be determined by the needs of the child. Once again, these needs have been already singled out during the case formulation and treatment planning in early stages of treatment. The treatment strategies selected for each child are guided by the AIP model and EMDR procedures, as well as by the specific needs of the child and family. If EMDR clinicians start to intervene without a clear landscape, they take the risk of providing a treatment that lacks direction and time may be spent in treatment strategies that do not serve a clear purpose. For example, an EMDR clinician working with a child struggling with the divorce of his parents identifies the presence of anger, and soon after intake, the clinician asks the child to write a letter. This letter, according to the clinician, is used to help the child express all his feelings of anger toward his parents. This clinician reports that she wants to eventually do EMDR therapy with this child, but she feels that he is not ready. When we look at this case and how treatment strategies have been selected, they evidently lack direction and appropriate case formulation. How does the letter fit into a comprehensive treatment plan? Does the child possess enough ability to regulate affect to sustain the expression of such feelings to his parents? In addition, this clinician appears to equate EMDR therapy with just the reprocessing phases of EMDR. From the moment a case is conceptualized using the AIP model, EMDR therapy is initiated. Moreover, it is not clear where writing a letter may fit in the eight phases of EMDR therapy. The purpose of the letter is also unclear. Is the purpose to create catharsis by helping the child release feelings of anger? If so, this is not the purpose of EMDR therapy. Integration and assimilation of maladaptive material, not catharsis, is the ultimate goal of EMDR therapy. Using this example, it is evident how, without a thoroughly organized clinical landscape, treatment has the potential of being disjointed, fragmented, and ultimately ineffective.

Developing containment before exploring trauma memories. When working with complex trauma, state change strategies should be taught before exploring traumatic material. In some cases, extensive preparation and stabilization should be done. This area will be extensively covered in the next chapter, and several strategies that can help the child and caregiver develop affect regulation will be thoroughly described.

SUMMARY AND CONCLUSIONS

Developing sound and thorough case formulations and treatment plans are pivotal to the final outcome of EMDR therapy. When creating the initial clinical landscape, an extensive exploration of the past, the present and the goals for the future is fundamental. When working with complex trauma, attachment insecurity, and dissociation, thorough exploration of the past and the present parent–child interaction and the quality of their attachment bond should be attained. Meticulous and comprehensive assessment of the history of trauma, losses, and attachment injuries of the child and the parent will lay the foundation for the development of treatment plans that can lead to successful outcomes. In the long run, spending sufficient time during the initial phase of EMDR therapy will save time and energy. This chapter emphasizes the need for developing comprehensive treatment plans that in turn can provide clear pathways and direction throughout the different phases of EMDR therapy.

APPENDIX: PARENT'S RATING SCALE

Name of Client: _____

Name of Caregiver: _____

Date: _____

I would like to know about your relationship with your child. This form lists areas of you, as a parent, and areas of interaction with your child. Please take some time to think about how easy or difficult it is for you to execute the following tasks. Using a scale from 0 to 10, where 0 represents no difficulty at all and 10 the highest level of difficulty, circle the number that best describes your ability to perform each task. Below each question please write an example of an interaction between you and your child associated with your rating. Please avoid wishful thinking and try to go more with your gut response. The more accurate this information is, the better I will be able to assist you and your child in reaching your goals in therapy:

1. Set boundaries with my child

    0 1 2 3 4 5 6 7 8 9 10

    This is an example _____
    _____

2. Have physical-nurturing contact with my child (eye contact, hugs etc.)

    0 1 2 3 4 5 6 7 8 9 10

    This is an example _____
    _____

3. Figure out what my child is feeling at any given time

    0 1 2 3 4 5 6 7 8 9 10

    This is an example _____
    _____

4. Figure out what my child needs at any given time

0 1 2 3 4 5 6 7 8 9 10

This is an example _____
_____

5. Help my child when he or she is hurt

0 1 2 3 4 5 6 7 8 9 10

This is an example _____
_____

6. Help my child when he or she is angry

0 1 2 3 4 5 6 7 8 9 10

This is an example _____
_____

7. Help my child when he or she is scared

0 1 2 3 4 5 6 7 8 9 10

This is an example _____
_____

8. Help my child when he or she is sad

0 1 2 3 4 5 6 7 8 9 10

This is an example _____
_____

9. Calm myself down when my child is acting out

0 1 2 3 4 5 6 7 8 9 10

This is an example _____
_____

10. Set boundaries with my child when I am not feeling good

0 1 2 3 4 5 6 7 8 9 10

This is an example _____
_____

11. Deal with my own worries and problems

0 1 2 3 4 5 6 7 8 9 10

This is an example _____
_____

12. Allow my child to explore the world safely on his or her own

    | 0 1 2 3 4 5 6 7 8 9 10 |

    This is an example _____

    _____

13. Trust my child

    | 0 1 2 3 4 5 6 7 8 9 10 |

    This is an example _____

    _____

14. Trust that as a parent I will be able to help my child

    | 0 1 2 3 4 5 6 7 8 9 10 |

    This is an example _____

    _____

15. Support and nurture my child when he or she is not performing or is underachieving

    | 0 1 2 3 4 5 6 7 8 9 10 |

    This is an example _____

    _____

16. Encourage freedom and spontaneity in my child

    | 0 1 2 3 4 5 6 7 8 9 10 |

    This is an example _____

    _____

17. Play with my child

    | 0 1 2 3 4 5 6 7 8 9 10 |

    This is an example _____

    _____

3

Phase Two: Preparation

*T*he work directed toward increasing the child's ability to tolerate and regulate affect, so that the processing of traumatic material can be achieved, is initiated during the preparation phase. The process of providing the neural stimulation to improve the child's capacity to bond, regulate, explore, and play should begin during the early phases of eye movement desensitization and reprocessing (EMDR) therapy. Stimulating neurogenesis and synaptogenesis by promoting the formation of new synaptic connections is necessary with children lacking appropriate developmental experiences. This is accomplished by providing repetitive and corrective experiences of safety and connection. Children with attachment traumas and dissociative tendencies will need more multifaceted work during the preparation phase. Due to the nature of these children's injuries and the pervasive quality of their deficits, what is done with simple trauma cases will not be sufficient or effective with this population. Throughout the preparation phase, different systems need to be accessed: the attachment system, the defense system, play and motivation systems, and emotional and affective systems. In many cases, the experiences necessary to develop a healthy sense of self were never part of these children's lives. According to Perry (2006), "Children growing up in chaos, neglect, and threat do not have fundamental experiences required to express their underlying genetic potential to self-regulate, relate, communicate, and think" (p. 28). Often, memories of safety and connection are completely absent in these children's lives. As a result, attempting to install resources or use state change strategies such as the "calm-safe place" may fail initially. The reprocessing of traumatic experiences cannot take place if the adaptive and positive neural networks do not exist (Shapiro, 2001). According to Perry and Hambrick (2008), "A neural system cannot be changed without activating it, just as one cannot learn how to write by hearing about how to write without practicing" (p. 42). With this in mind, the preparation phase with this population may involve activities and experiences that, in turn, create new neural systems and can bring the social engagement systems back on-line. If the child had never experienced moments of safety, then experiences of safety and regulation are promoted. If the child had not experienced appropriate and healthy nurturing touch, then experiences in which touch can be felt and integrated as positive and regulating should be encouraged.

When working with children with profound deficits, the preparation phase may begin by providing, through different avenues, the experiences of connection, nurturance, touch, play, and safety so that new memory networks can be formed in the child's system. Experiences in which the child feels internally regulated can create new patterns of neural activation, which, in turn, can be enhanced and integrated by the use of EMDR therapy procedures and protocols. Moreover, the utilization of adjunct approaches and activities, such as Theraplay, somatic interventions, ego state strategies, sandtray and play therapy, and physical play activities may be necessary, depending on the severity and complexity of the case. Moreover, models and theories, such as the neurosequential model of therapeutics (Perry, 2006), affective neuroscience (Panksepp, 1998, 2009), interpersonal neurobiology (Siegel, 1999, 2010), regulation theory (Schore, 2001, 2009), and the polyvagal theory (Porges, 2011), can enrich our understanding of the work necessary during the preparation phase of children with pervasive dysregulation of the affective system.

THE PREPARATION PHASE OF EMDR THERAPY AND THE POLYVAGAL THEORY

The Polyvagal theory presents a hierarchical model of the autonomic system (Porges, 2011). According to Porges, the bidirectional reciprocal communication between bodily states, visceral organs, and brain structure is mediated through the autonomic system. The polyvagal theory emphasizes the importance of the parasympathetic ventral vagal system that allows individuals to adapt flexibly to their environment, as well as to connect with others. Porges emphasizes how autonomic states are linked to social behaviors and prosocial emotions. In complexly traumatized children, the development of this system has been compromised due to the early dysregulated and traumatizing interactions with their environments and caregivers. As stated by Porges (2011), a defining feature of psychopathology is the person's inability to inhibit defense systems in safe environments and the inability to activate defense systems in the presence of danger. The inaccurate assessment of safety and danger may lie at the core of difficulties experienced by children with histories of abuse, neglect, and exposure to frightened and frightening attachment experiences. Children diagnosed with reactive attachment disorder exhibit, in Porges's words, "faulty neuroception" of danger and safety and compromised social engagement systems. According to Porges (2009), "Social separation and isolation from humans, regardless of age, leads to profound disruption in the ability to regulate physiological states and compromises both physical and mental health" (p. 119). Promoting the stimulation and activation of the social engagement system is an important goal of the preparation phase. Activities with other people that help the child experience a sense of safety and regulation will certainly start to stimulate ventral vagal structures. Play, fun, laughter, pleasure, movement, and touch will invigorate the ventral vagal system and the subcortical areas of the brain. Restoring some level of connection with others through therapeutic family sessions may be necessary for some children and their families during the initial phases of EMDR therapy. In addition, Porges (2011) brought up how social engagement depends on how well we can regulate the muscles of our faces and heads. The neural regulation of the facial and head muscles influences neuroception of safety or danger. Facial affect can activate neuroception of danger and result in compromised emotion regulation and social engagement. With this in mind, exercises that progressively stimulate the child's ability to make eye contact, modulate the voice, and display contingent facial expressions may be incorporated initially during the preparation phase and continue throughout the different phases of EMDR therapy.

ACCESSING AND STIMULATING DIFFERENT SYSTEMS DURING THE PREPARATION PHASE

Strategies and activities that have the potential of bringing integration of different affective and cognitive systems in the brain and promote emotional homeostasis should be incorporated into the different phases of EMDR therapy. With this in mind, when working with children with complex trauma, the preparation phase should incorporate activities and exercises that promote the development, integration, and healing of the following systems:

The attachment system: When working with this system, provide corrective attachment experiences that could create new and enhance existing neuronal networks in the brain. These experiences can create new firing patterns in the brain with positive associations about the self in connection to others. Strengthening the parent–child attachment bond and developing a safe and trusting relationship between parent and child will provide containment and emotional balance, and will expand the child's windows of affect tolerance. Theraplay activities could be very useful during the preparation phase and could be a very helpful adjunct approach to EMDR treatment (see Chapter 12). Engaging other adults in the child's support system who can provide corrective experiences is pivotal. A relationally invigorating atmosphere will provide the stimulation the brain needs to develop subcortical areas.

The defense system: When working with this system, provide opportunities for the child's social engagement system to develop and become available to the child. For many children, the long-term availability of the social engagement system has been compromised due to early and chronic trauma (Porges, 2009). Mobilization and immobilization responses have been conditioned, resulting in great deficits in social interactions. Fight, flight, activated freeze, and immobilization responses (Porges, 2011), can be elicited by even minor environmental stimuli. Making opportunities available to start exercising the social engagement system is important during the preparation phase. Encouraging parents to have these children participate in rough and tumble play, martial arts, dance, and music activities may be recommended as EMDR therapy is initiated. Having the body be an active participant in the therapeutic process by involving somatic strategies (see Chapter 11) can help soothe and regulate lower parts of the brain.

The play and exploration system: When working with this system, provide opportunities for play, laughter, and excitement. Animal and human researches have shown how play cannot take place when the organism is in a state of alarm or fear (Pellegrini, 2009; Panksepp, 2009; Brown, 2009). Children growing up in unsafe, chaotic, traumatizing, and neglectful environments have not had the opportunity to exercise their play urges. According to Panksepp (2009), the cortex and the social brain are developed and built through tools such as play, especially physical play. With this in mind, we have to wonder how the lack and deprivation of play that some traumatized children may have experienced could affect the development of social and affective circuits in the brain. As stated during the client history and treatment-planning phase, a thorough assessment of the play history of the child should be included. Parents should be highly encouraged to have the child participate in physical sports and physical playful activities as the child is undergoing EMDR therapy. Moreover, the incorporation of fun strategies and approaches within the EMDR treatment is fundamental in order to stimulate and maintain an active social engagement system as well as to promote the development of adaptive and positive memory systems in the child's brain. Keeping a good sense of humor and having laughter as part of the interactions with the child and the caregivers enhances the ability of the child and the caregiver to experience and tolerate positive affect. However, it is important that the clinician does it with enough attunement so the child can still stay within tolerable levels of arousal. Keep in mind that the child and the caregiver will have different levels of tolerance for connection and warmth. A child who has developed an avoidant pattern of attachment with his or her primary caregiver may find the warmth and nurturing interactions of the clinician highly activating and dysregulating. Providing exposure to closeness and nurturance should be done gradually as the child can tolerate it. However, the therapist needs to provide opportunities for the child and the caregiver to experience moments of closeness and connection. This can be done by incorporating Theraplay, directive play therapy, and nondirective play therapy strategies, where the caregiver and the child are involved in playful and fun interactions. In addition, the EMDR clinician can enhance these positive experiences that may include touch, feeding, singing, laughter etc., by using bilateral stimulation (BLS) while the child is experiencing these positive states.

The affective and emotional systems: Providing interactive experiences that can enhance the child's capacity to tolerate and manage affect should be an important part of the preparation phase. Helping the child feel a sense of containment is essential. Creating a secure harbor in which emotions, thoughts, and bodily states can be safely embraced, experienced, reclaimed, processed, and integrated is critical.

One of the main objectives of the preparation phase is to expand the child's ability to tolerate negative and positive affect. Safe place, resource development and installation (RDI), and containers, among others, constitute some of the strategies and protocols used during the preparation phase of EMDR therapy with children. The augmentation of the child's capacity to experience positive affect is a fundamental aspect of EMDR therapy. Experiences that promote the development of new and positive neuronal connections should be provided at this point and throughout the entire EMDR treatment. Working with the child's support system to stimulate the child's capacity to connect with others is pivotal. The child's need to connect, love, and socialize is biological; therefore, taking steps to meet this need and promote some level of connection with others can increase the child's sense of safety and containment. Modeling activities that include play, laughter, and connection can show the caregivers how to continue to provide these corrective experiences at home. All these positive affective experiences can then be enhanced by using bilateral stimulation (BLS) and resource development and installation protocols.

PREPARING CHILDREN FOR EMDR THERAPY

Talking to Children About Trauma

Children who have experienced trauma tend to avoid anything that is reminiscent of the traumatic event. The use of metaphors and analogies can help children create distance from what otherwise could be overwhelming. They also constitute a language that can easily access the right brain. In our dreams, we communicate through symbols, stories, and analogies. The values and traditions of every society and generation are passed onto the new generations through stories. EMDR therapy and trauma can be more easily embraced and understood through the use of analogies, metaphors, and stories. Below are some analogies that can be used to explain trauma to children.

1. **The "geode" analogy**: This analogy can assist children in looking at the potential positive outcome of working through the traumatic events in their lives. Geodes are rock cavities with internal crystal formations. All geodes hold unique shades, colors, and compositions despite the rough exterior. The unseen uniqueness held in each geode is only discovered when the geode is cracked open. When the covert crystals are exposed, the prize is found. When we look at trauma like the geode, the exterior is rough. However, it holds within its core the possibility for expansion and transformation. Only when we embrace it will we find the crystals in our life. According to Esly carvalho (personal communication, August 6, 2010), as a result of experiencing trauma and adversity, we may have learned lies about ourselves and about who we are. We may have learned that we are unlovable or bad, or that we do not deserve good things. We can tell kids how EMDR therapy can help us recover the truth about who we really are. Since the geode is the symbol of trauma and adversity, we invite children to metaphorically crack open the geodes in their lives so they can discover the truth about who they really are. We then find the crystals that represent the new sense of self found through the work with EMDR. This is a powerful analogy for older children, which can create the first bridge of communication about trauma and healing. Once the child has completed the work in therapy, you could give the child a geode as a symbol of the transformation accomplished through the therapeutic work. Once the child receives the geode, it is important to go through the different crystals and name them with the new positive emotions, cognitions and bodily states found throughout the child's therapeutic work.

2. **The pearl analogy:** EMDR clinicians attending one of my training programs in Ecuador inspired this analogy. The creation of a pearl is a truly extraordinary event. The life of a pearl begins with a foreign object entering the inner body of an oyster. In order to protect itself from the irritation caused by this foreign object, the oyster secretes a substance. Over time, this foreign object will be completely enclosed by layers and layers of the oyster's protective substance. The result is a marvelous and wonderful pearl, which represents the work of the oyster's protective and defensive system. This is a wonderful analogy that can help children understand, identify, honor, and celebrate what they have used to protect and defend themselves from negative events. In addition, it can help them see how they will never find the pearls they have constructed in their lives if they never open the shell. EMDR clinicians can be ingenious and invent ways to have children create their own shells with small colorful rocks that represent their "life pearls" and survival resources.

3. **The tree analogy**: The following analogy was created with the purpose of assisting children in understanding how challenging situations may offer opportunities for transformation. Out of the work we do to survive, unique qualities emerge in us. You can say, *"When a tree is in the dark or when the branches die, the tree continues to grow around, always searching for the light. The loss of a branch causes the tree to transform and grow in exceptional ways that give the tree its unique shape. When we go through challenging situations in life, we also have to stretch to find the light and with it an opportunity to grow and transform. My job as a helper is to support you in finding the light again in your life. Keep in mind that as you search for the light, special qualities in you develop and grow, making you the unique person you are."*

4. **The analogy of the bag of mixed-up stuff:** This analogy helps children understand what happens when we experience trauma and the potential negative effects of repressing these memories (Gomez, 2007). You can say, *"When we have yucky things that happen to us, we have many mixed-up feelings and many mixed-up thoughts. We do not feel good in our minds, bodies, and hearts. It is like carrying bags of mixed-up stuff. When we are so busy carrying all these bags, we do not have space in our hearts, minds, and bodies for the good feelings and thoughts. If we work on making those bags smaller or even get rid of them, we will have space for the good feelings and the good thoughts."*

5. **The brain's glasses analogy:** This is designed to help children understand how the experiences we have had in our lives have shaped the brain and colored our present reality. You can say, *"When we have bad experiences or events in our lives, our brains will pay much more or much less attention to anything that might be similar in some way to the bad thing that happened. The brain might see things much bigger or much smaller than they really are. The brain does not do this with a bad intention. It is actually making sure that we don't suffer or feel pain so we can survive. If the brain thinks that what is happening is too big, then we will act in ways that are too big. This might actually get us in trouble. If the brain thinks that what is happening is too small, then we will act in ways that are too small. This might put us in danger, because we might not defend ourselves in the presence of a real danger."* Give examples you may know or use examples from the child's life. Say, *"For example, I know that you have many experiences with kids bullying you at school. Now, when a kid says 'you have funny glasses' you punch him or push him right away. Once again, because, the experiences you had in the past with bullies, now your brain sees any remarks from other kids as, 'they are trying to bully me'. This is a way of seeing it that is too big, and as a result, what you do is also really big. For example, you have punched other kids, and this has gotten you in trouble. What is important about this is that when you have these big feelings and behaviors, it is not because you are a bad or a troubled kid, but because your brain is seeing things 'too big' or 'too small.' This is happening because of the bad or yucky things that happened to you in the past. Keep in mind that the brain does this to protect you and make sure that you survive and don't feel hurt. Now let's think about other things that your brain might see as too small or too big."* Continue to assist the child in identifying current triggers and current problematic responses. Remind the child that the goal is to help the brain, the heart and the body work on the yucky things that happened so they can see things as they really are, and respond in ways that help us be safe, get along with others and feel good.

6. **The "file" analogy:** This analogy works really well with older children or pre-adolescents. You can use this analogy with regular files or computer files, so use the terms accordingly. Say, *"When we have bad or negative events in our lives, the brain creates 'files' that contain all the feelings, thoughts, and body sensations connected to this event. When we have events that are not 'too bad,' the brain has the capacity to work on these files before storing them and locking them up as memories. What is stored has been sorted out and organized so the negative stuff has been let go, allowing us to keep the good stuff and learn from this experience. However, when the event is really bad or has happened several times, these files get overloaded and the brain can't do the work of sorting things out. As a result, these files are all messy and in pieces that are not put together or organized by the brain. Different life events we call 'triggers' can open up these files or click on them (if using the computer analogy). For example* (repeat some of the current triggers of the child), *when these triggers open up the files, we start to have again the mixed-up feelings, thoughts, and body reactions we had when the bad stuff happened. Because the brain has not organized all the pieces of these files, we don't even notice that these files are being opened. This causes*

us to behave or act in ways that could be 'too big' (exaggerated responses. Repeat some of the child's current responses, symptoms, or problems) *or 'too small'* (lack of reaction due to immobilization-shutdown responses being activated)."

Talking to Children About EMDR Therapy

After the concept of trauma has been addressed with the child, we have the perfect opportunity to introduce EMDR therapy. If you are using the geode analogy, say, *"I know something that can help you with the geodes in your life. We can work through these geodes and find the hidden crystals in your life and the truth about who you really are."* If you are using the tree analogy, explain how you both could work as a team to find the light in the child's life. By doing this, the child can grow stronger in the wounded areas. If you used the analogy of the mixed-up stuff bag, you can say, *"I know something called EMDR that can help kids make the bags of mixed-up feelings and thoughts smaller or even get rid of them. This way, you can have space in your mind, heart, and body for the good feelings and the good thoughts."* If you are using the analogy of the brain's glasses, you can say, *"I know something called EMDR that can help the brain with all the bad experiences you had in the past. This way, the brain does not have to see things in ways that are "too big or too small" but the size they really are."* If you are using the analogy of the "files," say, *"I know something called EMDR that can help you by working on those files that make you have* (repeat the child's symptoms and current problems). *EMDR can help you sort out the files, put the pieces together, and organize them so that when people or events click on these files, you don't have negative feelings and thoughts anymore. Instead, you remember what you learned from this difficult experience."*

Continue to explain EMDR therapy by saying, *"When we do EMDR, you will think about the bad or yucky thing that happened to you while moving your eyes from one side to another. When we do this, your brain can work on sorting out the files, putting all the pieces together, and organizing them so that you can let go of the mixed-up feelings, thoughts, and body sensations while keeping the good ones. If you have a hard time doing eye movement, we can tap or use headphones* (show the devices and allow the child to play with them). *When doing EMDR, you can say whatever comes to your mind, whatever you feel, or whatever comes to your body; there is no right or wrong way of doing EMDR."*

You can also use the book I authored called *"Dark, Bad Day...Go Away,"* which explains EMDR to children. It uses the digestion analogy to explain what happens in the brain because of adverse events and trauma, and how EMDR can help. Emphasize how EMDR can help children find the truth about who they really are. Say, *"When bad things happen to us, we learn a lot of bad things about who we are. We may have learned that we are bad or that we do not deserve good things in life. We may have learned to be sad or very scared all the time. Our bodies may have learned to feel tired or to be on the go all the time. When we do EMDR, we visit the memories we have of the bad things that happened to us so that we can find the truth about who we are. Remember, we are just visiting the memory. It is not happening again; it is just a visit in our minds. Then, we can discover how good we are and how we do deserve good things in life. We may learn to be happy and find our exciting feelings again. Our bodies may find a way to feel more energy and to be still and enjoy our calm moments. If we keep all the yucky stuff inside, we may never find the truth about who we are, and we will continue to live our lives based on lies. So let's take a trip to find the truth."*

Explaining the Different Forms of Bilateral Stimulation

When describing the various forms of bilateral stimulation (BLS), go over the different options and practice with the child. When explaining eye movement, you can use a set of finger puppets that I call "EMDR helpers." This team consists of a group of finger puppets with names that form the acronym EMDR: Elizabeth, Mario, David, and Robbie (Gomez, 2007, 2009). The EMDR helpers can also provide tactile stimulation if the child has difficulty using eye movement. You can also create a song for the EMDR helpers to make the process more playful and appealing for the child.

The eye movement can be done using magic wands, hand puppets, laser pens, and so on. The butterfly hug has been used widely in individual and in group settings with children and adults (Artigas, 1999). Drumming, walking, or stomping feet can also be utilized. In addition, paint brushes and feathers can be used to provide tactile bilateral stimulation.

Addressing the Potential Outcome of Experiencing Negative Affect During Reprocessing

This is an aspect of EMDR therapy that must be addressed early on; otherwise, we have the risk of children stopping the process once the negative affect is activated. Children may expect immediate relief after reprocessing is initiated. As a result, they might experience EMDR therapy as not helpful or even scary. They might also feel betrayed by the clinician who reassured them that EMDR therapy was going to help them feel better. Make the process predictable by saying, *"If you start to have thoughts, feelings, and body sensations that bother you, it is your brain's signal for letting you know that it is working on those files or bags and that some of the pieces of these files are coming up so the brain can put them together. It is important to let the brain do the work. However, if visiting those past memories or yucky stuff gets way too hard to do, you can stop doing EMDR at any time by saying stop or raising your hand."*

Emphasizing Present Awareness

Maintaining awareness of the present safety is crucial when reprocessing traumatic memories (Shapiro, 2001). Highly traumatized children tend to be avoidant of remembering traumatic events for the fear of getting trapped in these memories and unable to escape. They feel powerless to change or control the emotions associated with these memories. This may result in what many authors refer to as the "fear of the fear" (van der Kolk, 1996) or the "phobia of the trauma" (van der Hart, 2006). Making the process predictable and emphasizing the transitory and impermanent character of the "visit" to the memory can help children master this fear. The following is an example of how this issue can be addressed. You may say, *"We will just VISIT those memories in our minds and we can leave and come back at any time. We are not going back or staying there. These events or things are not happening again and no one will hurt you while we visit these memories. Remember that you are safe here and now."* Enough resources should be provided to increase the child's sense of safety and containment. Resource development for children with complex trauma will be extensively covered in this chapter.

Another analogy that can be used with children is the "pool analogy." This analogy is also helpful for EMDR clinicians to clearly conceptualize the work that often is necessary when working with complex cases. A symbol that can be used to represent the memories of trauma and hardship is a "pool." Simple trauma can be seen as a "pool" where the child, for the most part, can jump in right away. The child already has the life jackets (resources) necessary to dive into the pool (trauma and adverse events) fairly quickly. However, children with complex trauma come into treatment with deep and challenging pools, "phobia of pools," and without any floating devices. The initial work will be directed to helping the child develop appropriate floating devices and overcome the phobia of the pool. Children with complex trauma will be fearful of going into the pool even when having appropriate life jackets. As a result, strategies to go "in" and "out" of the pool will need to be utilized. Initially, the child will just put a finger inside the pool and then come back out. Later, the full hand can go in and so on until the child and the therapist can fully dive into the pool. When using this analogy, make sure it is used with children who do not have adverse experiences that happened inside a pool or that are related to drowning. Needless to say, children only need a simple explanation that conveys the "in" and "out" visits to the "pool" until the child can master these visits and leave the pool behind in the past. Children who enjoy swimming and water will find this analogy fun and enjoyable. The child can create life jackets that can help when visiting the pool. The life jackets and floating devices contain all the resources the child is developing. An actual life jacket can be brought up to the therapy sessions and all the resources can be taped to the jacket to make this more tangible to the child.

Explaining the Stop Signal

When teaching and practicing the stop signal, make sure you let the child know that we stop only if the feelings are too big and way out of what we can manage. On the other hand, give reassurance to the child. Let the child know that it is appropriate to stop and take a break. This does not mean that he or she is not brave or strong. Once again, remind the child *"as much as possible, we let the brain do the work; but if it gets way too hard, we can use our stop signal."* If this is not explained clearly, the child might use the stop signal every time the negative affect or the traumatic material is accessed.

Creating a Safe Place

Children who have experienced complex trauma and did not develop a secure foundation in their attachment with caregivers tend to have greater deficits in affect regulation. As a result, they are unable to identify a calm, safe, or happy place. They just do not possess the memory networks that contain information about feeling safe. These children never had the experiences that could allow these memory networks to form. Moreover, if these children are able to identify a calm or safe place, very often the safe place becomes contaminated after initiating BLS. The child may report negative associations to this place, or the child may start to access disturbing material very quickly when BLS is initiated.

When BLS is provided during the reprocessing of memories of trauma, it appears that synthesis happens in the brain, and the memory networks that contain maladaptive information bind and link up to the networks that contain adaptive and positive information (Shapiro, 2001). The binding and linkage of memory networks from different systems is what appears to result in the integration of the different aspects of the memory into a larger adaptive memory network. During the preparation phase, BLS is provided with the purpose of enhancing memory networks that contain information about resources and mastery experiences. The sets of BLS are slow and short with the goal of enhancing these networks, while preventing the child from accessing disturbing material. However, highly traumatized children may tend to access traumatic material more rapidly, even when developing and instal-ling resources. If we look at the conceptual cartoon of the brain of a type 3 case (see Chapter 1), we can hypothetically say that the networks that contain adaptive and positive information are almost nonexistent. As a result, when the memory system that contains information about safety is accessed and BLS is initiated, it could link up very rapidly to information that is maladaptive and disturbing. Moreover, children may move more rapidly into hyper- and hypoarousal and dissociative states, even during the installation of resources. Type 1 cases have been exposed to experiences of safety, nurturance, and connection with their caregivers. Finding a safe place is usually an easy task for these children. During RDI, the likelihood that these chil-dren could access disturbing information is minimal. On the contrary, type 2 and type 3 cases present with great deficits. Experiences of safety, love, and connection with their caregivers are minimal or totally absent. It is almost expected that these children could have difficulty identifying and utilizing resources or state-change strategies, such as the "calm-safe" place. Due to the pervasive nature of the deficits that these children present, extensive preparation may be necessary. Making the process fun and playful can facilitate this process. A 7-year-old boy who had experienced serious neglect in his early years was resistant to working with the calm–safe place protocol. Despite extensive preparation and having a good level of environmental stability, he always responded to any activity with, "That is boring." I had to come up with a fun activity to increase his level of motivation and participation. I found out that he really liked to play and eat potato chips. I asked him if he wanted to participate in a pretend TV show called *Who Wants to Be a Potato Chips Millionaire?* In this show, he would be playing for potato chips. He was really excited and agreed to play the pretend game I was sugges-ting. Then, I started the "show" by saying, " *Ladies and gentlemen, welcome to our show,* Who Wants to be a Potato Chips Millionaire. *We have here our first contestant. Please tell us your name."* Using a microphone, I asked basic questions about his life and explained how all the questions were going to be about finding a safe, happy place. Then, I said, *"Now, you will be playing for one potato chip; ready? Please find a place where you feel happy, calm, or safe. This can be a real or an imaginary place. Remember that this is a place where noth-ing bad or yucky has ever happened."* He was able to find a place and win his first potato chip. The next question was about the feelings he had when he thought about his calm, safe, happy place, and once he found them, he earned another potato chip. The entire time, I continued to play the role of a TV show host, and the child playfully followed each step of the calm–safe place protocol. When I asked this boy what had made it easier for him to work on his calm, safe, happy place, he stated that pretending to be on a TV show made it exciting. The goal here was not to positively reinforce each answer with potato chips, but to stimulate the play system and the social engagement system, and to make this activity fun and appealing for this boy while learning and practicing an EMDR state-change activity.

Some children who have difficulty finding a calm, safe, happy place may be able to discover it in their dreams. Ask about any dreams in the past where they felt calm, safe, or happy and ask the child to draw a picture or describe the place. If they have not had any dreams that contain such a place, tell them that they could ask their "dreaming self" or the "dreaming me" for a calm, safe, happy place. Let them know that some-times the "dreaming self" may have this special place and sometimes it may not. Let the child know that there is nothing wrong with having a "dreaming self" that does not have a calm, safe, happy place.

CALM–SAFE–HAPPY PLACE PROTOCOL

If the child went through the calm–safe place protocol successfully, motivating the child to actually use it when facing environmental triggers is an important goal. Every time the child is able to utilize the calm–safe place, his or her ability to change affective states and regulate internal states is enhanced. In order to assist the child in using the calm–safe place when needed, start by identifying where the triggers are occurring in the child's life. This will help you determine the best way to help the child remember to use the calm–safe place. If the child gets triggered mostly at night, then a glow in the dark picture of the safe place in the child's room might be helpful. If the child is triggered mostly at school, a transitional object or a napkin with the picture of the safe place that the child can carry in his or her pocket will be more appropriate. The following ideas will assist you in making the safe place more available, appealing, and motivating for children.

- Ask the child to create the safe or happy place in the sand box. Take a picture and give a copy to the child for his or her room.
- Have the child draw a picture of the safe or happy place and ask the child to use glow-in-the-dark paint to trace it. Later on, the child can put the picture of the safe place near his or her bed; this way, if the child wakes up scared, the safe place is visible to the child. The child may also draw a picture of the safe place or any other resource on a pillowcase using fabric markers (Figure 3.1).
- Have the child draw a picture of the safe, happy place on a small piece of fabric using fabric markers and instruct the child to take the napkin in his or her pocket to school. This ensures that if the child is triggered or is having upsetting feelings, the safe place will be more accessible to the child.
- Have the child pick an object to represent the calm–safe–happy place. It could be a small stone or figure that the child can keep at all times. If the child gets activated,

Figure 3.1 My helpers on a pillow case.

the transitional object will serve as a reminder of the safe place. Make sure you emphasize that the safe place is in the child's mind and heart and no one can take it from him or her. If the child loses the object, the child should know that the safe place always stays within.

- Use heart-rate monitors, HeartMath®, or EmWave® in combination with the calm–safe place protocol. This biofeedback technique can enhance the child's motivation to use the safe place when they need it. It is also useful for helping children connect to their body and internal states.

- Use manicures as a way to make the use of the calm–safe–happy place more motivating. Create a symbol for the safe place that is encoded on each nail. Symbols such as a dot, line, or a special nail polish color that is associated with the safe place can be used on the child's manicure. This is usually highly motivating for girls. In addition, the safe place will be, at least for a week, right in front of their eyes.

- Use arts and crafts and play therapy strategies. Create bracelets and necklaces with the cue word or elements of the safe place. This could increase the likelihood of the child using the safe place when feeling activated. When the child reports using the safe place successfully, the clinician can install this experience by using BLS. Ask for a clear image of the moment where the child used the safe place to move from a negative to a positive emotional state. Identify the emotions associated with this mastery experience and the location in the body. Then, provide short and slow sets of BLS. This can be done every time the child is able to utilize effectively the safe place or any other resource identified by the child. These experiences constitute acts of triumph (Janet, 1907; Ogden, 2006). During the preparation phase, it is important to create an atmosphere where the child can feel successful and empowered. Highlight even small attempts on the child's part to use the safe place or other resources installed and developed in therapy.

When the Safe Place Does Not Exist

Sometimes, despite all the efforts of the clinician, a child cannot find a safe place, or it becomes contaminated and negative after BLS is initiated. The calm-safe place protocol can also serve as a diagnostic tool and can help us identify the children who need extended preparation and the children with greater deficits in affect regulation. The following steps should be followed when a child is unable to identify a safe place:

1. **Thorough assessment of the level of safety and stabilization of the family and school environment:** Assess the child's family and school environment in more depth. Ensuring safety in the present is fundamental before initiating or pursuing any exploration or reprocessing of traumatic material. If the child is in a chaotic and traumatizing environment, stabilization of the family system should proceed or accompany any individual work with the child. If trauma is still happening in the present, part of the preparation phase should be dedicated to achieving an appropriate level of stability and safety within the immediate family system. If the child is being bullied at school, appropriate measures should be taken to ensure the safety of the child at school. Once an appropriate level of safety and stability has been achieved, you can try again using the calm-safe place protocol. This time, the child may have a different response.

2. **Identify here-and-now activities and moments of joy, safety or calmness:** To prevent the child from accessing negative affect too quickly, as you are trying to install the safe place, try making it more tangible and present. Identify moments or activities the child enjoys in the session with you. If you are playing with Play-Doh®, ask the child to notice the feelings experienced in the "here and now" as the child is engaged in this activity. If the child reports positive emotions, ask for the location in the body and install this moment of safety, joy, playfulness, or calmness in the present. Ask the child for an activity that he or she enjoys. If the child says that dancing is something that is enjoyable, play music and dance with the child. Pause for a moment and ask the child how dancing together feels and where those good feelings are hanging out in the body; then install it using very slow and short sets of BLS. Incorporating playful strategies will also be helpful in keeping the child in a positive emotional state. The following is the calm–safe–happy activity protocol. This protocol is appropriate for children who cannot find a safe place or who find safe places that rapidly become contaminated. If the child has difficulty getting through the entire protocol, use a simplified version and just "catch" the child in moments of joy during the session. Identify the emotions associated with the experience and the location in the body and install these positive states. Some children might not be able to use the entire protocol in the beginning. Only until the positive emotional states have been enhanced and experienced mindfully, during several sessions, might the child be able to pendulate from a negative into a positive emotional state.

CALM–SAFE–HAPPY ACTIVITY

This is adapted with permission from the EMDR Institute training manual. *"We are going to practice EMDR with good stuff today. Which EMDR helper would you like to have today?"* Give the child an opportunity to choose the puppet or puppets that are going to help to provide the BLS.

1. **Image:** If the child is already engaged in a playful activity that seems enjoyable, you may say, *"I can see that you are really into this, how much do you like what we are doing right now?"* If the child is not engaged in an activity that is enjoyable, you may ask, *"What are some of the things that you really like that we can do here together?"* Give menus like, *"Do you like to paint? Do you like to dance or listen to music? Do you like to play ball or play with Play-Doh®?"* Once you and the child are engaged in a playful, fun, or relaxing activity, check again with the child to see if the activity holds positive associations.

2. **Emotions and sensations:** You may say, *"How do you feel now as we are playing with* (say the name of the activity or describe what the child is doing in the present moment)?" If the child does not come up with anything, provide a menu of feelings. If the child reports positive feelings, then continue to assist the child in identifying the emotions and say, *"Do you feel happy, excited, glad, safe, calm? Where do you feel these feelings inside your body? You could use the feeling finder to find the feelings inside."* Do not go to enhancement unless the emotions are positive. If negative feelings and associations occur, assist the child in identifying a different activity.

3. **Enhancement:** You may say, *"I would like you to notice the activity you are doing or the game you are playing* (make a description of what the child and you are doing now), *the feeling that you are having right now* (repeat the feelings reported by the child) *and where you feel them in your body."*

4. **Bilateral stimulation:** You may say, *"Now as you are noticing the activity you are doing or the game you are playing and the feelings that you are having* (repeat the emotions reported by the child) *and where you have them in your body, I want you to do your butterfly hug, or follow with your eyes the puppet* (say the name of the EMDR helper selected by the child) *or let's have the EMDR helpers tap your hands."* You can also use *brushes and feathers to provide tactile stimulation.* Do four slow passes of BLS. Repeat two or three times if the emotions and positive associations to the calm–safe–happy activity continue to be enhanced.

5. **Cue word:** You may say, *"Can you think of a special word that can help you remember all the good feelings that you have now as you* (repeat the activity the child is engaged in)? *It could be any word you want.*
   You may say, *"Now I would like you to keep doing what you have been doing so far, and notice all the good feelings* (repeat the emotions identified by the child) *and repeat in your mind the word* (say the cue word) *and now follow* (repeat the EMDR helper's name selected by the child)."* Do four slow passes of BLS. Repeat a few times.

6. **Cuing with a neutral situation:** When working with children with complex trauma, allowing a child to practice with a neutral situation before going into a mildly disturbing event may be helpful (Adler-Tapia & Settle, 2008). You may say, *"I would like you to think about something from your life, like what you are going to do when you leave this office, a TV show, or a cartoon character. I want you to think about something that is not good or bad, but just neutral."* When the child has identified the situation, say *"Now I am going to say that special word* (repeat the cue word), *and I want you to think or actually start doing the cool game or activity we were playing together* (repeat the activity)."* Allow the child to think about the activity or actually play for some time. Then say, *"How do you feel now?"* If the child reports positive emotions, then say, *"Okay, just think about those good feelings* (repeat the positive emotions reported by the child) *and do your butterfly hug, or follow with your eyes* (state the EMDR helper's name) *or let the EMDR helpers tap your hands."* Do short and slow passes of BLS.

7. **Cuing with disturbance:** You may say, *"I would like you to think about something from your life that is a bit upsetting."* When the child has identified the situation, allow the child to stay in this negative state for a few seconds. Remember that we are also building affect tolerance. Say, *"Now I am going to say that special word* (repeat the cue word), *and I want you to start playing or doing that cool thing or game we were playing* (repeat the activity)."* Allow the child to engage in the calm, safe, happy activity for some time.
   You may say, *"How do you feel now?"* If the child reports positive emotions, then say, *"Okay, just think about those good feelings* (repeat the positive emotions reported by the child) *and do your butterfly hug, or follow with your eyes* (state the EMDR helper's name) *or let the EMDR helpers tap your hands."* Do short and slow passes of BLS. Keep in mind that, at this point, we are actually enhancing the state change the child accomplished and not the activity.

8. **Self-cuing with disturbance:** Say, *"I would like you to think again about that thing from your life that is a bit upsetting or that bothers you just a little bit. Let me know when you are thinking about it."* Wait until the child tells you he or she is thinking about it. You may say, *"This time you are going to do this on your own. You are going to use your special word*

and you are going to do that cool game or thing we were playing together." Allow enough time for the child to engage in the happy, safe activity. You may say, *"How do you feel now?"* If the child reports a positive difference, then say, *"Good job! Okay, just think about those good feelings again* (repeat the positive emotions reported by the child) *and do your butterfly hug, or follow with your eyes* (state the EMDR helper's name) *or let the EMDR helpers tap your hands."* Do short and slow passes of BLS.

9. **Practice:** Encourage the child to use the special word and the calm, safe, happy activity. If the parents were not present, spend some time with them and go over what you did and how they can prompt the child to use the cue word and the calm, safe, happy activity.

   You may say, *"Whenever you feel down or bad or you have mixed-up feelings, you can use your special word* (repeat the cue word) *so that it can help you remember the cool game or activity we did together and get the good feelings back. You could also do the cool game we played on your own so you can get the good and happy feelings back."*

Notice that BLS is added only after the child has been able to move from a negative to a positive emotional state. This is different to what is currently being taught during the basic EMDR training. In my clinical view, it is important to enhance the child's state-change ability when it occurs. Changing affective states constitutes an "act of triumph" that should be recognized and installed. However, we need to be careful to ONLY provide BLS when the child is in a positive affective state. At this point of treatment we want to prevent the activation of traumatic and maladaptive material.

The safe–happy place or activity protocol can be enhanced with tangible and playful prompts. For example, the child can choose a hat, cushion, or a color mat to stand on when thinking about the minor disturbance and a different one when thinking about the safe place. Every time the child goes from one affective state to the other, the child changes hats, holds a different color cushion or stands on a different mat. From the start, the child can choose the hat, cushion, or mat for the "small yucky thing" and another one for the safe, happy place or activity. The addition of tangible objects and playfulness will make this process more fun and appealing for the child.

CREATING CONTAINMENT

The child's ability to feel contained is achieved through various avenues. The first one is through the important relationships in the child's life. This includes the relationships with caregivers, friends, teachers, and therapists. Having parents and therapists who can effectively regulate the child's shifting internal states constitutes the cornerstone for the development of affect regulation (Schore, 2009, 2010). These dyadic interactions have the potential for providing the greatest sense of containment for the child. The second avenue comes from the pace of the therapeutic sessions. Keep the child engaged and stimulated enough, but not to the point of overwhelming the regulatory capacities of the child's system. Different activities and objects can actually assist the child in feeling more contained and regulated. In my clinical experience, the use of puppets, blankets, cushions, umbrellas, and other toys and objects can enhance the child's sense of containment. Using all these objects creatively can do wonders for children. The following are some of the imaginative and playful strategies that I have developed to create a sense of containment for the child during the different phases of EMDR therapy.

The Shy Blanket and the Invisible Hat

This blanket is used with the purpose of helping the child feel contained while exploring, embracing, and processing disturbing material. The shy blanket is a wool blanket that children can hide under and still see the world; children can see, but they are not seen. This blanket should have some weight to provide a sensory experience of containment as well. While under the blanket, children can perform actions that they could not tolerate otherwise, such as having eye contact with the caregiver, speak unspoken words, and complete defensive responses during EMDR reprocessing sessions. They can also start to explore adverse and traumatic events with the clinician while feeling contained under the blanket. Similar to the shy blanket is the invisible hat. This hat is made of materials that allow the child to see others, but the child is not seen. It can accomplish the same outcome as using the blanket and can be used in similar ways.

The Cushion House

Places where children can feel more contained in the therapy office can be built with a bit of creativity. A cushion house can be made under a table by surrounding the table with cushions. Umbrellas can also be used to create an "umbrella house." These tangible containers are introduced early on in therapy and can be used at any point during EMDR therapy. These tend to be more useful when the exploration, processing, and integration of disturbing material is taking place.

The idea of the cushion house was born years ago after working with a 6-year-old child who had acted out sexually on another child. He was experiencing a lot of shame and embarrassment as this incident was being addressed in therapy. After asking him what he needed in order to "help the brain chew up the mixed-up feelings and thoughts," he stated that he needed to feel safer and expressed the desire to hide. He identified home as the place where he felt safe and where he wanted to go and hide. I asked the child if we could make my office a bit more like home by creating a little cushion house for him. When he heard about the house, his eyes lit up. A few minutes later, he was willing and opened up to processing this memory. He went inside the house as I continued to work with him from the outside. The majority of the reprocessing of this memory was done while he was inside the cushion house. He even invited his mother to join him inside the house. During the installation of the positive cognition and the body scan, he was able to do the work outside the cushion house. At this point, he no longer needed this level of containment. In my clinical experience, this simple strategy can help some children feel more contained and stay within appropriate windows of tolerance. However, children come to therapy with a wide range of needs and challenges. As a result, what could be helpful for one child may be counterproductive for another child. With this in mind, children who have been forced to stay in confined spaces may not find the idea of going to a cushion house appealing; in fact, it could be too arousing and dysregulating.

The Helpers

Having finger and hand puppets and stuffed animals labeled as "helpers" is very useful. Children can identify the animals that will be their helpers so they can always be nearby to provide support. When doing exploration of distressing material, having the helpers around may help create a safe and supportive atmosphere. You can have helpers for different situations, problems, or feelings. In my office, I have a big white tiger named Coco. Children are told that Coco likes to help kids when they feel scared. Morris the cat likes to help children who are having embarrassing feelings. They like to help by sitting next to the child or by letting the child pet them. Once again, creating a playful, fun, safe, and supportive atmosphere in your office can facilitate the use of EMDR protocols and procedures.

Walkie-Talkies

When using other strategies for containment, such as the shy blanket, the cushion house, or the umbrella house, walkie-talkies not only can make it more fun and appealing, but also can facilitate communication between the child and the therapist. If the child has a need for distance from the clinician, the communication can still happen through the walkie-talkies. It usually makes communication really fun and playful. By keeping the play and the social engagement systems active during EMDR sessions, we are also keeping the child within tolerable levels of arousal. The entire exploration of memories, the assessment phase and the reprocessing phases can be done while the child is inside the cushion house or under the shy blanket. The communication between the child and the therapist happens entirely through the walkie-talkies.

Imaginary Containers

Containers have long been used by clinicians for a wide range of therapeutic approaches, including EMDR therapy. The following exemplifies how containers can be introduced to a child. You may say, *"We are going to create a really cool thing that you can use to help yourself when you are having mixed-up thoughts or feelings. Let's start by creating in your mind or by drawing a picture of an imaginary container, jar, or box. This jar or box is very special because you can put anything that bothers you or that is mixed-up inside it. First, choose the shape of your jar or box. Once you have the shape, choose the material you are going to use to build your container. It could be made of metal, wood, glass, or any other material you may want. Once you have the shape and material, pick the color. Now, make sure that it has a lid. You can also pick different things to decorate your container. Once it is decorated, I want you to pick the place where you are going to leave your container. It could be my office or any other place you may want. You can also choose the protector of your jar or box. You can have Spiderman or an angel or any important helper guard and keep your container safe."* Once the child has created the container, ask him or her to practice putting anything that may be disturbing inside it. Say, *"Now, we are going to practice. Let's start by getting all the mixed-up thoughts you may have and put them in the jar. Next, let's find all the mixed-up feelings and put them in the jar. Now, let's go through your body and find anything or any part that feels yucky or mixed-up and put the yucky stuff inside the jar. Good job! How do you feel now?"* If the child reports a positive emotional state, ask where these feelings are located in the body and enhance this positive state using slow and short sets of BLS. During following sessions, ask the child about situations in which the container was used successfully. These become mastery experiences and acts of triumph that, in turn, can be enhanced with BLS.

DEVELOPING BOUNDARIES

Children growing up in neglectful and traumatizing environments usually lack a healthy sense of personal boundaries. They either have no boundaries or they have built walls around themselves. The majority of children with complex trauma do not know the language of boundaries. When boundaries have been violated, helping the child and the caregiver develop a healthy sense of personal boundaries should be included as part of the preparation phase. The somatic, cognitive, and emotional information needed to construct and shape a healthy sense of personal boundaries and identity might be missing in these children. For children who were sexually abused by their caregivers, closeness and connection were shaped through sexualized interactions. As a result, subsequent responses to others when in search of intimacy and connection will be highly sexualized. For children who have never experienced healthy and appropriate touch, imagining during reprocessing sessions what would it be like to receive nurturing healthy touch is just a foreign language. The memory networks that contain the alphabet of this language should be taught before reprocessing these memories.

Boundary exercises and Theraplay activities can actually provide the experiences that can construct the neural networks of healthy and nurturing connections and touch. When doing boundary exercises, have the child create tangible boundaries. Use hula hoops, cords, and strings to mark the physical boundaries. Use color and light to help the child visualize the "personal bubble." Invite the child to visualize the bubble made of a color that helps them feel safe and protected. This bubble can be of any shape and size. Have them touch "the bubble around them" and help them have a sensory experience associated with having this "personal bubble." Talk about how we have different bubbles that protect us. Say, *"The physical bubble helps us keep our bodies safe and protected. The feelings bubble keeps us protected from other people's feelings and helps us know where our feelings end and where the feelings of others begin. The mental bubble protects our minds. It prevents the mind from taking in ideas or things that others say that may not be good or we do not believe in."* Ask the child to notice these "bubbles" and the emotions and where these feelings are located in the body; enhance them with slow and short sets of BLS if the reports of the child are positive. If the child experiences negative emotions, do not use BLS. Continue to collect data and identify what about this exercise triggers negative reactions. This can become a target that will need to be reprocessed later on.

Help the child have a gentle experience of having his or her boundaries invaded. Cross the child's boundaries by first allowing a stuffed animal or a doll inside the child's bubble. Ask the child to notice what feelings or thoughts come up and how the body feels when the bubble is invaded. Ask the child to put the stuffed animal back outside the bubble and to notice how it feels to have the bubble and space cleared up again. You can also get a bit closer to the child or place your hand inside the child's bubble. Once again, ask the child to notice or observe thoughts, feelings, or what the body is saying about this experience. Encourage the child to experiment setting boundaries by putting the hands up or by pushing your hand away gently to make you stop. Ask the child to notice the feelings, thoughts, and bodily states that arise after successfully setting this boundary. If the child reports positive feelings after placing a boundary with the hands, identify where these feelings are located in the body. Enhance with slow and short sets of BLS. Ask the child to notice the feelings and somatic reactions of being in a room with you, knowing that he or she can have his or her own protective bubble. If the child reports positive reactions, identify the location in the body and enhance it with slow and short sets of BLS. For some children, you may have to do boundary exercises more than once. In addition, encourage the caregiver to honor these boundaries at home. If the parent continues to violate the child's boundaries at home, the information you provide and the one that is received at home may be confusing to the child. Therefore, the parent should be getting information on boundaries as well and engaging in boundary exercises. The sessions on boundaries with the caregiver should be done individually and not in the presence of the child (see Chapter 5).

THE IMPORTANCE OF TOUCH

A very complex and essential organ of the body is the skin. It possesses receptors to the somatosensory cortex and the anterior cingulated cortex in the limbic system (Carlson, 2001). According to Cozolino (2006), "Light touch and comfortable warmth leads to increases in oxytocin and endorphins that enhance social bonds through an association with a feeling of well-being" (p. 103).

Cozolino emphasizes the importance of touch and physical contact for attachment and psychobiological regulation. He states how positive dyadic interactions with the mother can increase the cortisol receptors in the child's brain, creating a biochemical safeguard for stress. Sexually abused children, who have created associations of intimacy and connection through sexualized interactions with caregivers or other important adults in their lives, need to learn the new alphabet of bonding and attaching. Nurturing, healthy, and honoring touch will be an important corrective experience that can create new neural patterns of activity. When the memory network that contains the information about the sexual abuse is activated during EMDR reprocessing, the linkage of these neural networks with the adaptive ones, if they do not exist, will not take place. This could compromise the reorganization and integration of the information held in these memory networks. Sufficient external and internal input is needed for reorganizing and integrating the brain and the system of a highly traumatized child. Creating the atmosphere within the therapeutic process for healthy and warm touch to occur between the child and the caregivers should be initiated during the preparation phase. Theraplay and other playful activities can be very helpful in incorporating the element of touch in therapy. When both the child and the caregiver can mutually enjoy these warm and positive interactions, these experiences can be enhanced later on by using BLS (see Chapter 12).

The Helping Luggage and the Trip Analogy

This exercise and analogy are designed to assist children in identifying the challenging aspects of accessing and processing a disturbing event. In addition, it helps them identify the resources needed to manage these challenges. This analogy of a trip is used to help children understand the temporary nature of the work they will be doing when reprocessing a trauma memory. Emphasis is placed on "visiting" the memory, which implies that we can go in and out and we do not have to stay. The "visit" is done with five purposes: (1) identifying the challenges, (2) identifying the resources needed to manage the challenges, (3) identifying peritraumatic resources, (4) building affect tolerance and expanding the child's windows of tolerance, and (5) reprocessing and integrating disturbing material. The following illustrates how to introduce this strategy: You may say, *"We are going to do this cool make-believe activity. We are going to pretend that you are going on a trip to the North Pole. First, I want you to think about what may be challenging for you in the North Pole.*" Allow some time for the child to identify challenging situations, and then say, "*Now that you have all the things that might be difficult for you, let's pack the helping luggage that you will bring. Inside this luggage, I want you to bring all the things that will help you with all the challenges and difficult situations you may have when traveling to the North Pole.*" The child can draw a picture of this luggage or just tell you what is inside. You can also give menus to assist the child in identifying challenges and resources. If the child said that the cold weather might be difficult, you may say, "*What do you need to bring with you so you can help yourself feel warm when it gets really cold? Do you need a warm jacket or a blanket or a small heater?*" Once the child has identified all the resources, you may say, "*Now, we are going to pretend that we are going on another trip, this time to the desert. This place is really, really hot. Let's think about what might be difficult for you and what you need to bring in your helping luggage.*"

Once all the challenges and the resources have been identified and the luggage has been packed, say, "*Now, we are going to go on another trip. This time we are going to visit the memory of that yucky thing that happened to you. Let's think about what might be challenging or difficult for you when visiting this memory and let's pack your helping luggage with all the things that you need to deal with the difficult stuff.*" This time it is important that you create some real luggage. You can use a small bag or a box to represent the luggage. Provide menus to support the child's efforts in identifying challenges and resources. You may say, "*Sometimes kids may feel too scared or may think that if they visit the memory, it will happen again, or the feelings are too big or they don't feel safe or strong, or sometimes they worry about what I may think about them. Sometimes kids feel bad about themselves and they may worry that if we visit the memory, I will not like them anymore.*" Have the child talk, draw, or write about the challenges. Once the challenges are clearly identified, assist the child in selecting the resources needed. You may say, "*Now, let's think about all the things that are difficult for you and find what you need to bring in your helping luggage.*" Once the resources have been singled out, have the child draw a picture of them and install one at a time using a resource protocol (Korn & Leeds, 2002; Shapiro, 2005, 2010), or the RDI protocol adapted for children (Adler-Tapia & Settle, 2008). Once the resources have been installed, put them inside the bag. Make sure the child brings the luggage for all the reprocessing sessions.

If the child worries that "visiting" the memory may affect the relationship with the clinician, provide reassurance. It is important that the clinician comes from a place of acceptance and what is said to reassure the child is genuine. The following is an example of what may need to be conveyed to the child: "*I am so glad that you trust me enough to share your worries with me. I want you to know that what I may find out about you and the yucky thing that happened to you will not change how I see you, how I think of you, how I feel about you, and how I care about you.*" The child might want something tangible as a reminder of this promise. It could be a small card from the clinician or a drawing or an object that can be placed inside the luggage. You may say, "*If you ever have doubts about my promise, you can look at this card or object and remember what I told you today.*"

The Harvest Analogy and Peritraumatic Resources

The recall of peritraumatic resources might be associated with a lower probability of developing PTSD. After studying under Dr. Pat Ogden in March 2010 how to identify somatic peritraumatic resources, I was inspired to create a playful strategy for children. The harvest analogy came to mind to assist children in exploring these resources.

This analogy can be used in conjunction with the trip analogy. Once the child has iden-tified the resources needed to visit the trauma memory, have all these resources placed around the child. You may say, *"Now that we have all these things inside your helping lug-gage, let's pick the first yucky memory we are going to visit. The goal of this first visit is to find anything that you remember that was positive and good. You can also bring helpers with you as you visit this memory. I want you to look at anything that you did or that others did to help you. We are going to start with the things that happened right before the yucky thing, then we are going to go right to the moment when the yucky thing happened, and then we are going to go to all the things that happened right after. We are going to bring a special basket to harvest and pick up anything that you find as we visit this memory."*

Provide menus for the child as you explore resources that were used before, during, and after the traumatic event. Keep in mind that at this point, we are assist-ing the child in accessing what he or she did to survive or the things that others did that were helpful. We are looking for any somatic, emotional, or cognitive resource; as well as relational, symbolic resources and mastery experiences. We may be also looking at simple things such as nature. Maybe after the event, the sun came out and made the child warm, or just seeing the stars gave some sense of strength to the child. The attuned presence of the clinician can facilitate this experience. Knowing when to slow down and pause or keep going will be determined by the responses given by the child. Using menus not only will assist the child in finding resources that otherwise are below awareness and still implicitly encoded in the brain, but also will keep the child focused and within appropriate levels of arousal. Remember that we do not want the child at this point to access the disturbing aspects of the memory. You may say, *"Let's start our visit by thinking or drawing what happened right before the yucky or bad thing we are visiting. Let's look at anything that you remember about that day or night that was positive or good. It could also be something that was later on helpful. A thought you had, a feeling, something your body did or felt, or something that others may have said or done. It could be just anything that you saw, heard, touched, or tasted. Once you find it, let's put it in your special basket."* Allow enough time for the child to access resources.

If the child becomes disturbed as a result of this exercise, you can stop, take a break, and continue later on once the child feels ready again. Please be aware that each child may respond differently, and there will be moments when the strategy being used may not work well for a specific child. If there are ruptures in the therapeutic work, there are always opportunities for repair. If the child quickly accesses disturb-ing material and becomes agitated, use another state-change strategy. Once the child is able to successfully change emotional states, this experience becomes an act of tri-umph: the child was able to "visit" the memory and still be safe; the child did not get hurt again and was able to put the memory aside, bringing the positive feelings back. It is important to help the child see how the visit will last only for whatever time he or she feels comfortable with.

Once the child is able to come back to emotional balance, help the child see this as a mastery experience. You could also install this act of triumph using BLS. If the child is responding positively to this exercise, you may say, *"Now, let's go to the time when the bad thing happened. Let's start with your body. Notice anything that any part of your body did to help you. Maybe you ran and your legs helped you get away, or you put your hands in front and your hands protected you. Maybe your body chose not to move so that it would not get hurt, and by not moving, you managed to stay alive. Maybe you fought really hard and pushed away, and by fighting, your body kept you safe and helped you survive. Let's think about any words that you said, or maybe, not saying any words was what helped you at that time. Let's look at any thoughts you had that gave you strength and courage or anything that you saw in your mind that helped you make the pain smaller. Let's think about any feelings you had that helped you survive. Maybe you felt really angry, and the angry feelings helped you fight, or you felt really scared and this fear helped you stay still so you would not get more hurt. Maybe you went to a special place in your mind, and this actually helped you get through this difficult thing. Maybe you numbed your body or your feelings, and that is how you protected yourself. Now, let's think about any person, pet, or angel that helped you as you were going through this yucky thing, or something that was said, or a smile, or a helping hand that you received."*

Remember to be mindful of the pace, the tone of voice, and the pauses you make so the child is able to search for these resources while maintaining focused attention and emotional balance. Knowing ahead of time, some of the details of the traumatic event will be helpful. Gathering this information from the caregivers or any other sources will allow you to assist the child in identifying peritraumatic resources. Every time the child finds a resource, ask the child to imagine putting it in the basket. The child can also draw a picture of the resource and put the drawing inside a real basket. When the child finds a positive recall, it is important that the clinician joins in with enthusiasm and excitement for the child. Highlight how brave that was and how proud the child should be for all the things that helped him or her survive.

Once all the peritraumatic resources have been identified, take one at a time and embody them. Identify the feelings about it and how the body feels about this resource. Ask the child to drop the content of the traumatic event and stay with just the good feeling about this resource and the bodily states. If at any point during the exploration of peritraumatic resources the child becomes too aroused, use the positive resources the child has inside the helping luggage. If the child starts to have dissociative reactions, bring attention to this resource. Help the child understand how dissociation helped him or her survive. Once the child has mindfully noticed this reaction, assist the child in becoming more present in the body. The simplest strategy to restore present orientation is to ask the child to stand up and walk. Talk about how this dissociative response was a survival skill that helped the child endure this experience. Once you finish this exercise, encourage the child to give the basket a name, such as, "My survival skills," "How I became a hero," or "The things that make me a hero." This exercise helps by changing the orienting response of the child. Children who tend to orient to the negative aspects of the self and others often miss what they did or what others did that was positive or that helped them survive. On the other hand, it helps them see from a new perspective what otherwise will be negative and shameful. In addition, it also builds affect tolerance.

The Survival Kit and the New Helping Kit

This exercise is designed to help children transform survival skills and resources into healthier coping mechanisms. These resources are not necessarily linked to a specific memory like in the previous exercise. This is about identifying the general resources utilized at this point by the child to manage triggers and disturbances and replace them with more adaptive ways of coping. Say, *"I wanted to tell you a bit more about something I call survival skills. These are the things that we do to make it through difficult times. To help you understand what survival skills are, let's pretend that, in the past, you had to live in the North Pole. Because the North Pole was so cold, you had to wear heavy jackets and warm boots. These jackets and boots really helped you survive and make it through the very cold weather. Let's say that after a while, you moved to a very warm place like Arizona in the summer. Although, now you live in a very warm place and you don't need to survive the cold weather, you still continue to wear your heavy jacket and your warm boots. While the jacket and the boots helped you survive in the North Pole, now they make your life more difficult. The same thing could happen when we have lived in places or had to go through things that were tough. We probably had to wear jackets made of angry or scared feelings to survive. We may have had to wear jackets to cover our feelings and pretend we didn't have them because having feelings was too difficult. We may have had to leave the body and watch ourselves from a distance. Even though the jacket and the boots really helped us survive, now the same jacket and the same boots may make life harder. Let's find the jackets and boots that you had to wear to survive the yucky things that happened to you. We are going to put all these things you did in your survival kit."* Once the survival skills have been identified, assist the child in selecting new adaptive resources. Support the child through the process by offering menus of potential resources (e.g., the safe place, relational and symbolic resources, mastery experiences, breathing exercises, music etc.). Create "the new helping kit" with all the new installed resources to replace the old survival kit. In addition, you want to honor what the child has done to survive by emphasizing how the jackets and boots from the past were good and helpful in ensuring the child's survival. However, these heavy jackets do not let the child receive and enjoy the sun and the warmth the he or she may have around now.

CREATIVE RESOURCES FOR CHILDREN

Relational Resources

These are extremely important resources for children with insecure patterns of attachment. Caregivers, family members, teachers, friends, angels, religious figures, and a higher power are examples of relational resources. A team of helpers (Greenwald, 1999) is a very powerful resource. Different names can be used to represent this resource: "My circle of safe people," "My helping circle," and so on. The team may include people, superheroes, animals, God, and angels who assist the child in feeling supported, strong, and calm. Children can draw pictures of the team, create it in the sandtray, make it out of clay or Play-Doh, or bring pictures and create an album with them. Once the team has been singled out, the child is encouraged to identify the feelings associated with this resource, and where these feelings are experienced in the body. The clinician provides BLS as the child is thinking about the team of helpers while noticing the emotions and bodily states. The child is then invited to bring all the helpers into the heart and keep them there. If there is turmoil, the child can access the helpers and the associated affect by reaching to the heart. Sometimes, the child may want to have a perpetrator or other characters known by their violent and even criminal behavior as part of his or her team. Remember that whatever the child brings into the session offers a great opportunity to get to know the child at a deeper level. I never prevent a child from having someone be part of his or her team. However, careful and caring exploration will be needed. For instance, you may say, *"I can see that you want to have your uncle be part of your team! I am so glad you are bringing that up since it seems important to you. You know we are trying to have on your team only the people, animals, and so on, that are safe and help you feel secure and strong, right? So I am a bit confused since I know he was not safe to be around at times."* The child may say that his or her uncle was also nice at times and took care of him or her. *"I can see how you had moments where you felt cared for by him. It seems like your uncle had a part of him that was not safe and was hurtful, but at times he showed a part of him that was nice and caring. I wonder if for now we may want to keep him on a 'waiting list' for your team until we know that it is safe to have him on your team?"* If the child insists on having the wounding person, another option may be to have only the part of his or her uncle that was safe and caring join the team and not invite the part that was hurtful. The same strategy can be used with other characters that possess unsafe qualities.

MASTERY EXPERIENCES AND ACTS OF TRIUMPH: MEDALS, DIPLOMAS, AND TROPHIES

Identifying and installing positive experiences and developmental milestones attained by the child can be a good starting point. Time lines can greatly assist children in connecting with their mastery experiences. It also constitutes the beginning of creating a coherent narrative of their lives and who they are. What better examples to rediscover or to rebuild the self than the acts of triumph they have performed throughout their lives? In addition, children with histories of neglect and trauma do not orient to what they have achieved and the positive aspects of the self; on the contrary, they focus on what they perceive as negative in themselves. The child may need menus to rediscover their achievements. Start by drawing a line in the middle of a blank piece of paper and letting the child know you both will be creating the very special story about a "hero child" or a child with a "big hero inside." Let the child know this will be a story about him or her. Ask the child to draw pictures of each experience on top of the line. It is important to begin with experiences before and after birth. A nine-year-old girl who had a damaged umbilical cord was born without any problems. According to the doctor, the cord did not rupture only because the baby turned toward the cord at the moment of her birth. This child had heard about this story and it became an incredible mastery experience. This information was placed within the time-line, and the incredible strength of the child was highlighted. Learning to eat, walk, go potty, run, speak, sing, read, write, and draw, among others, are achievements and mastery experiences that may be explored and brought up to the child's attention.

Each time the child identifies a developmental milestone attained, give the child a medal. Use stickers and place them on the drawing that represents the child. Then, draw a string around the neck so it looks like a medal. Identify the emotions the child is experiencing in connection to this act of triumph and the location in the body. You could ask how the body is letting him or her know how it feels good, happy, or proud; how the body speaks about this experience. Then, install it using slow and short sets of BLS. Go through the entire life of the child until the present. At the end, you could ask the child to once again listen to the entire story of a brave and amazing kid. Start with "once upon a time," and go through all the mastery experiences while the child listens. You could have the caregiver tell the story as well. In addition, you can provide very slow BLS while the child is listening to the story. At the end, the caregiver and the child can create a medal. This can be done by cutting a piece of paper in any shape the child chooses. Then, put a string or ribbon through the paper to make it look like a medal the child can actually wear around the neck. This medal can be decorated with stickers, glitter, and so on.

USING NATURE AS A RESOURCE

Children with a scarcity of resources due to being exposed to relationally impoverished environments can find a wealth of resources in nature. The following are potential resources for children:

1. **Seasons:** Identify the child's favorite season. For example, if spring is the selected season, ask the child to imagine a wonderful spring day and draw a picture of it. Assist the child in creating a specific sensory-based picture of what feels good about this season. Make sure nothing bad has happened during this season. Then identify the emotions and location in the body and provide BLS.

2. **Nature sounds:** In order to identify nature sounds, it is helpful to have a CD with sounds, a sound machine, or a stuffed animal with recorded sounds. Play different sounds and ask the child to notice the ones that make the mind, body, and heart feel good. Some stuffed animals have recorded sounds of a heartbeat. This could also be a powerful soothing sound. Install the sounds that are soothing and instruct the child to use them whenever the mind is having mixed-up thoughts, whenever the heart is having yucky feelings, or whenever the body is having mixed-up feelings. The caregiver can be instructed to use these sounds to soothe and regulate the child when activated by environmental stimuli. At bedtime, the caregiver can create rituals that include sounds and soothing touch.

3. **Colors and light:** Children usually respond to color and they may already have a favorite one. If different colors are favored by the child, identify the different feelings associated with each color and ask the child to bring the color or colors associated with calm, safe, or happy feelings. Schedule a "color day" and ask the child and the parent to wear the color selected by the child. Make sure you also wear something of such color. I keep different colored hats that are used for "color day." Ask the child to bring a special object of the color that elicits positive affective states. Invite the child to just notice the feelings experienced while "feeling" the color. Then ask the child to notice what the body is saying or communicating about this color and how the body communicates it. If the responses continue to be positive, provide slow and short sets of BLS to install this resource. The child could then pick a transitional object of the selected color and carry it. The child is instructed to use it when experiencing emotional turmoil.

   Light can also be used as a resource. The child can imagine a light connected to a relational resource, such as the parents, a higher power, angels, and so on. The child is instructed to imagine the light of a special color connected to the heart of the caregiver. The child can also create a special shape around it for containment and protection: children can create pyramids, lighthouses, forts, squares, and so on. Once the imaginary shape is created, the child is invited to jump inside the shape. Once again, if the emotions and body states are positive, they are identified and enhanced using BLS. This resource can be used in the presence of the caregiver. If a caregiver is not currently present in the child's life, a simple shape that surrounds the child can be used. However, if the child has any positive spiritual or religious figures, the shape can be attached or connected to such relational resources.

4. **Animals:** Pets and animals that we find in books and stories could be very powerful resources for children. Asking for the favorite animal and the qualities the animal possesses that are appealing to the child is a good starting point. Identifying past encounters with this animal, if any, could provide a more tangible and sensory experience for the child. Once a clear picture of the animal and its qualities has been created, identify the feelings and how the body communicates these positive feelings. Needless to say, the child should not have any traumatic or negative experiences associated with this specific animal.

Imagining how it would feel to have the qualities of the animal, such as strength, power, playfulness, and calmness, should be encouraged. This experience and resource can be installed using BLS once the emotions and location in the body have been identified. It is important to emphasize the special use of these qualities so they are not used to harm or hurt. The child can create an animal helper that can be kept inside the heart. Every time the animal helper's qualities are needed, the child can reach inside the heart and connect with the special animal and its qualities.

ANIMAL-ASSISTED THERAPY

The use of real pets can be helpful with children who have grown up in chaotic, dysregulating, and traumatizing environments. Dogs and cats are usually the best pets to bring into the office. Dogs, especially, are highly driven to connect and nurture. I do not encourage the use of reptiles, insects, or rodents, even though the child can learn valuable lessons from these pets. If the child already has a close relationship with a pet, this could be a good bridge into building connections with humans. Inviting the pet to the session could be very motivating to the child. Time should be allotted during the first session for the pet to explore the office until it feels comfortable and safe. A wide range of therapeutic activities can be used with pets during the different phases of EMDR therapy. During the preparation phase, the pet can be a resource for developing mindfulness about others, mental and emotional states, empathy, as well as self-regulation. Noticing and guessing what the pet may be feeling could exercise the child's mirror neurons and capacity for attunement to others. The child may be asked to gently touch the pet and notice what happens inside. The child is invited to notice the feelings and the bodily states that arise associated with the contact and connection with the pet. The child should be instructed just to notice the feelings and where the feelings are "hanging out" in the body while the clinician provides slow and short sets of BLS. If the pet is a dog that knows tricks, this could become a mastery experience for the child, as the dog obeys the commands provided by the child. In addition, the pet can become part of the team of helpers that the child carries inside the heart. Regulation exercises that engage the child and the pet can be very useful. Activities that involve slowing down and speeding up while remaining mindful of what is happening inside the child and the pet's body can help the child recognize emotions and somatic reactions.

OBJECTS AS RESOURCES

Children may already have dear and important objects that carry positive associations. Stuffed animals, tokens, and special gifts can serve as resources as long as they elicit positive emotional states. Ask the child to bring such objects and have the child hold them while he or she identifies the emotions and bodily states. Once again, use BLS to install them. When the child is ready to move into trauma processing, instruct the child to bring these special objects. They can also help the child feel more regulated and within appropriate levels of activation during the reprocessing of disturbing events. Moreover, they can be used instead of the calm, safe, happy place if needed during reprocessing or as a closure procedure.

PREPARING FOR THE POTENTIAL AFTERMATH
OF EMDR THERAPY SESSIONS

The immediate post-EMDR therapy session responses can vary significantly from client to client. Many children experience an immediate relief of symptoms after the initial reprocessing sessions of EMDR therapy. When working with simple PTSD and single trauma incidents, the response may be immediately very positive. However, when working with complex, chronic, multiple, and severe trauma, the response after the initial reprocessing sessions may be full of emotional charge. Some of the children and adults receiving EMDR therapy have reported feeling "emotionally sore" or "emotionally raw" right after the initial reprocessing sessions. However, for the most part, the "soreness" does not tend to last and tends to improve after a few days. Some clients have actually reported that after the "soreness," they tend to feel better than they felt before the EMDR reprocessing session. With this in mind, preparing for the potential "soreness" that some clients may experience is relevant. It is also important to highlight that not all clients receiving EMDR therapy experience the "emotional soreness." Many clients actually report feeling better right away. However, when working with highly traumatized children, we want to make the process safer and more predictable by letting them know the following: Say, *"When doing EMDR, we will be exercising different muscles that, for the most part, have not been used in a while: the helping myself muscle, the feelings muscle, and the memory visiting muscle. When we exercise these muscles, we may feel sore in the beginning. As we continue to exercise, the muscles get stronger and they will not hurt as much or will not hurt at all. Let's prepare so that if we feel sore, we already have a plan."* Encourage the child to use the resources developed and installed during the preparation phase. A really playful way of preparing for the potential "soreness" is by making the EMDR reprocessing day a special day. You can create a special name for this day with the child. Some children call it "my special pampering day," "the loving myself day," or "the taking care of myself day." The child and the parent may be prepared to have a special day together. The child may have time on that day for special music, a treat, and so on. Children for the most part will look forward to the day they exercise their muscles and they get nurturance from different sources. Children can also be encouraged to use the "helping box" and the various resources previously installed between sessions.

SUMMARY AND CONCLUSIONS

The complexity of the clinical landscape of dissociative and insecurely attached children calls for a multifaceted application of EMDR therapy. Throughout their lives, these children have failed to attain basic developmental milestones. Addressing developmental deficits and providing experiences that can promote the development of new and adaptive memory systems is fundamental with this population.

Integration and reorganization of maladaptive networks during EMDR reprocessing requires the presence of adaptive memory systems (Shapiro, 2001). Stimulating the formation of such networks through the exposure to positive, regulating and attuned interactions with clinicians and caregivers is an important goal of the preparation phase, that should continue throughout the entire treatment. During the preparation phase, the child should be exposed to experiences that expand his or her capacity to tolerate and modulate positive and negative affect. In addition, due to the complex and intricate nature of the clinical presentations of these cases, comprehensive and extensive preparation may be necessary. This may include a team of clinicians that can work not just with the child but with the entire family system. Children with complex trauma may come from relationally impoverished and chaotic environments. As a result, finding resources and positive experiences of connection and safety may be challenging. The EMDR clinician needs to be creative and skillful in accessing and developing new resources. This chapter offers a wide range of ideas and strategies for children that are in need of a more comprehensive and multifaceted treatment.

4

The Skill-Building Phase and EMDR Games

Children who have not internalized a sense of security and safety due to trauma experienced within the caregiving system tend to have difficulty regulating internal states. New situations, even when they are positive, may increase the level of arousal and internal disorganization. These children have a greater need for predictability, structure and organization in their everyday lives. All the strategies offered in this chapter are intended to provide a rich variety of playful opportunities to address what otherwise would be extremely challenging. Exploring trauma memories and current triggers may be challenging for traumatized individuals. Moreover, some of the traumatic and adverse events may have occurred pre- verbally and as a result they still remain encoded implicitly. In addition, traumatized children tend to exhibit avoidance from anything that might be reminiscent of the traumatic event. As a result, incorporating a variety of playful and creative approaches to the exploration of what could be potentially disturbing to the child, may facilitate this process.

THE IMPORTANCE OF PLAY

It is important to differentiate exploration and play since they both often get confused. Anthony Pellegrini has done extensive work in the field of play. According to Pellegrini (2009), when children and animals are presented with novel stimuli, exploration takes place initially. As the object or situation becomes familiar, play begins. "*While the child at play is characterized as being relaxed, with positive affect and relatively low heart rate, in exploration the child displays flat or negative affect and an increased heart rate* (p. 17).

We could conclude that familiarity and a sense of safety with an object or situation increases playfulness. During the initial stages of eye movement desensitization reprocessing (EMDR) therapy, the accessing and exploration of disturbing material should be titrated to minimize dysregulation of the child's system and maximize stabilization. During my early training in EMDR, children were only exposed to the procedural steps of EMDR therapy right when the trauma memory was about to be reprocessed. We were expecting children to access a traumatic event, identify cognitions, emotions and where the emotions are located in the body while using two measure scales: validity of the positive cognition (VoC) and subjective units of disturbance (SUDs). They were exposed to a fairly new situation and experience while thinking about a traumatic event. These were questions that children had never been asked before. Most of these children did not even have the ability to identify thoughts, emotions or body sensations. Without the cognitive, emotional and sensory literacy, children with complex trauma may have great difficulty accessing the different aspects of the memories of adversity during the assessment and reprocessing phases (desensitization, installation and body scan). In my clinical experience, it is important to allow children to explore and play with elements of EMDR therapy procedural steps during the preparation phase, before trauma memories are accessed and reprocessed. Allowing children to explore and become familiar with the different aspects of EMDR therapy enhances the child's ability to explore traumatic material while being in playful states and feeling safe and contained.

The assessment phase of EMDR therapy is designed to create a baseline and to access the different aspects of the traumatic or negative event. However, accessing the various parts of the memory requires the ability to identify cognitions, emotions and somatic reactions. Most children do not possess the ability to access such information held in their memory networks due to different factors such as: The lack of cognitive, emotional and sensory literacy and the lack of exposure and familiarity with questions and strategies used to access this information in therapy. Most children and even adults have difficulty identifying and labeling emotions, thoughts, and somatic reactions. With this in mind, a period of skill building with children where they can get acquainted with the procedural steps of EMDR therapy may facilitate the accessing, processing, and integration of trauma memories. Incorporating playful approaches is critical in order to increase the child's sense of containment and safety. Playfulness also keeps the social engagement system active and has the potential of maintaining dual awareness and optimal levels of arousal. When children are in safe, playful states, trauma memories can be explored, accessed, processed and integrated more effectively. The use of the skill-building phase gives an opportunity to expand the child's ability to tolerate affect. It is imperative that the clinician is attuned enough to the child's shifting internal states. If the child becomes too activated and the level of arousal is too high while playing EMDR games, the attuned clinician will need to slow down or provide distance or containment. At this point the child should have access to the stop signal, if needed. In addition, the clinician should be attentive to changes indicating that the child's social engagement behaviors are reduced and the child is moving out of appropriate windows of affect tolerance. Some physiological changes to look at are: Respiratory rate, skin tone, pupil dilatation, eyelids dropping, voice intonation, facial expressions, reduced awareness of sounds and the clinician's voice, among others. Present awareness should be maintained while exploring traumatic material. Playful exploration of experiences that elicit negative affect can also give the child a sense of mastery. Expanding the child's capacity to access traumatic material and build affect tolerance is a goal of the preparation and the skill-building phase. The clinician's ability and comfort level with affect is critical when working with highly traumatized children. Children can experience the clinician's discomfort as dysregulating and disorganizing. The clinician's internal state could increase the child's feelings of containment, safety, and sense of internal regulation. However, it can also generate the opposite reaction.

When working with children that dissociate, the assessment and exploration of dissociative experiences and the development of a plan to manage dissociation should precede the utilization of EMDR games.

The incorporation of a skill-building phase and EMDR games can greatly enhance and facilitate the utilization of EMDR therapy with children who have a history of complex trauma. The skill-building and EMDR games can help by:

- Assisting the clinician in building rapport with the child
- Engaging the child's play system to modulate affect while the child is exploring and processing memories that could activate negative affect and high arousal states
- Building affect tolerance
- Making EMDR therapy protocols and procedures more predictable, familiar and concrete for children
- Making the child feel a healthy and age appropriate sense of power and control as the traumatic material is accessed, processed and integrated
- Using play to help the child stay within manageable levels of arousal while the child is identifying, accessing and reprocessing trauma memories, thus facilitating integration
- Helping the child get acquainted with EMDR therapy procedural steps
- Assisting the child in identifying resources and memory networks that contain positive information
- Assisting the child in identifying potential targets for EMDR reprocessing
- Helping the child develop cognitive, emotional and somatic literacy
- Helping the child follow the procedural steps of EMDR therapy more effectively

The EMDR games are classified depending on the landscape of the brain that is addressed as well as the aspect of EMDR therapy that is introduced. Some EMDR games work with cognitive skills, others work with emotional skills, while others work with the body and the language of sensation. These games engage the participation of the right as well as the left parts of the brain.

The following are the EMDR game categories:

- EMDR games that exercise cognitive skills and assist the child in identifying positive and negative cognitions
- EMDR games that address the emotional system and assist the child in identifying emotions
- EMDR games that address the body and somatic reactions
- EMDR games that address the two measure scales: VoC and SUDs

With these categories in mind, many existing games and exercises can be potentially turned into EMDR games. Even though a number of games and strategies will be presented in this chapter, select the games and strategies that fit each child's needs, affect tolerance and learning and communication style.

The following are some of the EMDR games I developed using cubes, cards, balls and bowling pins that contain cognitions, emotions and body sensations.

DEVELOPING COGNITIVE LITERACY

Children with complex trauma tend to have greater deficits and difficulties in identifying and verbalizing thoughts, emotions, and body sensations. According to Cozolino, "When a child is left in silence due to parental inability to verbalize internal experience, the child does not develop the capacity to understand and manage his or her own world. The ability of language to integrate neural structures and organize experience at a conscious level is mostly unavailable" (p. 232). Children with disorganized and ambivalent strategies may present with increased activation in the right hemisphere. People with excess of right hemisphere flow without enough linkage to the left hemisphere may suffer from emotional outbursts and dysregulation of the affective system (Siegel, 2010). For these children, soothing the right hemisphere as well as stimulating the left to promote horizontal integration, even during early stages of EMDR therapy, is crucial. On the other hand, children with avoidant strategies may present with reduced activity in the right hemisphere in favor of the left hemisphere. Distancing and reducing participation from the right hemisphere may have served as a coping mechanism to avoid the pain and hurt from the lack of connection with important figures in their lives (Siegel, 2010). Stimulating the brain through play and games that promote the participation of both, the right and the left hemispheres, creates the stage for the rapid and appropriate processing and assimilation of trauma memories.

The identification and verbalization of thoughts, emotions and somatic reactions should be part of the preparation phase with complexly traumatized children. Building neural networks that connect language and affective states as well as exercising the "cognitive muscle," the "emotional muscle," (Panksepp, 2009) and the "somatic-sensory muscle" constitutes the initial road toward neural growth and integration. Even though integration occurs more rapidly during the reprocessing phases, a great deal of integration and processing is already taking place during the early phases of EMDR therapy. A study conducted by Cresswell et al. (2007) concluded that affect labeling improved neural regulation.

Participants in this study were asked to choose the affect label from a pair of words that matched the target face. Results show reduced amygdala responses during affect labeling. According to Siegel (2010), "We can use the left language centers to calm the excessively firing right emotional areas. The key is to link the left to right, not replace one imbalance with another" (p. 116). With this in mind, stimulating horizontal communication in the brain (right and left) as well as vertical (brain stem, subcortical and cortical areas) may constitute the foundation for integration and adaptive information processing.

It is important to highlight that, during the assessment phase, even though the cognitive aspect of the memory network is identified first, this is not reflective of a greater importance. According to Shapiro (2001), "Although the person's negative beliefs and self-attributions are transformed simultaneously with the other manifestations of the trauma, they are not given greater weight than sensory experiences" (p. 44). In fact, Shapiro has emphasized how "*the affect feeding the person's beliefs is the pivotal element of pathology*"(p. 44). Even though beliefs do not posses greater importance or play a causal role in the development of pathology, they may be used to access the memories laying the foundation of current symptoms. When identifying cognitions with children, a challenge is presented due to their cognitive development. A negative cognition in EMDR is interpretive rather than descriptive. However, children tend to provide descriptions rather than interpretations and self-attributions. EMDR games can help children become aware of the self-attributions and interpretations they have made about themselves and how these interpretations continue to affect how they experience life. Negative cognitions such as "My mother did not love me" or "I was afraid," even though are only descriptive statements, represent age appropriate negative beliefs for very young children. Some children may bring up an event-related belief such as: they left me or he was mean to me. If this is what feels appropriate for the child, we should honor the child's choice. However, we should ask first, "*What does it say about you that they left you. Let's find a mixed-up thought or something yucky that you learned about yourself because they left you.*" Children could be encouraged through the use of EMDR games to identify the self-referencing belief if a mere description or an event-related belief has been provided by the child.

The following represent some examples of negative and positive cognitions that are appropriate for children. Remember that a negative cognition is:

- A presently held belief
- A self-referencing belief
- An irrational belief
- A belief that has resonance with the memory

NEGATIVE COGNITIONS–POSITIVE COGNITIONS

Adapted from Shapiro (2010)

RESPONSIBILITY: Defective

I am bad.	*I am good*
There is nothing good about me	*I am good*
I can't be loved	*I can be loved*
I am not good enough	*I am fine as I am*
I can only have bad things	*I can have good things*
I am ugly	*I like myself the way I am*
I am stupid (not smart enough)	*I am smart*
I am not important	*I am important*
I am weird (don't belong)	*I belong*
There is something wrong with me.	*I am okay as I am*
I can't do anything right.	*I can do many things right*
I am weak	*I am strong*
I don't belong	*I belong*
I don't deserve to be loved	*I deserve to be loved*

RESPONSIBILITY: Action

It's my fault.	*It is not my fault*
*I should have done something**	*I did my best*

*I did something wrong**
*What does this say about you? (e.g., does it make you think: I am bad/I am stupid).

SAFETY/VULNERABILITY

I cannot trust anyone	*I can choose who I trust*
I am not safe	*I am safe now*
Bad things are going to happen.	*I am safe now*
I can't let my feelings out	*It is safe to let my feelings out*

CONTROL/POWER

I am weak . . . . *I am strong*
I can't ever be happy . . . .*I can be happy*
I can't stand it . . . .*I can handle it*
I can't get what I want . . . . *I can get what I want*
I can't help myself . . . .*I can help myself*
I can't ask for help . . . .*I can ask for help*
I can't get out/I am trapped . . . . *I have choices now*
I can't trust my myself . . . . *I can trust myself*

PLAYING WITH POSITIVE COGNITIONS
Using Positive Cognition Cubes

These cubes contain positive cognitions appropriate for children (Figure 4.1). Clinicians can purchase plain wooden cubes and write on each side a positive belief. Encourage the child to share any other positive beliefs that might not be written on the cubes. You will need the numbers from 1 to 7 to form the VoC or The Thought Scale. For younger children, use large foam or paper numbers and put them on the floor so the child can stand on the numbers to have a more tangible, concrete and sensory experience of The Thought Scale. The following is an example of how to use and play with positive cognition cubes and the VoC scale:

"I know a game that we can play with these really cool cubes that have the good thoughts that kids sometimes have. This game is about discovering the good thoughts we have about ourselves now. I also have this thing called The Thought Scale. The Thought Scale helps kids check out how true the good thoughts feel to them. Let me show you how it works." Throw the cube and say out loud the positive cognition written on the cube. Say out loud if you have this positive belief or not. If you do not have it, say it, and throw the cube again until you get one that you have. Once you find the positive cognition that you have, talk about the events or people that make you have this positive thought. Then, stand on The Thought Scale and model for the child how to use it. Walk on the VoC scale; explain how 1 means that the good thought DOES NOT FEEL true and 7 means that the good thought FEELS really true. Tell the child it is his or her turn. *"Okay, let's roll the cube and find a good thought that you have now about yourself. Tell me about what things in your life make you have this good thought and use The Thought Scale."* Once the child has identified a positive cognition, you may say, *"Think about that thing that makes you have the good thought and stand on The Thought Scale. Walk on it while you are thinking about the thing that makes you have the good thought. Stop when you find the right number. Remember that 1 means that the good thought doesn't feel true and 7 means that the good thought feels*

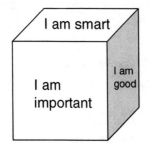

Figure 4.1 A positive cognition cube.

really true. When you do this, check your gut or heart feeling, not the one in your head." Write the good thought on a piece of paper and place it near the number 7 or you can stand up next to the number 7 and hold the cube with the good thought in front. Continue to play, finding good thoughts and walking on The Thought Scale. If the child has a positive cognition with a low VoC, most likely the child has the opposite negative cognition. Ask what prevents the child from fully believing that this good thought is true. *"I can see that the good thought* (repeat the PC reported by the child) *feels just a bit true. Can you tell more about this? Is there a mixed-up thought that you have about yourself that doesn't let you believe that this good thought is true?"* Document all the PCs reported by the child. This represents information about positive and adaptive neuronal networks the child already has. Later on they can be enhanced using BLS or using the Resource Development and Installation protocol (RDI). On the other hand, if the child reports having negative cognitions, you can ask about events or past memories associated with it.

Using Positive Cognition Cards

The use of cards offers a great opportunity to play and use a wide range of card games. You could purchase illustrated cards that contain positive cognitions appropriate for children, such as The Thought Kit for Kids (Gomez, 2009). You could also download art clips from the Internet and create your own cards. Once you have the laminated cards, the following games will help you introduce the use of positive cognitions and the VoC with children. Place the positive cognition cards face down and play with the child uncovering each card. Remind the child of the stop signal and how important it is that the child lets you know when any of the games feel too uncomfortable or overwhelming. *"I have these cards with the good thoughts that kids might have sometimes. I also have this cool thing called The Thought Scale. The Thought Scale helps kids check out how true the good thoughts feel to them. Let me show you how it works."* Model the use of The Thought Scale to the child. Uncover the first card and read the positive cognition written on the card out loud. Identify what in your life makes you have this positive belief about yourself. Stand on The Thought scale and walk on the VoC. Explain how 1 means that the good thought DOES NOT FEEL true and 7 means that it FEELS really true as you think about the event or situation in your life that is associated with the positive cognition. Then, let the child know it is his or her turn to uncover a good thought card and to use The Thought Scale. Once again, if the child has a positive cognition with a low VoC, ask what prevents the child from fully believing that this good thought is true (see games with cubes).

You can also give all the positive cognition cards to the child. Then, ask for positive cognitions that the child currently has on one side and the ones the child does not have on the other side. Then, you can take one cognition at a time and ask for the events or situations associated with the positive cognition and use The Thought Scale.

Using Positive Cognition Balls and Bowling Pins

If you have a child that needs movement, or cannot stay still, using balls and bowling pins will be more effective. You will need to buy plain balls and bowling pins. Write on the ball or bowling pins positive cognitions appropriate for children. Have The Thought Scale available, as well. Throw the ball to the child and ask the child to focus on the positive cognition written on the ball that is more visible. Ask the child to notice if this is a good thought that he or she has. Follow the same scripts used for games with cubes and cards. If you are playing with bowling pins, ask the child to roll the ball.

Then, ask the child to look at the pins that are still standing that have positive thoughts and pick the ones the child has about himself now. Pick one at a time and ask for the events or situations that elicit this positive cognition. Use the scripts used with cubes and cards to play with The Thoughts Scale.

PLAYING WITH NEGATIVE COGNITIONS

Using Negative Cognition Cubes

Once again, you will need to have wooden cubes and write negative cognitions suitable for children on each side (Figure 4.2). The following exemplifies how to use negative cognition games. *"I know a game that we can play with these really cool cubes that have the mixed-up thoughts that kids sometimes have. Let me show you how it works."* Throw the cube and say out loud the negative cognition written on the cube. Tell a short story of a time when you had this thought. Make sure it is something that is appropriate to share with your client that is simple and easy to understand. This is done with the purpose of modeling self-disclosure as you build trust and rapport. Tell the child it is his or her turn. Remind the child that your office is a safe place where kids can talk about their feelings and thoughts or anything that bothers them. Document the negative beliefs and events reported by the child. If the cube lands on a negative belief the child does not have, ask the child to throw it again until a negative belief is found. Once you have the negative cognition you may say, *"What makes you have those mixed-up thoughts? Let's think about anything that you hear, touch, see or smell or anything that people say or do that makes you have this mixed-up thought about yourself."* Once the child has identified the event or situation associated with the negative cognition you may say, *"When you think about that* (repeat the situation identified by the child that is associated with the NC) *and the mixed-up thought* (repeat the NC identified by the child) *what feelings do you have now?"* You can also have cards with feeling faces to assist the child in identifying emotions. Document all the information provided by the child. Notice how, with this exercise, you are identifying current triggers, past adverse or traumatic events and also the negative cognitions associated with these memory networks. You could follow up with a float back to identify other past events associated with the negative cognition selected by the child. The use of the float back and affect scan is covered later on in this chapter.

Using Negative Cognition Cards

You can purchase illustrated negative cognition cards such as the ones found in The Thoughts Kit for Kids (Gomez, 2009) and The EMDR Journey (Courtney, 2009), or you can create your own. Once you have the cards, give the set of cards that contain the NCs

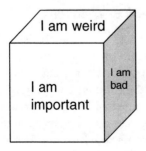

Figure 4.2 A negative cognition cube.

to the child and say, *"All these cards are about mixed-up thoughts that kids sometimes have. I would like you to look at them and pick the mixed-up thoughts that you may have about yourself now. If there is a mixed-up thought that you have that is not on any of the cards, you can tell me, write it or draw a picture of it."* Once you have the NCs, ask for the one that bothers the child the most and say, *"What makes you have this mixed-up thought* (repeat the NC reported by the child)*?"* Let the child know that he or she can use different forms of communication. The child can use drawings, verbal or written communication.

Using Negative Cognition Balls and Bowling Pins

Write on bowling pins, soccer or beach balls NCs suitable for children. Using the negative cognition ball or the bowling pins you may say, *"Let's play a special ball game or bowling game. This ball (or bowling pins) has the mixed-up thoughts that kids sometimes have. Let me show you how it works."* Throw the ball up and receive it back in your hands and read out loud the negative belief that is in front of you when the ball lands in your hands (Figure 4.3). Tell a short story of a time when you had this thought. Make sure it is something that is appropriate to share with children. Then, throw the ball to the child and invite him or her to explore the negative beliefs. If the ball lands on a negative belief the child does not have, throw the ball again to the child until a negative belief is found. Follow the same procedures used with cubes and cards to assist children in identifying environmental stimuli that elicits the negative cognitions, the emotions and the location in the body.

DEVELOPING EMOTIONAL LITERACY

The Feeling Finder

Assisting children in identifying feelings and the location of these emotions in the body is an important aspect of EMDR therapy and a significant aspect of integrating and processing memories. The feeling finder makes the process of identifying emotions in the body concrete, playful and appealing for children. The feeling finder could be any object that the child can use to scan the body from head to toe. I have used magnifying glasses and other objects that might be appealing for children. When you show children how to use the feeling finder, you can add playful sounds such as beeping or buzzing. These sounds are performed by the clinician and later on by the child, as the body is scanned from head to toe for feelings and their location. The following illustrates how the feeling finder can be used.

Figure 4.3 The mixed-up thoughts ball.

"Now, we are going to use a really fun thing called the feeling finder or detector. The feeling finder helps kids find feelings in their bodies (model for the child how to use the feeling finder adding buzzing or beeping as you scan your body). *Let's practice finding feelings in your body. When you think about that* (repeat the situation identified by the child that is associated with the NC) *and the mixed-up thought* (repeat the NC identified by the child), *what do you feel now?* (provide cards with feeling faces). *Now, use the feeling finder and see where you feel the* (repeat the feelings identified by the child) *in your body?"*

Using Feeling Cubes

These cubes contain different basic emotions appropriate for children. Clinicians can purchase plain wooden cubes and write different feelings on the cube. For younger children, draw a feeling face on each side of the cube (Figure 4.4). *"I know a game that we can play with these really cool cubes that have feelings that kids sometimes have. This game is about discovering the feelings that we have now. Let me show you how it works."* Throw the cube and say out loud the emotion written on the cube. Say out loud if you have an event or situation in your life that makes you have this feeling. If you do not have it, say it, and throw the cube again until you get one that you have. Once you find a feeling that you have, talk about the events or people that make you have this feeling. Tell the child it is his or her turn. *"Okay, let's roll the cube and find a feeling that you have now in your life. Tell me about the things in your life that make you have this feeling. Now, let's use the feeling finder and find where this feeling is hanging out in your body."* You can also use a mirror to help the child connect with the body and how it communicates this feeling. Children with complex trauma tend to be detached and dissociated from the body. Bringing awareness to how the body experiences and communicates different emotions initiates the journey toward integration. Making feeling faces and using a mirror so the child has the experience of watching his or her own faces and labeling the emotion is a fun and highly integrative activity. You may also make a feeling face yourself and ask the child to copy it and label it. If the parent is present during the session, the parent could also be the one making feeling faces. Be aware that for some children with attachment traumas and injuries, the parent's faces representing emotional states can be highly triggering.

Once the emotion has been identified along with the location in the body, you can also ask the child about the cognition associated with this emotion and event. *"When*

Figure 4.4 The feeling cube.

you think about (repeat the situation identified by the child that is associated with the emotion) *and the feeling* (repeat the feeling identified by the child) *and where you feel this feeling in your body,* what *mixed-up thought do you have about yourself now?* You can provide the cards, the cubes or the ball that contain the negative cognitions. Write all the events reported by the child so you can start to organize all the events in chronological order to develop the targeting sequence.

Using Feeling Cards

A wide range of card games can be used with the feeling cards (Figure 4.5). You will need to create laminated cards with illustrated feeling faces to assist children in identifying and connecting with a wide range of emotions. You could also download art clips from the Internet and create your own cards. You can place all the feeling cards face down and play with the child, taking turns uncovering each card and labeling the emotions. When the first card is uncovered, encourage the child to identify any situation, person or event associated with this feeling. Use the feeling finder so the child can practice finding the location in the body. You can also ask the child to take all the feeling cards and select the ones that he or she has now. Then, you can take one feeling at a time and ask for the events or situations associated with this feeling. You can also create a feeling ball by writing or drawing feeling faces on a plain soccer ball or beach ball. Use the feeling ball to help the child identify and access feelings as you play with the child, throwing the ball back and forth. Another game can be developed by writing feelings on bowling pins and identifying feelings as you bowl with the child. Every time a feeling is identified, ask for the present and past events associated with this feeling. Facial expressions and body postures associated with each emotion can be explored.

Developing Sensory Literacy

Information processing and the resolution of traumatic memories are achieved through the intervention of different systems and occur at different levels of human experience:

Figure 4.5 Feeling faces.

Cognitive, emotional and sensorimotor. With this in mind, the use of games that stimulate the development of sensory literacy in children constitutes an important aspect of the skill building phase. The use of somatic interventions during the different phases of the EMDR therapy will be extensively covered in Chapter 11.

DEVELOPING THE TARGETING SEQUENCE WITH CHILDREN

When developing the targeting sequence with the child, it is important to use the information contained in the targeting sequence created by the caregiver and the information gathered with the child while playing EMDR games. When a caregiver is not present, use the information provided by case managers and other adults involved in the child's life. Oftentimes the use of the EMDR games is sufficient to gather the information needed to develop the targeting sequence. However, other playful approaches and strategies are listed in this chapter that are also effective in assisting children in the process of identifying potential targets for EMDR processing. If the caregiver is present while the child is identifying targets or playing with EMDR games, it is important to have some time to clarify the role of the caregiver in the course of the EMDR sessions. This topic will be extensively covered in Chapter 5.

Creating the targeting sequence with children oftentimes is not a straightforward process. Several factors need to be taken into consideration when addressing traumatic material:

1. **The use of nonverbal forms of communication**: When recalling trauma memories, many traumatized children are unable to use words. Speech production, language comprehension and language processing have been associated with the Broca's area of the brain, which is located in the left hemisphere in the inferior frontal gyros. This is an important area that seems to be highly affected by trauma. Research conducted by van der Kolk (1996) using PET scans with individuals diagnosed with PTSD during the recall of traumatic events showed a significant decrease in activity in the Broca's area. These findings point toward the inability of traumatized individuals to use words when experiencing dysregulated affective states. These individuals may be somatically and emotionally activated but unable to put experiences into words. With this in mind, having nonverbal forms of communication available in therapy is essential. This can assist children in organizing and integrating their internal reality when identifying, selecting and processing trauma memories. Art, drawing, and play therapy strategies can assist children in communicating more effectively the content of traumatic experiences that may be encoded in the brain at a somatic and implicit level.

2. **The use of playfulness and play during the identification and processing of trauma memories:** Keeping the social engagement system active and maintaining dual awareness while exploring traumatic material is critical during the different phases of EMDR therapy. When the child has a sense of connection to the clinician and as a result feels contained and internally regulated, the exploration of disturbing material can be accomplished. Play can greatly facilitate the connection and sense of safety the child experiences with the clinician during EMDR sessions.

3. **Keeping the child within appropriate windows of tolerance:** When accessing disturbing information during the preparation and reprocessing phases, the clinician needs to be an effective regulator of the child's system. During the process of

identifying traumatic and negative events with the child, the clinician's level of attunement to the child's internal state is crucial. Knowing when to explore trauma memories, when to provide distance, or when to switch the subject and engage in a different activity is what makes EMDR therapy multifaceted and at the same time fascinating with complex trauma cases. The clinician's ability to regulate the child when the child's level of arousal is too high or too low greatly impacts treatment outcome. Clinicians' internal state and verbal and nonverbal communication hold the potential for regulating or dysregulating the child. If the clinician is often depressed and in a hypoaroused state, or if the clinician is bothered and frustrated by the child or the child's behaviors, the dyadic transactions between the child and the clinician can actually be disruptive to the child's system. These interactions can actually become a barrier for the appropriate exploration and processing of implicit and maladaptive material. The clinician's voice tone and voice quality, eye contact, touch, physical proximity and facial expression can be conducive of an internal sense of regulation of the child or, on the contrary, it can create an internal state of turmoil. An attuned clinician is aware of how his or her own interactions with the child may facilitate or inhibit the process of accessing and integrating the child's disturbing material. All the strategies described in this book that are geared toward assisting children during the eight phases of EMDR therapy will be more effective in the hands of an attuned and mindful clinician.

Several strategies are listed below to assist children in the process of identifying experiential contributors to the current symptoms as well as the current stimuli that activates these memory networks. In addition, strategies to aid children in identifying pre-verbal memories will be addressed. You can choose the one that is more appropriate depending on the child's preference, communication style and special needs.

USING THE FLOAT BACK AND THE AFFECT SCAN WITH CHILDREN

The float back and the affect scan are extremely helpful in assisting individuals in linking the present to the past. However, understanding these strategies might be difficult for children. The following is a helpful way of using the float back or affect scan with children. Keep in mind that by the time you are doing a float back or an affect scan, the information needed has already been identified during the use of EMDR games. You already have the present triggering event, the NC and the emotions. If the child was unable to find any negative cognition and was able to identify the emotions and bodily states, an affect scan can be used. The following is the script for the float back:

Float Back Script

"Now that we know what bothers you in the present, there is something we can do to help the brain find the memories of yucky things that happened to you in the past. It is called 'the detective work exercise.' I would like you to think about (repeat the current triggering event) *and the mixed-up thought* (repeat the NC identified by the child previously while engaging in any of the EMDR games) *and the feelings* (repeat the feelings identified by the child), *and let your mind do some detective work and find other times in your life where you had the*

same thoughts and the same feelings. When you find them you can draw a picture, write them or talk to me about them." When you do detective work, have the detective gear ready. Have a magnifying glass and a detective hat to make it more playful and appealing for the child.

If the child has not been able to identify the cognitive aspect of the memory, but is able to communicate the emotions and the location in the body, you can do an affect scan (Shapiro, 2001).

Affect Scan Script

"I would like you to think about (repeat the current triggering event) *and the feelings* (repeat the feelings identified by the child previously while engaging in one of the EMDR game activities) *and where you feel them in your body, and let your mind do some detective work and find other times in your life when you had the same feelings in your body. You can tell me, write them or draw a picture of anything that comes to your mind."*

USING DRAWINGS TO ASSIST CHILDREN IN CREATING THE TARGETING SEQUENCE

Sometimes, children have difficulty verbalizing and disclosing negative or traumatic experiences to the clinician. The following is a method to assist children in identifying current triggers and potential targets for EMDR reprocessing. If the child dissociates, the clinician should pay close attention to any behavioral or physiological changes. (See Chapter 7 for preparation strategies with dissociative children). You may say, *"I am so glad that we are getting to know each other. I already know many things about you, things that you like and make you feel good and things that are yucky and make you feel mixed-up. We are going to talk about some of those things that are upsetting for you. We are going to listen to the different languages that children and humans speak. We are incredible creatures and can speak different languages. We have a mind that speaks the language of thoughts, a heart that speaks the language of feelings and a body that speaks the very special language of sensations. Let's start by looking at some of the yucky things or problems that you have. What are some of the things that you worry about now?"*

If the child is unable to identify any problems, or the child mentions very minor issues and does not mention any of the problems reported by the parent, you may say, *"I want you to know that I already met with your* (mother, father) *and they told me a few things that you might be having trouble with. I want you to know that I am a helper for kids and families and it is important that I know what is really happening so I can help you and your family. This is the reason why your* (mother, father) *told me about all those things about you and your family. I want you to know that this is a very safe place for children and you can tell me anything that bothers you or worries you. I hope you can help me be the best helper I can be for you. Please know that good helpers are really interested in getting to know the children they help, so they try to get as much information as they can to truly know and understand children."* Bring up some of the problems or symptoms reported by the caregiver. Clearly establishing how issues of confidentiality will be handled will create an appropriate atmosphere for trust to develop. Children should be reassured that issues will be openly and honestly discussed with the purpose of helping the child heal and assisting the parents in being the best parents they can be. Start with a minor issue to see if the child can tolerate it. Needless to say, if the child denies the reports of the caregivers or refuses to address the issue, honor the child's need for distance from this subject. It may be too overwhelming and a greater level of stabilization may need to be attained before exploring this issue.

You may say, "*I heard from* (mom, dad, case manager) *that* (say something very general about the problem, such as: I heard about some yucky things that happened to you with a grown up, or that there are some problems at school, or that there are times that you get sad or mad. Let the child know that he or she can talk about it, draw pictures about it or write about it). "*Tell me about the last time that yucky thing, problem or worry happened. You can also draw a picture of the problem or I can draw it for you if you would like.*" Give the child a piece of paper. If the child does not want to draw the problem or issue, you can draw the scene the child is describing on a piece of paper to make it more tangible and concrete for the child.

"*When you think about* (repeat the problem or worry identified by the child) *what mixed-up thoughts do you have about yourself?*" If the child is unable to identify a negative cognition; give the set of cards, the cube or the ball that contain NCs to the child and say, "*All these cards, ball or cubes have mixed-up thoughts that kids sometimes have. I would like you to look at them and pick the mixed-up thoughts that you may have about yourself now. If there is a mixed-up thought that you have that is not on any of the cards you can tell me, write it or draw a picture of it.*" Once the child has provided the NC, draw a thought bubble next to the scene that you or the child has drawn that represents the problem. Write the NC inside. See Figure 4.6. You may say, "*Okay, good job. Now, I want you to think about* (repeat the problem or worry identified by the child and point to the picture created by you or the child) *and the mixed-up thought* (repeat the NC identified by the child) *and let's find out what feelings you have now.*" Draw a heart next to the picture created by you or the child and write all the feelings the child reports inside the heart (see Figure 4.7). If the child is unable to identify emotions, give the cards, cube or ball that contain feelings to the child and say, "*These cards, cube or ball have feelings that sometimes kids have. I would like you to look at them and pick the feelings that you have when you think about* (repeat the problem or worry identified by the child) *and the mixed-up thought* (repeat the NC identified by the child)."

Figure 4.6 Drawing by a 7-year-old girl of the current trigger with the accompanying negative cognition.

Figure 4.7 Using drawings to assist children in developing the targeting sequence.

Float Back

You may say, *"Now, I want you to think about this problem or worry that you have and the mixed-up thought* (repeat the NC identified by the child) *and the feelings that you have. Now, let your mind do some detective work and find other times in your life where you had the same thoughts and the same feelings."* Write any events reported by the child. When the child reports an event, ask for an earlier one until you find the earliest event. *"Okay, good job. Now, I want you to continue to do detective work and find other times where you had the same thoughts and the same feelings."* If the child cannot come up with any events and you have information obtained from the caregiver that can assist the child, you may say, *"You know, I heard from* (mom, dad, case manager) *that something happened* (say a general statement). *Do you remember that? I wonder if when you think about this thing, you have the same mixed-up thoughts and feelings we have been talking about."* Write the events in chronological order and identify the level of disturbance associated with each event. Keep in mind that we are still in the preparation phase. We are just starting to explore the adverse events and the trauma memories that are laying the foundation for the current symptoms. This information will be used to create the overall clinical land-scape and the targeting sequence. This exploration should not take place unless good enough levels of stabilization and preparation have been established with the child. If the child shows signs of emotion dysregulation, slow down the process or completely stop. Instead, use strategies that assist the child in developing affect regulation skills.

Affect Scan

This is used when the child is unable to find a negative cognition, the child is more open to talking about feelings, or doing the float back did not provide enough information about past trauma memories. In this case, the affect becomes the access route to the memory network.

You may say, *"When you think about* (repeat the problem or worry identified by the child), *what feelings do you have now?"* Draw a heart next to the picture created by you or the child and write all the feelings the child reports inside the heart (see Figure 4.7). If the child is unable to identify emotions, give the cards, cubes or ball that contain the feeling faces to the child and say, *"These cards, cube, ball have feelings that kids sometimes have. I would like you to look at them and pick the feelings that you have when you think about* (repeat the problem or worry identified by the child). *Now, let's use the feeling finder and find these feelings in your body and tell me where they are."*

You may say, *"Now, I want you to think about this problem or worry that you have and the feelings and where you feel them in your body. Now, let your mind do some detective work and find other times in your life where you felt the same way."* Write any events reported by the child. When the child reports an event, always ask for an earlier one until you find the earliest event by saying, *"Okay, good job. Now, I want you to continue to do detective work and find other times where you had the same feelings"* If the child cannot come up with any events and you have information obtained from the caregiver that can assist the child, you may say, *"You know, I heard from* (mom, dad) *that something happened* (say a general statement) *do you remember that? I wonder if when you think about this you have the feelings we have been talking about."* Write the events in chronological order and identify the earliest event, the easiest event to remember and the worst.

THE MEMORY WAND

The memory wand offers another playful approach to the process of identifying traumatic events with children. In order to use this strategy, the following supplies are needed (Figure 4.8):

- Ribbons of different colors
- A wooden stick
- Tape
- Blank stickers
- A scale with the numbers from 0 to 10 (SUDs scale)

The ribbons are the objects used to represent the trauma memories and the wooden stick holds them together to form a special wand. The following is an example of how to introduce this exercise to a child. You may say, *"I am so glad that we are getting to know each other. I already know many things about you, things that you like and make you feel good and things that are yucky and make you feel mixed-up. We are going to talk about some of those things that are upsetting for you. I know a really cool thing that we can do together;*

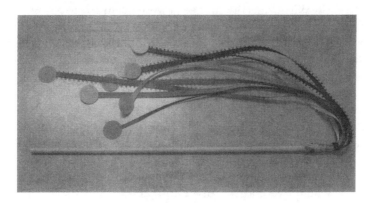

Figure 4.8 The memory wand.

it is called 'The Memory Wand'. This wand is very special because it is about all the yucky or bad things that have happened to you or are still happening to you. I have all these ribbons of different colors, a wooden stick, blank stickers and tape to create your wand. I also have something that I call 'The Bothering Scale'. 'The Bothering Scale' helps kids check how much things bother them or make them feel bad. Let me show you how it works. 'The Bothering Scale' has numbers that go from 0 to 10. The number 0 means that it does not bother you or that it feels neutral and the number 10 means that it bothers you a lot. I would like you to think about all the yucky or bad things that you have gone through and have survived from. Pick a ribbon to represent each of those negative things. When you pick the ribbon, I want you to think about the yucky memory and use the 'Bothering Scale' to make the ribbon short or long, depending on how much thinking about that memory bothers you now. Now, let's begin creating your 'Memory Wand' and practicing with 'The Bothering Scale'. Think about the first yucky memory and pick the ribbon. Using 'The Bothering Scale', think about how much it bothers you now or how bad it feels now. Remember that 0 means it is neutral and 10 means it bothers you a lot. Now, cut the ribbon exactly at the number that you picked using 'The Bothering Scale' and tape it to the wooden stick. Using a sticker, write down the title of this memory so we remember what this memory is about and put the sticker at the bottom end of the ribbon. Good job! Now, let's do the same thing with the other yucky memories you have." You could also use the EMDR games and ask the child about the mixed-up thought, the emotions and somatic reactions associated with this memory. You can use the cards, the ball or cubes to assist the child in identifying these aspects of the memory. You may say, *"When you think about* (repeat the negative event identified by the child), *what mixed-up thoughts do you have about yourself now? What feeling do you have now as you think about that yucky thing that happened? Where do you feel this feeling in your body?* You can provide the cards, the cubes or the ball that contain cognitions, emotions as well as sensations. Notice how the child responds as this information is being accessed. Be attuned to the child's nonverbal and physiological responses that tell you to keep going or to slow down. Keep in mind that each child will have different windows of affect tolerance. Some children will be able to tolerate a more in-depth exploration of the disturbing material while others will just benefit form a simple exercise like the wand without any other questions.

When the child has finished the process of creating "The Memory Wand," highlight the strength the child has demonstrated during this exercise. It is important that you suggest that the wand stays in your office since the wand will be utilized again during the target selection and re-evaluation phase. This wand provides information about past trauma memories, current symptoms or triggers and level of disturbance associated with each. When selecting targets, the clinician may start with the earliest, most recent, worst or least disturbing event depending on the child's ability to tolerate affect. A type 1 child with the ability to utilize resources effectively will most likely be able to tolerate the reprocessing of the earliest or worst event. On the other side, a type 3 child without extensive preparation may become highly dysregulated if you start with the earliest or worst memory.

"The Memory Wand" will also be used during the reevaluation phase once all the past memories and current triggers have been reprocessed. During the reevaluation of all the trauma memories, 'The Memory Wand' offers a playful opportunity to review the level of disturbance of each memory. At this point, when the memory does not hold any disturbance, each ribbon can be cut from the wand and replaced by a new ribbon that holds the new adaptive and positive information about the self. The use of the wand during the re-evaluation phase will be thoroughly described in Chapter 10.

THE "BAG OF MIXED-UP STUFF"

If you used the analogy of the "Bag of Mixed-up Stuff" to explain trauma and EMDR, creating the "Bag of Mixed-Up Stuff" would be the best option to assist children in the process of identifying past trauma memories and current triggers. The following supplies will be needed in order to create the bag:

- A bag made of paper, fabric or other material
- Stones of different colors and sizes
- Construction paper in three different colors: red, yellow and green
- Blank stickers (used with stones only)

When you create the bag, the child can choose stones or drawings to represent the trauma memories. The following is a way to introduce and explain this exercise. You may say, *"We talked about how when we have yucky things that happen to us, we have many mixed-up feelings and many mixed-up thoughts. We do not feel good in our minds, bodies and hearts. It is like carrying bags of mixed-up stuff. Let's create your own 'Bag of Mixed-Up Stuff.' Here is a bag and some stones of different colors and sizes. The stones represent the yucky or bad things that happened to you or things that still bother you now. I would like you to think about the first yucky or bad memory of what happened to you and pick the stone that will represent it. If this memory bothers you a lot now, pick a big stone. If the memory bothers you just a bit, then pick a very small stone. Make sure you pick the size of the stone based on how much this memory bothers you now or how bad it feels now. You can write a title of the memory on this sticker and put it on the stone to remember what this memory is about. Once you are done with all your memories then put them inside your bag."* If you used the "Geodes" analogy to explain what trauma is to the child, you can combine the analogy of the "Bag of Mixed-Up Stuff" and the "Geodes". Use the stones to represent "the geodes of our lives" and encourage the child to find all the geodes that he or she may have. Place emphasis on how we do this with the purpose of finding the unseen uniqueness held in each geode. Even though opening each geode may at times be challenging, we do it with the goal in mind of finding the crystals hidden in each geode. Remind the child of how these crystals symbolize strength, a new sense of self, wisdom and a new appreciation for life.

If the child is using drawings, you may say, *"Let's create your own 'Bag of Mixed-Up Stuff'. I have paper of three different colors: Red, yellow and green. On these pieces of paper you can draw all the yucky or bad things that happened to you, or things that still bother you now. I would like you to think about the first yucky or bad thing that happened to you, and pick the piece of paper that will represent it. If this memory bothers you a lot now, pick a red piece of paper; if the memory bothers you a bit, pick a green piece of paper; and if it bothers you somewhat in the middle, then pick a yellow piece of paper. Then, you can draw what this memory is about. Once you are done with all your memories, put them inside your bag."* Encourage the child to leave the bag in your office and find a special place where the bag will be safe. If the child insists on taking the bag home, a special contract should be created with the child and the caregiver. Special care should be provided to prevent the parent and other family members from accessing information that the child regards as private. Providing corrective experiences where the child feels respected, honored and where good boundaries are modeled is important. The parent and the child should also be instructed to bring the bag to each therapy session. However, to avoid potential boundary violations, the clinician could suggest leaving the bag in the therapist's office. Later on, after all the memories have been reprocessed, the stones and drawings can be replaced for stones or drawings that contain the new positive and adaptive information about the self. When this happens, then the child will be able to take the bag home.

THE "FILES OF MY LIFE"

If you have used the "files" analogy to explain trauma and EMDR, the child can create a box with all the files of the trauma memories and current triggers. If you used the computer analogy, the files can be drawn on a computer illustration. Figure 4.9 shows an illustration done by a 12-year-old using the "files" analogy.

At the end of treatment, once all the past memories and present triggers have been fully reprocessed, new "files" can be created that contain the new adaptive information. These "files" reflect the new view about the self, about others, and about the future.

TIME LINES

Timelines are very helpful when it comes to identifying positive as well as negative life experiences. Mastery experiences and developmental milestones can be identified so they can be installed as resources later. Negative and traumatic experiences can be singled out as the child recounts life experiences. Pictures can be very helpful and can facilitate the recollection of past memories. A big enough piece of paper should be used to place all the pictures or drawings of the various life stages and important moments in the child's life. The time line should begin with prenatal experiences and memories. This includes information the child may know about each stage of life. If there is a picture of the mother when she was expecting the child, glue the picture to the time line. Then, invite the child to share the present feelings connected to that specific time. Identify the thoughts, feelings and bodily states resulting from looking at the pictures of each developmental stage. The following are questions that may be helpful in assisting the child in accessing past explicit as well as implicit information about the self. How do you feel now as you think about the time when your sister was born? What mixed-up thoughts do you have now about that time in your life? You could also create distance by asking about the "younger self" or the "little you." How do you think the "little you" was feeling inside mom's belly? Was the "little you" happy, sad or worried? Was there anything bothering the "little you?" Is there anything the "little you" needed that the

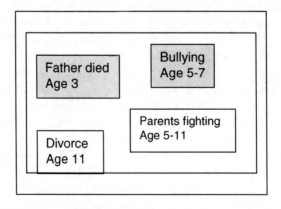

Figure 4.9 Files analogy.

"little you" did not get? Is there anything the child knows about what was happening in his or her family at that time? We are also interested in the stories the body can tell us about that time in the child's life. It is important to assist the child in listening to how the body can tell the story. Invite the child to notice what happens inside when looking at the pictures of each developmental stage. In addition, invite the child to notice if the heart or the mind know anything about any given age or time. If the parent is present, instruct the parent not to disclose any traumatic events that are not known by the child. We are mostly interested in the stories that the child has and how they have been encoded in the child's brain. If the child reports that he or she was feeling scared after birth, invite the child to notice what may have been creating the fear. If the child reports a somatic reaction such as tingling sensations in the hands, invite the hands to participate in telling the story. What are the hands saying? Letting the hands take us where we need to go to get the story can be very powerful. The hand can draw, move or hide. It is important not to force the language of the body but to also teach the child interoceptive awareness. Once the time line is completed, the memories of mastery experiences can be installed using BLS and the negative experiences can be placed in the targeting sequence. Some memories where words are absent may come up in the form of emotions or bodily states. These can become targets later on and can be processed. These memories should be included in the targeting sequence as well. Shaky hands and scared feelings associated with the birth of the first sibling can be a target. A full assessment and reprocessing can be done just with the shaky hand, the fear and the image of a specific life developmental stage, age or event.

MEMORY DETECTORS: EXPLORING PREVERBAL MEMORIES

This creative strategy can assist children in doing developmentally appropriate float backs. A memory detector can be created using a stick and attaching or gluing a piece of paper of any shape to one end of the stick. This detector should mirror and look like a metal detector. Also, a big enough paper should be placed on the floor where a time line of the child's life has been already created. This time line is a very simple one that includes basic drawings representing different developmental stages, starting with pregnancy. Clinicians may want to have pre-made time lines that can be used with different children. In order to create the time line, draw a line on a long enough piece of paper. On this line draw a picture of a pregnant mother with a well-defined baby inside. Then, draw a new-born baby, followed by a drawing of a toddler, school age child and so on. Once the time line and the memory detector are ready, take a current trigger for the child and identify the following: The image, the negative cognition and the emotional responses associated with the current trigger. Attach the drawing of the current trigger, the negative cognition and emotions to the "memory detector" using tape. Stand in front of the time line with the child while holding the memory detector and act as if you both were looking for metal or gold. In this case, instead of searching for metal, you are searching for memories associated to the current trigger. You could add a "beep" sound to make it more playful. You may say, *"Now that we have found the thing that bothers you, the mixed-up thought and the feelings you have, let's use our 'memory detector' and find other times that you remember having the same mixed-up thoughts and the same feelings. When we look for memories, we let our hearts or gut feelings guide us. In fact, the memory detector is inside you and the power to feel and find stuff from the past that may still bug you. We are going to start our search really early, so let's start with the time when you were inside mom's belly. Notice what happens when you think about that time in your life and check if the feelings and mixed-up thoughts you have now were present back then, or see if these feelings you have now were also felt then, or see if the "little you" may have felt the same yucky stuff you feel now."* Keep in mind that we are searching for the implicit somatic memories that may be connected to the current symptoms. In addition, children may know information connected to early developmental stages that may have a connection to the current symptoms. For example, a 7-year-old girl came to therapy because she was getting extremely angry at her mother. She always accused her mother of not loving her. She also accused her father and sister of not loving her enough. The negative belief identified by this child was of course "nobody loves me" and the feelings were anger, sadness and frustration. When this child used the memory detector, she started looking at the time when she was in her mother's womb. She immediately said that she already had this negative thought and feelings back when she was in her mother's belly. She actually said that she had heard that she had ruined her mother's life. She went on and said that because she was inside her mother's belly, her mom had to quit school. When more questions were asked, she stated that her mother wanted to be a doctor but she could not do it because of her. The mother corroborated this information later on and stated that she had to give up school to raise her children. She reported that the child might have heard a conversation she had a long time ago with her husband in regards to this issue. The mother recognized that her pregnancy was unexpected and initially she did not want to have this child because she wanted to pursue her career. However, she was happy with her family and this issue had been left in the past. Neither the caregivers nor the child had disclosed this information until the memory detector was used.

Moreover, if the parent has pictures of the child at different ages, the time line can be done using pictures of the child, as well. Make note of all the memories reported by the child so they can be placed in chronological order in the child's targeting sequence.

THE STORY OF A HERO: ONCE UPON A TIME…

Stories are wonderful ways of accessing adaptive as well as disturbing memories. In addition, stories offer a child-friendly and appealing approach to memory identification. This is also a good way of helping children see the heroes that live inside them. Emphasizing how their stories are actually the stories of bravery and survival can begin to give new meaning to their life experiences. As in the time lines, start with the story of the child before birth. Invite the child to give the story a title that honors the strength of the child. The child may tell the story by writing or drawing. The clinician can also serve as the secretary of the child by writing important aspects of the story while the child draws the pictures. The parent can also be invited to participate by being the writer. In order to make it appealing to the child, have stickers and scrap booking materials so the child can also decorate and highlight important experiences. Special stickers can be used just for positive experiences while others can signal the presence of difficult or negative events. Encourage the child to let the mind, the heart and also the body participate in the story. Let the child know that while at times the mind may say that a certain part or event in our lives was good and positive, the body may say the opposite. The body may get buzzing, tingling or pressure feelings as we think about a time in our lives that signal to something that may have been yucky or difficult. While we pay attention to our thoughts, we should also pay close attention to the feelings in the heart and the body reactions. Let the child know that the mind may want to protect us by convincing us that something was really good when in reality it was really difficult. The mind does not have bad intentions; it is just trying to protect us. This is why it is important to listen to the whole story as the mind, the heart and the body tell it. When the child is writing about a specific time or event, take time to pause and ask what the heart and or the body are also saying. It may take longer to write a story with these kinds of elements. However, as the child works on the story, the child is also using mindfulness and developing emotional, somatic as well as cognitive literacy. In addition, vertical as well as horizontal integration in the brain is stimulated. Once the story has been written, the clinician could take all the mastery and positive experiences and install them using BLS. The negative and traumatic events are then placed in chronological order in the targeting sequence. Throughout the story it is important to always highlight the child's ability to survive.

MEDALS, TROPHIES, AND DIPLOMAS

Medals, trophies and diplomas can accompany time lines and stories. They are used to highlight once again the child's strength and survival abilities. As the child is recounting the story or creating a time line, moments of bravery as well as survival resources can be identified. A medal can be given to the child or the "little self" every time a challenge is overcome. A round or square sticker can be placed near the picture of the "little self" or a medal can be created for the child by the parent. Use ribbon, paper, glitter and jewels to create an impressive medal. These "medal moments" can be installed by using BLS. Identify the emotions and location in the body as the child is aware of the moment of survival or strength and add BLS.

IDENTIFYING CURRENT TRIGGERS

Exploring the present stimuli that elicits and activates traumatic material is an important aspect of EMDR treatment. The following are playful strategies that can provide assistance to children in the course of identifying triggers.

Things That Make Me Have Mixed-Up Thoughts and Feelings

This strategy is based on the exercise, "Things that remind me of the sexual abuse" (Crisci, Lay, & Lowenstein, 1998). The purpose of this strategy is to assist the child in doing a deep exploration of all the present triggers using the five senses. For this exercise, you need six sheets of blank paper. Write on top of each sheet the following statement:

> Page 1: Things that I see that make me have mixed-up feelings, thoughts and body sensations.
> Page 2: Things that I touch that make me have mixed-up feelings, thoughts and body sensations.
> Page 3: Things that I smell that make me have mixed-up feelings, thoughts and body sensations.

Page 4: Things that I hear that make me have mixed-up feelings, thoughts and body sensations.
Page 5: Things that I taste that make me have mixed-up feelings, thoughts and body sensations.
Page 6: Things that people say or do that make me have mixed-up feelings, thoughts and body sensations.

Ask the child to draw pictures on each page of what elicits negative thoughts, emotions and somatic reactions. You may say, "*I have this cool exercise that can help us find the things in your life that make you have mixed-up feelings, thoughts and body sensations. Our brains and bodies talk to us in so many ways. Our brains talk to us with words, our hearts with feelings, and our bodies with sensations and movement. Let's start with the first one. I would like you to think about anything in your life now that you SEE that makes you have mixed-up feelings, thoughts and body sensations. You can draw on this page all those things that make you feel mixed-up.*" Provide the same instructions to assess all the potential triggers. In another session, you can use the cards, cubes and balls to help the child do a more thorough exploration. Then, you can assist the child in identifying the specific negative thoughts, emotions and sensations associated with each trigger. A float back or an affect scan can be done to assist the child in exploring past adverse and traumatic experiences that are laying the foundation for the current symptoms.

My Buttons

This exercise was inspired by Paris Goodyear-Brown (2010). The following supplies are needed:

- Buttons
- Paper dolls or body outlines
- Glue

The following represents how this strategy can be introduced with children. You may say, "*I have this paper doll that is going to represent you. I also have all these buttons that will represent all the things in your life that make you feel mixed-up. I would like you to think about things that you see, things that you touch, things that you hear, things that you taste and things that people say or do that make you have mixed-up feeling and thoughts. Once you have one, you can pick a button that represents this thing in your life. Now, let's find where you feel this in your body and glue the button on that part of the body. Let's write around the button a small sentence on what this button is about.*" Do the same thing with al the other triggers. If time allows, or during the following session, EMDR games can be introduced to help the child find the cognition and the emotions. A float back or affect scan can be done to identify past experiences associated with the current trigger.

IDENTIFYING DISTURBING EVENTS AND RESOURCES WHILE ASSESSING READINESS FOR TRAUMA PROCESSING

A really helpful exercise inspired by Paulsen (2009) and later on adapted for children (Gomez, 2006), can assist clinicians in assessing the child's readiness to endure EMDR trauma processing. This strategy provides information regarding current triggers, past adverse experiences, as well as resources. In addition, it captures how the child perceives subjectively his or her own ability to utilize resources and cope with hardship and adversity in the present. For this exercise, you will need two balloons of different colors. One balloon will represent the child's current perception of the past and current problematic situations. The second balloon will represent the child's perception of current resources available and his or her own ability to utilize them when facing difficult situations. The following script exemplifies how to introduce this exercise: You may say, *"This really cool exercise is about getting to know you better and also helping you get to know yourself better. I have these two balloons for you; the first balloon will represent all the things that are difficult for you in the present and all the yucky things that have happened in your life. Take a minute to just think about all these yucky things and see how big they feel to you now, in your heart and gut. Then, take the first balloon and blow it up, or if you want I can do it for you until it reaches the size of these yucky things you feel inside. Please make the balloon big, medium or small depending on how big all the yucky things feel to you now. If the yucky things feel kind of small, make the balloon small. If the yucky things feel in your heart and gut pretty big, then make the balloon really big."* Once the child has the balloon ready, invite the child to write on the balloon all the present and past negative events. Make sure this information is documented or written on a card. Continue by saying, *"The second balloon represents all the good stuff that you have in your life that help you feel good, all the good things that you do or others do that help you when you are having mixed-up feelings and thoughts. Once again, when you think about all the good things you do to help yourself, check in your heart and gut and see how big they feel and blow the balloon as big as you feel it inside."* Invite the child to write all the resources on the second balloon. It is important to look at the size of the two balloons. If the balloon representing resources is smaller than the balloon representing the amount of disturbance, it clearly speaks for the need to develop more resources. It also shows the need to enhance the child's capacity to utilize the existing resources more efficiently when facing turmoil. If the amount of trauma exceeds the capacity of the system, trauma processing could further dysregulate the child. Let the child know you both will be working on making the balloon with the "good stuff" bigger. After the balloon is big enough, you both will be working on making the balloon with the "yucky stuff" smaller. This exercise can be used several times throughout the preparation phase to assess if the child's capacity to manage affect and disturbance has increased. If this exercise is used more than once, the child will not need to write on the balloon all the trauma memories or triggers unless new ones have surfaced.

EXPLORING TARGETS ASSOCIATED WITH PARENT-CHILD INTERACTIONS

The following is a playful way of exploring and identifying parent-child interactions. These interactions may have resulted in the development of mechanisms of adaptation, such as: Controlling behaviors, pleasing, role reversing, avoidance and dismissal of attachment relationships, anxiety and preoccupation toward attachment figures and clinginess, among others. Parental behaviors and responses such as: Enmeshment, neglect, rejection, emphasis on overachieving, conditional love, dismissive, preoccupied and disorganized behavioral strategies toward attachment relationships, among others, should be identified. The challenge of identifying such patterns of interaction lies on their implicit nature. The following is a playful, child-friendly interview founded on aspects of the AAI. For this interview, a good selection of sandtray figures and animals are needed.

1. Ask the child to pick three figures that represent the relationship with each parent. If there are other important attachment figures then include them as well. The child may have a biological parent for the first five years and an adoptive parent for the last two years. The child should identify figures and memories for both the biological and the current adoptive parent. More than four attachment figures can be overwhelming for the child, mostly when trauma and loss are accompanying the memories associated with such relationships. Make sure to focus only on primary attachment figures. You may say, *"I really would like to get to know you better, so how about if we start by getting to know your relationship with your parents or how you get along with them. Please tell me about your life, your family and the people that have taken care of you."* Allow time for the child to tell the story and identify the primary attachment figures. Continue by asking about the nature of the relationship with each caregiver by saying, *"I would like you to pick three figures or animals that represent or show how your relationship is with your mother."*

2. Once the child has identified the figures, take one at a time and ask the child to describe the figure and how it is descriptive or connected to the relationship with the parent. Say, *"Let's start with the first figure that represents how your relationship with your mother is. Please tell me first about the figure that you picked. Then, I would like you to tell me how this figure represents your relationship with your mom."* Allow the child to describe and talk about the figure. Sometimes the child may forget to connect it to the relationship with the parent. If this is the case, gently prompt the child to talk about how the figure or animal shows in any way how he or she sees the relationship with the parent. Go to the next figure and descriptor of the relationship with the parent until all four figures have been described. Then, ask the child for specific memories or current events for each figure. For example, if the child chose a teddy bear because the relationship with the mother is very nurturing and loving, invite the child to talk about or draw pictures of the "loving" memories with the parent. As in the AAI, first look at the group of figures and descriptions with respect to the relationship with the parent. Then, identify specific events that support such descriptor or adjective. The memories could be from current or past events with the parent. Notice if adjectives or descriptors are very negative, negative, neutral, positive or very positive. Then look for specific details of each memory to identify potential incidents of:

   ▓ Rejection
   ▓ Neglect
   ▓ Intrusive and involving parental behaviors
   ▓ Loving or unloving behaviors
   ▓ Pressure to perform and achieve
   ▓ Role reversing

Notice if the child is open to sharing attachment experiences, expressing feelings, acknowledging hurts or, on the contrary, if the child may be close and guarded. Be observing of signs of idealization or derogation of the parents as well as remarks about not having or not remembering any specifics about the past or current interactions with the parent. On the other hand, be aware of expressions of anger or anger-provoking events. The clinician should be attentive to any reference to self-blame, parentification and role reversing. Identify negative, adverse or traumatic events as well as losses associated with the main attachment figures. Be attentive to fear responses or potential dissociative reactions. This playful interview does not constitute a formal standardized instrument. This is just a playful way to learn more about the parent-child relationship using some aspects of the AAI system with children. The information collected should be an important part of the clinical landscape. The reprocessing of negative and maladaptive experiences with the child should be done when the parent is working on changing such patterns of interaction. Otherwise, the parent will continue to enhance such mechanisms of adaptation and, ultimately, the memory networks that contain them.

The "Heart Jar"

The "heart jar" is a wonderful exercise that not only serves as a therapeutic tool and a resource, but a tool to explore the quality of the connection between the child and the parent. When doing the "heart jar" exercise, there is an exchange of positive interactions that include: Eye contact, physical contact, giving and receiving compliments and loving statements. When doing the heart jar, the child and the parent are invited to create a very special container that can be placed in the heart. They can imagine it, visualize it, actually draw it on a piece of paper or create it using Play-doh®. You may say, *"We are going to imagine, draw or make something really, really special that we can have in our hearts. It is called the 'heart jar.' This jar is special because it is for us to keep good and special stuff that we feel or have with others we care about, especially the people we feel close to, like our parents, etc. Every time we have a special moment, like a hug that feels good, a compliment, a smile, etc., we can put all these in our heart jars. We do it in a really simple way; we look at the person giving us the good special stuff, then we breathe it in and imagine putting it inside the heart jar. We can decide what and how much we take inside the jar. So let's start by having you and Dad create the jar in any way, shape, color and material you want it.* Once the child and the parent had enough time to create the jar, ask them to describe their jars. *"Now, we are going to practice putting good stuff in the heart jars. Parents always start and give kids special things to put in their heart jars. Kids, on the other hand, can choose to give or NOT to give special things to the parents for their heart jars. Some kids choose to do it and some others choose not to, either way it is okay. When we put stuff in the heart jar, first, we hold hands; second, we look at each other's eyes; and third, we say or do what we are giving to the other person for the heart jar. Then the other person can "breathe" it in as much or as little as they want to take for the heart jar. Let's start with Dad. Dad, I would like you to connect your heart to your voice, and as you look at John's eyes and hold his hands, just say or do something good and really special that comes from deep within your heart."* Once the parent has finished with the exercise, the child is encouraged to breathe as much or as little as he or she wants, and put it inside the heart jar. The child is asked if he or she wants to give something to the parent to put in his or her heart jar. Remember that children are free to do it or not. Noticing in every step how the parent and the child act and work together will provide valuable information and insight about their ability to tolerate positive interactive experiences. How do they respond to eye contact? Are they both open to the experience of having physical contact? Is the child open to taking in what the parent is giving for the heart jar? The content of what the parent provides for the child may have a lot of meaning as well. Some parents may express love, but very conditionally such as, "You make me very happy when you do well at school," or, "This week you did everything I asked you and you made me very happy, what a good kid you are." Some parents will provide statements that do not show much connection such as, "You have really nice eyes and you are a very pretty girl." The mother of a 5-year-old girl, when asked to "put something" in her heart jar, expressed to her in such a loving voice how proud she was of her and how honored she felt to be her mother. She went on to say what an amazing and strong little girl she was and how much love she had in her heart for her. This mother conveyed with her entire body, her eyes and her voice the deep love she had for this child. This was a very moving moment even for me as a clinician. I felt honored to be able to witness the love this mother had for this child. Looking at what the parent is saying verbally and nonverbally, how the right and the left hemispheres participate in the experience, can be very enlightening. On the other hand, we should be observant of the child's reactions. Does the child seem overwhelmed by the parent's responses, or on the other hand does the child seem calm and open to receive the eye contact, the physical touch and what the parent is providing for the jar? Some children may actually refuse to take anything that is given by the parent, while others may try so hard to give to the parent as many compliments as he or she can to make the parent's jar as full as possible. The parent should be encouraged to practice at home with the heart jar to promote closeness and connection with the child. However, many parents with difficulty tolerating closeness and connection oftentimes come back the following session reporting that they forgot to use the heart jar.

Since this exercise may actually be dysregulating and activating for both the child and the parent, a closure exercise should be used before ending the session, such as going to the safe place or engaging in some playful physical activity. Time should be allotted the following session with the parent alone and then the child alone to explore their experience with the heart jar exercise. The heart jar experience, for children and their parents with avoidant and dismissing strategies, may be highly activating and, as a result, it may elicit negative affect. On the other hand, children and adults with ambivalent and preoccupied strategies, may be extremely enmeshed and want the jar to be filled at all times. A father of an 11-year-old girl, felt very hurt when his daughter chose not to give anything for his heart jar and expressed during the following session a deep sense of sadness that was reminiscent of what he experienced as a child with his father who was very rejecting. He was highly preoccupied with his daughter not having enough closeness with him. This experience served as the medium to link the current parental behaviors to the father's past attachment injuries.

The heart jar exercise has been the vehicle for may of the parents and children in my clinical practice to access deep attachment wounds that can later be targeted and reprocessed. When exploring the experience of the heart jar exercise, positive responses as well as disturbance may arise. The positive moments and experiences may be explored more deeply by identifying the emotions and bodily states. Then, they can be enhanced by using BLS. When disturbance arises, they can also be explored. If appropriate, a float back or an affect scan may be used to access past experiences that underlie the current activation and annoyance. It is important to identify where the disturbance comes from. Is it elicited by the eye contact, the physical contact, or receiving positive interactive experiences or, on the contrary, giving something positive to the other? The heart jar and its different aspects in fact may be by itself a target that can be reprocessed with standard procedural steps.

SUMMARY AND CONCLUSIONS

The skill-building phase and the use of EMDR games are geared toward assisting children as they explore disturbing and traumatic material. Maintaining the child within appropriate windows of affect tolerance and keeping the social engagement system active through play, allow the child to explore what otherwise could be potentially dysregulating. The clinician's attuned and playful presence is an important contributor to the child's internal sense of containment and regulation. Dissociative and insecurely attached children exhibit a pronounced difficulty tolerating affect. As they explore traumatic material they could become hyperaroused or hypoaroused easily. As the child is able to playfully explore memories that were overwhelming in the past, a new sense of mastery starts to emerge. The preparation phase and, within, the skill-building phase, offers the opportunity to enhance the child's integrative capacity by developing sensory, emotional and cognitive literacy and awareness. Games that enhance the child's capacity to identify, label and explore the body, emotions and cognitions carry the potential for stimulating right and left hemispheric activity as well as cortical and subcortical brain areas. Even though greater levels of integration are achieved during the reprocessing phases of EMDR therapy, the games and playful activities described in this chapter can begin to promote and stimulate different levels of information processing while enhancing the child's capacity for affect tolerance.

5

Working With Parents and the Family System: The AIP Model and Attachment Theory

*T*he inclusion of parents and caregivers throughout the eight phases of eye movement desensitization and reprocessing (EMDR) therapy is essential for best treatment outcome with highly traumatized and internally disorganized children. "Parental responses serve both to amplify and reinforce an infant's positive emotional states and to attenuate the infant's negative emotional states. These repetitive experiences become encoded in procedural memory" (Kandel, 2006, p. 374). For children where the parent has been the wounding agent, these recurring injuring experiences provided by the caregiver on a daily basis could continue to reinforce and shape neural systems. Trying to process and integrate these maladaptive neural networks while the caregiver constantly reinforces them could affect EMDR therapy outcome. A caregiver's understanding of the role of repetitive parent-child interactions in the developing brain and sense of self is fundamental. On the other hand, clinicians' understanding of the caregiving system and its relevance in the transmission of the parent's attachment style into the next generation is also pivotal. According to George and Solomon (2008), the development of the caregiving system and the resulting caregiving behaviors is the product of complex transactions between biological and experiential factors. Specifically, when working with children with disorganized attachment and dissociative tendencies, understanding the "disabled caregiving system" (George & Solomon, 2008) is necessary. These authors have proposed that the caregiving system of disorganized children is characterized by failures of protection, relinquished caregiving, and helplessness. When working with children of parents with abdicated caregiving systems, repetitive daily parent-child interactions can continue to enhance maladaptation. Moreover, frequent negative and dysregulated interactions with the caregiver will maintain the child in a constant state of internal activation. When the child stays in persistent states of hyper- or hypoarousal, these states will become sensitized and eventually will become traits (Perry, 2009).

Parental stress, depression, psychopathology, and lack of appropriate support have been identified as important factors that influence the quality of parental care. It is also important to highlight that the parent's current caregiving difficulties may not only be rooted in his or her own unresolved past attachment trauma and loss, but also in current experiences of distress. Lyons-Ruth and Jacovitz (2008) were unable to differentiate between organized and disorganized groups of infants while interacting with their mothers under low-stress conditions. However, under stress even parents with an earned-secure category in the Adult Attachment Interview (AAI) can develop attachment disorganization in their children. According to the AIP model, present stressful situations can serve as the activating stimuli that bring these memory networks of early attachment traumas back to a state of activation. When these networks are activated, it causes the individual to act in ways that are more consistent with the past than with the present (Shapiro, 2001).

Many researchers have singled out the mother's perception of the infant and their relationship as the most relevant factor that influences parental care (e.g., Bokhost et al., 2003). According to George and Salomon (2008) the mother's awareness and view of the infant and their relationship is heavily affected by the mother's own memories and feelings about her own attachment experiences. As presented by Sroufe et al. (2005), it is important to highlight that parenting behaviors are not static and they actually change in response to the child's developmental stages. In addition, each child may elicit different parental responses in each parent or caregiver. In clinical observations, certain patterns of sexualized seductive parenting behaviors exhibited by mothers with history of sexual abuse or sexual exploitation have been noticed (Sroufe & Ward, 1980). These parental behaviors were not observed toward all the children of the same parent and they also seem to be present only when the infant or child did not follow through with the requests of the parent. Similar observations were made in parents that engaged in physical abuse. Several important aspects were observed that are worth highlighting: First, the sexualized care was only triggered by the male infant or child. Second, it was elicited when the parent experienced stress and was unsuccessful in getting the child to comply. Third, the parental behaviors, whether sexualized or physically abusive, tended to escalate as the parent's level of stress increased, starting with subtle displays to more marked overt displays (Sroufe & Ward, 1980). Looking at these findings through the AIP perspective (Shapiro, 2001), we see how the child's behavior, gender, or temperament at different developmental stages have the potential to activate the memory networks containing the parent's early experiences of either sexual or physical abuse. In the case of parents exhibiting sensualized parenting behaviors, the infant's gender and response that stressed the mother seemed to serve as the activating agent. It is worth noting how each infant's prenatal experiences and genetic makeup will result in the newborn's overall temperament. The characteristics and temperament of the infant, in turn, may activate different memory systems of the parent, resulting in potentially dysfunctional parent-child interactions.

The following case illustrates this point: A 5-year-old girl was brought to counseling because of her frequent temper tantrums when she was not given what she wanted. The mother described the child as manipulative and defiant. According to the mother, this child was very difficult to soothe since she was a baby and was colicky for the first six months of her life. Her oldest daughter, on the other hand, was described as a very quiet and compliant child. Even as an infant, she was quiet and easy to soothe. When a more thorough assessment was performed, the mother was able to identify negative beliefs, emotions and bodily states associated with the behaviors of her child. The mother stated that she felt out of control and thought that she was an incompetent mother. Her history revealed experiences of separation from her biological parents and rejection and neglect from her adoptive parents. We can see how the temperament of the youngest child had the potential to activate the mother's memory systems containing the information of her unresolved adverse attachment experiences. When this mother was asked to describe the responses she had toward her child when she was exhibiting temper tantrums, she stated that at times she spanked her repeatedly, yelled at her, and other times she just locked herself in her room while her child continued to scream outside her door. The unresolved trauma and adversity of the mother clouded the mother's capacity to attune to the child's needs and respond contingently. The child's current needs and behaviors were seen, interpreted and experienced by the parent through the lenses of unintegrated and unresolved memories. It is worth highlighting that the abusive and rejecting behaviors from the mother were only elicited when the mother was unable to soothe the child, and her responses escalated as the child continued to challenge the mother's regulatory capacities. The oldest child, however, did not elicit such responses even as an infant due to her calm temperament. These memory networks that remain in a latent state, in the absence of triggering events, most likely will remain deactivated. However, it will be almost impossible to have a life free of triggers and environmental stimuli that once again hold the power to bring these memory networks back to a state of activation.

Moreover, parental responses that create dysregulation in the child's system also appear to be related to the parent's capacity to reflect, represent and give meaning to the child's internal world. Studies looking at maternal insightfulness have yielded information in regards to the extent to which parental insight into the child's point of view and mind is predictive of infant attachment.

A study conducted by Koren-Karie, Oppenheim, Dolev, Sher, and Etziom-Carasso (2002) assessed the insightfulness of 129 mothers of 12-month-old infants. The mothers watched videotapes of their infants and themselves. Later on, the mothers were interviewed about their own thoughts and feelings as well as the mothers' own subjective experiences of the thoughts and emotions of their infants. The findings show that mother's insightfulness was associated with sensitive parenting and infant attachment security. This refers, according to Fonagy & Target (1997), to *"the caregiver's capacity to hold the child's mind in mind"* (p. 152). Other studies conducted by Meins, Fernyhough, Fradley, and Tuckey (2001) and Meins et al. (2002) using videos and free play have shown how the parent's reflective capacity on the child's behavior is predictive of attachment security. This reflective capacity is referred to as mind-mindedness. Sleed and Fonagy (2010) have proposed a link between the parent's state of mind with regards to his or her own attachment experiences, the parent's responses and interactions with the child, and the parent's capacity to represent the mind of the infant. The activation of the parent's attachment memories seems to interfere with his or her capacity to understand and resonate with the mind of the infant. In other words, the parent's state of mind with respect to his or her own attachment history may directly affect the parent's ability to create an organized, coherent, cohesive and integrated narrative and view of the infant. The resulting parent's representations of the child's mind may directly affect the contingency and congruency of the parent's interactions and responses toward the child.

A striking finding in the study of Ainsworth et al. (1978) showed how babies that ended up developing avoidant patterns of attachment with their mothers were held as often as other infants. However, the mothers of these infants did not hold them when the infants actually showed signals of wanting to be held. The Ainsworth team observed how these mothers actually distanced and turned away when the infant showed them explicitly that they wanted to be hugged or picked up. A viable hypothesis considering how these mothers may have had dismissing states of mind with regards to their own attachment histories is that the neediness of the baby actually activated the memories of early maladaptive attachment experiences. In addition, the strategies used by these mothers in response to the lack of emotional availability of their own caregivers would have once again become activated by the infant's responses. In the Minnesota longitudinal study (Sroufe et al., 2005), it was found that the caregiver's psychological understanding of the infant was a strong predictor of the quality of parental care. Some caregivers failed to understand the needs of the infant and perceived him or her as "needy." Other mothers failed to perceive the infant as an autonomous being and saw him or her as responsible for meeting the parent's needs. Two important variables were found to be significant in the quality of parental care: The capacity to understand and perceive the infant as a separate being and the capacity to perceive the infant as a being in need of care.

Another aspect that is worth exploring is the potentially detrimental effect of exposing infants and children to conflicting and contradictory representations of the self and the parent. According to Liotti (2009), "parental communications that are frightened or confused, but not obviously maltreatment of the infant may set dissociative mental processes into motion. Pathological dissociation, in infancy, is a primary failure in organizing multiple and incongruent models of the self and other into unitary mental states and coherent behavioral states rather than an intrapsychic defense against unbearable pain of severely traumatic experiences" (p. 56). These confusing, incongruent, and disorganizing parental behaviors may be the result of behaviors that are set in motion by the activation of neural networks containing information about the unresolved trauma and loss of the caregiver. As long as the caregiver's memory systems remain unprocessed and unintegrated, the child may continue to be exposed to the same experiences that laid the foundation for the development of dissociative mechanisms. The following case exemplifies how the caregiver's activation of maladaptive neural systems perpetuates the child's exposure to multiple and incongruent models of the self and other. An 8-year-old girl adopted at the age of two was brought to therapy by his two adoptive parents. She had extreme anger outbursts, mostly directed toward her mother. She engaged in name-calling and even threats of death toward her mother. The child reported no memory of the moments of rage and the resulting behaviors. The crisis lines were called multiple times and frequent hospitalizations were necessary. A variety of medications were used unsuccessfully and, at times, the frequent change of medication made things worse for this child and the entire family. The parents received extensive psychoeducation in therapy and specific strategies to manage the child's outbursts. After investigating step by step the parent-child interactions, the mother stated that she had an extensive history of abuse by her father and mother. When the child became agitated and called her names, no longer was she in her adult state, she felt once again victimized, and her child was perceived as a perpetrator. As a result, the mother was unable to respond as the adult mother she was while utilizing the strategies provided in therapy. The father stated that the mother completely changed during the confrontations with her daughter. Sometimes the mother became extremely fearful and acted like a "younger person," according to the father. Other times, she became agitated, yelled, and threatened the child with abandonment. After these confrontations, the mother felt extremely guilty, and to compensate, she allowed the child to get and do anything she wanted, including eating extra candy or breaking important house rules. In addition, as a result of the mother's inability to manage the child's affect, she felt highly incompetent when this child was threatening her, so she called the crisis lines endlessly, even when there was not an imminent danger. The child reported that the frequent calls to crisis lines, doctors and mental health professionals made her feel "bad," "abnormal," and "sick." The child stated that she had to constantly hear her mother on the phone repeating all the "bad" behaviors she had and how problematic she was. On the other hand, when the child was agitated, the father remained highly detached and peripheral. Sometimes the father also became agitated and restrained the child by using physical force. Despite all the efforts of many different therapists that worked with this family over the years, no improvement was made. In fact, things continued to escalate and got worse.

When looking at this clinical picture, it is clear that unless the parents' own past trauma and attachment experiences are appropriately assimilated, integrated and resolved, their responses will only continue to further dysregulate this child, promoting internal disorganization and dissociative states. If the mother continues to experience and respond to her child as if she was at times a perpetrator, a victim and a rescuer, this child most likely will not have the opportunity to develop memory systems containing appropriate and healthy representations of the self and other.

Based on all the above findings and constructs, the work with caregivers and parents of insecurely attached, dissociative and traumatized children is pivotal. Assisting caregivers in developing the capacity for mentalization (Fonagy & Target, 1997; Sleed & Fonagy, 2010), mind-mindedness (Mein et al., 2002), mindsight (Siegel, 2010), insightfulness (Koren-Karie et al., 2002), metacognitive monitoring abilities (Flavell, 1979; Main, 1991), all of which are constructs linked to infant's development of attachment security, is fundamental.

We can conclude that parents' coherence of mind in regards to their own attachment experiences is linked to parents' narrative coherence of the infant's world. In order to promote the parent's ability to have insight, reflective functioning, empathy and, ultimately, coherence of mind, the parent's past unresolved attachment experiences, traumas, and losses will need to be integrated, assimilated and moved to an adaptive resolution.

One of the fundamental goals of EMDR therapy is to promote integration and synthesis of neural systems. When we become integrated and achieve greater levels of completeness within ourselves, we get to fully embrace who we are, and as a result we are able to fully embrace and resonate with others. According to Siegel (2010), "resonance requires that we remain differentiated – that we know who we are—while also becoming linked" (p. 63). As stated early, parents with insecure states of mind may achieve differentiation, but are unable to connect and link with their children and, as a result, strongly promote premature independence. Other parents are unable to become differentiated and may fail to perceive their children as separate organisms, resulting in enmeshed parent-child relationships.

The participation of caregivers of children with experiences of trauma and adversity occurring within the caregiving system is critical. The question remains as to when and how to do the work with caregivers within EMDR therapy.

Even though the work with caregivers is heavily initiated during the preparation phase, it should continue throughout the eight phases of EMDR therapy. Stabilization of the caregivers and the family system greatly expands the child's internal sense of safety, containment and regulation. Promoting change in the dysfunctional and dysregulated family interactions can be addressed at different levels within the eight phases of EMDR therapy. Parents come with different ideas and expectations about therapy and their own involvement in the child's healing process. Some parents want to clean up the house, some are willing to clean up a room and some just want to clean up a table. With this in mind, expectations about treatment should be clarified early on. The level of participation may vary depending on the needs of the child and the willingness of the caregivers to be an active participant. Using an honoring, caring and respectful approach, the clinician should promote accountability and participation on the caregiver's side. In my view, three potential levels of involvement and intervention with caregivers may be appropriate. Keep in mind that appropriate consents should be obtained with regards to providing direct interventions with caregivers. In addition, clarification on who will be the primary client, in this case the child, should be openly discussed. In addition, including another clinician(s) that can work with the caregivers may be necessary. If this is the case, close communication among clinicians should be maintained.

Some parents may need only psychoeducation in order to promote change in the parent-child maladaptive interactions. Other parents will need to work on improving their ability for affect regulation, in addition to receiving psychoeducation. However, for best treatment outcome, most parents of dissociated, fragmented and insecurely attached children will need to reprocess the memory networks associated with their own attachment traumas and injuries that continue to cloud their perceptions of their child. As long as the parent continues to enhance multiple and incongruent mental models about the self and other, the integration of the child's memory networks might be compromised.

During phase one of EMDR therapy, the AAI represents a very powerful instrument for EMDR clinicians when working with complex trauma cases. If parents are unable to promote attachment security in their children due to the presence of dismissing, preoccupied or unresolved states of mind, the work with the child may be slowed down or compromised. Considering that the administration of the AAI takes between 60 and 90 minutes, it could easily be incorporated as part of the initial history taking. It may save a lot of time and effort to clearly delineate the dyadic interactions and the specific attachment patterns of the child with each parent and the states of mind of the caregiver with regards to attachment experiences.

Deciding on when and how much to include the parent is always a complex question and decision. For the most part, when children exhibit symptoms or have difficulties connected to trauma, adversity, or chaos originating within the parent-child relationship, the parents should be included as much as possible. The parent's choice to partake at one of the levels of participation delineated in this chapter should be foremost honored. However, enough information in regards to the benefits and pitfalls of fully participating or completely withholding participation should be openly and gently discussed with the parents. With this information, the parent can ultimately make an informed decision of the short- and long-term potential consequences. The following is a list of potential parental difficulties that will very often lead to the need of providing EMDR therapy to the caregiver:

- Parents with dismissing, preoccupied or unresolved states of mind with regards to their own attachment experiences.
- Parents with past unresolved traumatic experiences and or losses.
- Parents with intrusive or controlling parenting styles.
- Parents that tend to reject and neglect the child.
- Parents that tend to pressure the child to achieve. Perfectionist parents who are unable to provide true unconditional love.

- Parents with sexualized and role reversing tendencies. It may not necessarily be a parent that engages in sexual activity with the child but the caregiver that covertly relates to the child as if the child was the partner. A parent with poor physical and emotional boundaries that emotionally engulfs the child to meet personal needs.
- Parents with diffused boundaries that have relinquished their parental role. As a result, the child is treated as a peer, partner or caregiver.
- Parents lacking the ability for self-regulation.
- Parents experiencing any medical or psychological disorders that can interfere with their ability to interactively regulate their children.
- Parents exhibiting frightening or frightened responses in their interactions with their children.
- Parents that engage in physical, emotional or sexual abuse with their children, spouse, etc.
- Parents with poor support systems and high stress.
- Parents that dissociate.
- Any parent engaging in dysfunctional parent-child interactions that continue to wound the child and reinforce maladaptive memory systems.

LEVEL I—PSYCHOEDUCATION

Helping parents arrive at a deeper level of understanding of their parental role using the AIP model, attachment theory, regulation theory and interpersonal neurobiology principals will create a solid foundation. Providing the information in a simple and easy to understand manner is fundamental. Metaphors and analogies are helpful when presenting information that otherwise could be foreign and dense to the average parent. It is important to emphasize how metaphors are also the language of the right hemisphere. Keeping in mind the ultimate purpose of assisting parents in developing a deeper and clearer understanding of their parental role will assist you in finding the best way of conveying this information. The following are analogies that may assist parents in achieving this goal. These analogies also have facts and theoretical constructs that can engage the left hemisphere. These, however, are not the only ways to convey this information; in fact, some parents may respond better to a more linear and factual explanation. If that is the case, provide information on current literature from attachment theory, neurosciences and adaptive information processing.

The Mirror Analogy: Understanding Basic Principles of Attachment Theory and AIP

This analogy is intended to assist parents in understanding how the child's sense of self does not develop in isolation, but through the repetitive interactions with important attachment figures. It helps parents bring awareness to the current dyadic exchanges with their children that may be enhancing adaptive or maladaptive memory networks. Say, *"When we come into this world we have a brain, a body and a nervous system ready to be shaped by experience and the environment it encounters. At this time we have all the ingredients to form a sense of self, but we need experiences from those closest to us to form and develop a conscious sense of self since we do not have one yet. It is like the parent has a mirror in front, and we can see the reflection of the self through this mirror."* Place a real mirror in front of your chest, facing the caregiver. *"Through this mirror, we learn if we are good or bad or if we are lovable or unlovable. Our parents' words, actions, internal states, facial expressions, presence or absence mirror who we are and what we are worthy of in life. Each experience is encoded in the child's brain and also in the parent's brain. These mirror experiences form files in the child's brain that contain all the information about the self, the parent and the world. These files are usually locked, unless something or someone in our environment opens them up. When these files are opened or activated, all the emotions, bodily sensations and beliefs about ourselves are also in a state of activation. This causes us to have emotions, thoughts and bodily sensations in the present, that are reminiscent of the past experiences we had with important mirror figures in our lives. In other words, the past can continue to shape how we respond to the present and, ultimately, how we shape our future. With this being said, I would like you to take a minute to just notice what your child may see on this mirror on a daily basis. Can you think of what you say or do, or what your nonverbal signals communicate to your child? What do you think your child needs to see, feel or hear about himself or herself? What did your child receive early on from you and others to form files about the self, about you, and about the world?*

Establish a clinical landscape of the parenting behaviors and interactions that promote the development of a positive healthy sense of self as well as a sense of internal regulation. On the other hand, include the parenting behaviors that promote disorganized, avoidant or anxious attachment patterns and, ultimately, dysregulation of the child's system. In addition, even parents that are capable of promoting attachment security in their children may have had experienced adversity and trauma. They may show coherence of mind when discussing these experiences and, in the view of the AAI, this may be a sign of resolution of these experiences. It is important to keep in mind that the AAI does not look at the level of disturbance associated with these memories; instead it looks at the coherence of mind and of the narrative when exploring these experiences (Hesse, 2008). A parent categorized as having secure-autonomous state of mind with regards to attachment experiences may have memories that still hold disturbance and, as a result, have the potential of being activated in the present by the child's behaviors or other stressors. Helping the parent understand how the neural networks containing adaptive and maladaptive experiences are the cornerstones and mediators of the way they are parenting and responding to the child in the present is fundamental.

An important aspect of securely attached dyads is the capacity of the caregiver to repair moments of rupture in the parent-child daily interactions. According to Schore (2009), the capacity of the parent to reattune in a timely manner, after having moments of misattunement, will result in positive states of arousal and the modulation of negative arousal. Helping the parent recognize moments of misattunement and the importance of timely repair should be part of the initial stages of treatment with caregivers.

The Thermostat Analogy: Understanding Regulation Theory Principles

This analogy is designed to assist parents in understanding their role as external psychobiological regulators of the child's system (Schore, 2009). In addition, it helps parents see the potential pervasive consequences of leaving the child experiencing prolonged states of negative arousal. Say, *"When we are born, our brains, bodies and nervous systems don't have the capacity to manage and regulate internal emotional states. It is like having a brand new thermostat that is learning to manage and modulate how we feel internally. Nature, however, has provided external thermostats for all of us: Our parents, caregivers, and other important figures in our lives. The constant interactions between the child's and caregiver's thermostats will result in the appropriate development of the child's thermostat. However, if the caregiver's thermostat allows the child's internal states to get really high or really low without any intervention, to cool it down or warm it up, the child is left experiencing very high and very low internal states. Sometimes, the parent may feel really stressed and anxious or sad and depressed. The infant or child may actually feel the parent's feelings; heart beat, muscle tension, and fearful gestures. These experiences can actually create a lot of fear and very high or very low emotional states for the child. Now, it is the very same thermostat that the child needs to be regulated by, the one that is actually creating chaos and dysregulation. As a result of not having an external thermostat and having to stay in very high or very low emotional states, the child's thermostat never develops appropriately. The combination of genetic influences and all the experiences the child has been exposed to since or before birth shapes the way this thermostat responds to life's demands. The child's thermostat is still trying to regulate the high and low emotional states, but usually we do not notice it or label these attempts as bad or problematic. Aggression, gaze avoidance, stealing, hoarding, defiance, thumb sucking, rocking and even self-injurious behaviors are actually attempts to regulate these emotional states. The more the child's thermostat uses these strategies to regulate the self, the higher the probability of this child becoming an adult with more enduring and lasting difficulties regulating highs and lows. In fact, the intergenerational transmission of thermostats and regulatory strategies is well known by now. Caregivers that grew up with parents with thermostat difficulties may have difficulty regulating their own and their children's highs and lows. With all this in mind, in order to help your child develop healthier ways of finding balance, we have to provide on a daily basis interactive experiences that can help your child feel regulated and develop an efficient thermostat. In order to provide these experiences for your child, we have to start by working on attuning your own thermostat. An important goal of treatment will be assisting you in becoming the best thermostat you can be for yourself and your child."* Teaching parents about the tools that nature has provided for them to interactively regulate and interactively synchronize with their children is the first layer for developing parenting skills conducive of attachment security. Parents' internal state, ability to resonate with the child's internal states, capacity to connect through touch, eye contact, tone of voice, and facial expressions, among others, constitute some of the basic tools for attunement and emotion regulation. Assess the current ability of the caregiver for regulating the child by saying, *"Can you tell me about your own thermostat and your ability to use it when you experience high and low emotional states? Where do you tend to go more often, to the high emotional states, such as anger, high anxiety or fear, or to the low emotional states, such as sadness, depression or just emotional numbness? How do you think the early experiences with your parents affected the way you regulate yourself and your child now? What emotional states would you say are more often present in your child? Which ones are easier for you and your child to manage? Which ones are more difficult for you and your child to manage? What do you notice your child doing to regulate high and low emotional states? What are some of the things you do to help your child regulate emotional states? How is this similar or different from the way your own parents helped you regulate your highs and lows?* Ask for specific examples. Once a clear landscape has been delineated in terms of the parent-child interactions, provide education and role play different parenting strategies. It is important to do this exploration within an emotional environment that is free of judgment. This exploration and work is about healing both the child and the parent. Invite the parent to be your co-investigator. Encourage curiosity, not judgment. The work of Dan Hughes in his book, *Attachment Focused Parenting*; Karen Purvis and her book, *The Connected Child*; and Heather Forbes and Bryan Post in the book *Beyond Consequences Logic and Control*, provide very helpful and hands-on strategies. In addition, the books by Daniel Siegel, *Parenting From the Inside Out*, and *The Whole-Brain Child* are great resources for parents.

These books are easy to read and provide the information in a clear and simple way. They constitute a very good resource for parents of children with complex trauma.

Teaching Parents How to Parent From the AIP and Attachment Perspective

Most parents bring their children to therapy with the vision of changing them. According to Forbes (2009), the question parents must ask themselves should be how can I understand my child and my child's unmet needs, instead of how can I change my child's behavior. Stimulating the parents' curiosity and motivation in order to get to know the child at a deeper level should be promoted. Biological and adoptive parents of children with severe dysregulation of the affective system, get often to the point of restraining, yelling, and distancing from these children, increasing their level of isolation and disconnection from the parent. It is a difficult task for a parent to promote a healthy bond with a child that engages in what I call "pushing" and "pulling" behaviors. I want you close, but get away from me, is the constant message these parents receive from their children. These behaviors, often seen in children with attachment traumas and reactive attachment disorder (RAD), could be extremely difficult to manage. Very often, this is connected to a great dilemma these children endure: The fact that the caregiver activates the attachment system and the defense system simultaneously (Liotti, 2009; Main, 1995; Schore, 2009). The person that the child's survival depends upon is the same person that activates animal defenses. Staying present, while resonating through love and acceptance with appropriate boundaries, is the key to success when the child has these two systems activated. When working with adoptive parents, explain how when past caregivers exhibited frightening or frightened behaviors, the child experienced these caregivers as a source of fear and danger. As a result, the child's defense system was stimulated, causing the child to want to fight or run away from the parent. The child, unable to escape the source of danger, opted for surrendering and potentially going into trance-like states that seem to be the beginning of the development of dissociative responses (Liotti, 2009). Another system that was also stimulated by these parents was the attachment system. This system is organized to ensure that the child's needs for connection and ultimately survival are met. Now, when the new parent attempts to get close, set a boundary or care for this child activation of neural systems that hold the information about past dysfunctional parent-child attachment interactions is inevitable. When these neural systems are activated, the animal defenses, along with conflicting biological forces that drive the child to seek proximity, get entangled. When parents learn to recognize that their child is not bad, evil, or damaged, as many desperate parents come to believe, but instead they learn to recognize their pain and the deep and profound injuries, healing can begin. When presenting this information to biological parents that have been the actual source of fear and danger to the child, caution should be used. It is important to encourage healthy accountability without triggering guilt and shame. Holding this information until the parent is at a place where this material can be shared may be appropriate.

LEVEL II—SELF-REGULATION

An important goal of the preparation phase of EMDR therapy is to assist parents in developing the ability to regulate themselves and their children. According to Schore (2011), "attachment is the regulation of interactive synchrony" (p. 21). Parent-child interactions conducive of attachment security show the presence of affect synchrony that creates positive states of arousal and interactive repair. These two processes ultimately result in the development of self-regulation (Schore, 2010). However, children growing up in stress-provoking and affectively impoverished environments already exhibit pervasive affect dysregulation. If the child continues to interact on a daily basis with a caregiver who exhibits interactive asynchrony, the future may not be a promising one. These cases may require extensive and direct work with the caregiver or the parent. Enhancing existing resources, developing new resources, and ultimately helping parents access and utilize these resources when in the presence of the child's activating behaviors is critical at this stage of treatment. This level of intervention within a comprehensive EMDR treatment includes: Teaching parents relaxation skills, grounding exercises, boundaries, mindfulness, calm-safe place and RDI. It also involves exercises geared toward assisting the parent in developing or enhancing the capacity for attunement, empathy, emotional connection, affective communication, and reflective functioning. If the child's clinician is the one working with the parent at this level, appropriate consents should be signed. In addition, proper information should be provided to assist the parents in making an informed decision. At this point, a referral can also be made to another EMDR clinician.

Relaxation and Grounding Exercises

Parents of children with pervasive dysregulation of the affective system face the daily challenge of parenting these children. Relaxation exercises, such as the light stream (Shapiro, 2001), progressive muscle relaxation (Jacobson, 1938), visualization and imagery exercises, where the caregiver finds a place of peace and comfort, can be very beneficial. Oftentimes, parents need grounding exercises and can benefit from attending yoga classes. Encouraging the parents to include physical exercise in their daily routine as well as to teach them mindfulness will be helpful.

Assisting Parents in Developing Attunement

The concept of attunement is very complex and requires the ability to resonate with the system of another human being. Helping parents expand their capacity to fully experience their own feelings and bodily states may be a good starting point. In addition, working closely with parents and assisting them in experiencing and noticing the child's responses and shifting internal states may be extremely beneficial. The use of mindfulness and mindsight (Siegel, 2010) with caregivers throughout the eight phases of the EMDR therapy can assist parents in developing sensitivity and to begin to truly connect with their children. The use of therapy videos can be very powerful in assisting the parent and the clinician in accomplishing this goal. Sessions where Theraplay and Play Therapy activities are used can be videotaped with the appropriate consents from the caregivers or other entities involved. The video becomes and excellent assessment and teaching instrument. The clinician can thoroughly explore the parent's capacity to reflect and give meaning to the child's responses and internal world. The clinician observes the videos of the child with the caregiver while the clinician uses questions to identify the parent's internal reactions to the observed behaviors. The clinician also explores the meaning and narrative the parent creates about the child's behaviors and responses.

Many therapeutic modalities use videos to enhance the parent's capacity to be connected and attuned to the child's needs. Theraplay, among others, encourages the use of videos to promote the parent's awareness and ability to understand the child's internal world and needs.

The clinician may videotape play sessions where the parent, child and clinician are present, or sessions with just the child and parent. Later on, the clinician can watch the tapes with the parent to observe the child's myriad of responses while practicing mindfulness and attunement. When watching play sessions, stop the video often enough to observe different responses of the child and the parent. The following questions are helpful in eliciting awareness, mindfulness and attunement: *"What are you noticing inside and in your body right now as you observe what your child is doing? What is your body communicating to you about this moment? What is your heart communicating to you about this moment; are you aware of any feelings? What is your mind communicating to you about this moment; are you noticing any thought? What do you notice your child may be experiencing right now in the video? What do you notice that your child may be needing right now in the video? As you become more aware of what your child is experiencing and needing now, what do you notice or experience in your body right now? As you notice what your child feels and needs, what would you like to be able to do or say to you child? How do you think this response will affect how your child is feeling and behaving? When you responded in the video by* (repeat the parent's response from the video), *what do you notice happening with your child? Did he or she calm down or become more agitated? Did your child become more connected or, on the contrary, more distanced from you? How was your child communicating to you that he or she had enough stimulation or that he or she needed more of your active presence?"* Be aware that you may tap into the parent's unresolved attachment and developmental traumas. If that happens, in a gentle way invite the parent to be mindful of this response and how the reaction to the child is connected to his or her own past attachment experiences. At this point you may encourage the parent to put the traumatic or adverse event and the associated affect in a container. A container can be created at this point with the parent. If the parent is still within appropriate windows of affect tolerance, gently invite him or her to explore how these past experiences are affecting the interactions with the child in the present. In addition, when the parent experiences moments of self-awareness and a mindful understanding of the child's mind, pause and invite the parent to notice what feelings are present. If these feelings are positive, identify the location in the body and install them using slow and short sets of BLS. As you continue to work with the caregiver while watching the video, take any opportunity to enhance any positive reactions and moments of self-aware-ness in association with mindfully understanding, feeling, and resonating with the child. Always first highlight any positive steps taken by the parent, any new insight or positive understanding of the child's responses. Then, identify the emotions associ-ated with this new awareness, thought or insight. Third, identify the location in the body, and last, install it by using BLS.

The following describes the initial process of understanding the parent's internal representations of the child. A 7-year-old was brought to therapy by her adoptive mother because she had been diagnosed by the psychiatrist with a potential bipo-lar disorder. It was reported that this child had suffered extensive trauma before her adoption at the age of three. The mother reported that her child had great dif-ficulty sleeping at night and became agitated easily. The mother described this child as manipulative and deceitful. Playful activities were videotaped for two consecu-tive sessions and observed later on by the parent and the clinician. During the ses-sion, this child wanted to change activities constantly and stated that she was bored very often. She also said she wanted to eat even though the mother stated that she had had a large meal before the session. The clinician paused the video often to assist the mother in noticing her internal responses. The mother expressed annoyance with her child's behaviors and even with the activity. The mother constructed a narrative that involved a child that "knew really well" what she was doing and was just trying to manipulate the therapy session. The mother also stated often that her daughter was just like her own mother, deceitful and hardheaded. This session provided a clear picture of the nature of the parent-child relationship. The mother was constantly battling with the child's negative affective states, which in turn activated the mother's negative attachment experiences with her own mother. As a result, the adoptive mother's responses were usually charged with annoyance, irritability and anger. Becoming so immersed in her own experiences clouded this mother's capacity to have empathy and attunement to this child's deepest needs for connection and love.

Once a baseline was established, the clinician started working on helping the mother become aware and mindful of her internal affective, cognitive and somatic responses as she watched her child's behaviors. In addition, the clinician worked on assisting the mother in becoming consciously aware of the meaning she was attaching to the child's responses and internal world. The clinician worked gently on providing other alternatives and helping her expand the capacity for reflection and insight. The clinician offered other options and gently invited her to notice the fear and anxiety the child was experiencing and the changes in posture, eye contact, voice and activity level that were showing changes in physiological arousal. It was discussed at the appropriate time with the mother the intrusions of her attachment experiences when perceiving her child's behaviors and how they influenced her perception. This preparation work started to create some level of integration and awareness about the self and the child. There were moments where the mother was able to notice the child's needs and to see her behaviors as mechanisms of adaptation. At some points, the mother was able to truly understand when and why the child moved away from her or avoided eye contact. When this happened, I highlighted the fact that she had been able to see beyond her own pain and hurt. I asked her to notice what it felt like to have this new awareness. When this mother expressed positive feelings, the clinician invited her to notice her emotions and where they were located in the body, and to engage in BLS. Other times, the responses were tinted with negative emotions. Needless to say, BLS was not provided at those times. The moments where negative emotions were experienced served in the process of identifying neural systems activated by the child. These memories were then presented back to the mother so she could make an informed decision in terms of moving to the third level of EMDR intervention with parents. The mother's memories that clouded the view of her child were placed on a targeting sequence and were later processed using full EMDR therapy reprocessing procedures. The work with videos created the appropriate climate to identify and access the parent's memory networks, interfering with her ability to have empathy and engage affectively with her child without becoming dysregulated. In my clinical experience, even if parents do not choose to reprocess such memory systems, some level of processing and understanding is already achieved. Just arriving to a place of understanding may have the potential to at least minimally affect the parent-child interactions positively. In addition, some parents need some time to think and integrate at some level the insight they have gained. They often come back later to do more work. The truth of the matter is that the house does not have to be cleaned up all at once. Parents may choose to do part of the work now and come back later on for more.

Developing Boundaries

Bringing awareness to the parents' personal boundaries is extremely relevant. How can parents recognize the boundaries of others and teach their children about their personal space if they cannot recognize their own? How can we develop a coherent and cohesive sense of self if our own sense of space and boundaries are not acknowledged? In my clinical experience, parents with insecure states of mind with regards to their own attachment experiences tend to have a very poor sense of their own boundaries. These parents may violate the child's boundaries by becoming intrusive and enmeshed, as it usually happens with parents with preoccupied states of mind. On the contrary, parents with dismissing states of mind may violate boundaries by being too distant. The parent with unresolved states of mind may violate boundaries by engaging in frightening or frightened behaviors. At times, the child may experience the parent as being too intrusive and at times as being too distant and detached. Educating parents about how we develop our sense of personal boundaries should be done during the preparation phase. If parent-child interactions are marked by boundary violations, the child's process of individuation is constricted and thwarted. Depending on the parent's current state of mind with regards to trauma, loss and attachment experiences, specific sets of challenges and strengths may be present. When working with boundaries, assisting the parent in identifying boundary tendencies is usually helpful. In addition, identifying the driving forces of parental responses is relevant. For instance, a 12-year-old child who was exhibiting extreme anger toward his mother stated that he felt smothered by the level of closeness from his mother as well as the uninvited physical expressions of nurturance. I asked the caregiver to focus on the moment of wanting to hug her child while noticing whose needs were being fulfilled at this moment. The mother responded that she was the one who actually needed the hug. The mother was actually very sincere in telling me that she wanted to experience the same feelings she used to have when her father held her. The mother, in fact, reported that she believed that children were supposed to meet their parents' needs. She added that this was a clear message she had received as a child by both of her parents, mostly her father.

Boundary Exercises for Parents

Ask the parent to sit comfortably as the clinician sits far but in front of the parent. Test different levels of physical distance until the parent can find a distance that feels mentally, emotionally and somatically appropriate. Encourage the parent to be mindful as the thoughts, emotions and bodily states are explored with different levels of distance. Once the parent finds the right distance, encourage him or her to physicalize the boundaries using pillows, cords, etc. Invite the parent to notice his or her physical boundaries and invite the parent to notice the bodily states and emotions associated with them. If the emotions associated with noticing the physical boundaries are positive, invite the parent to identify the location on the body and provide slow and short sets of BLS. If the parent reports negative reactions, do not use BLS. We are only enhancing what may be positive in association with the awareness of having boundaries. However, if the parent can tolerate the emotions or bodily reactions, a further exploration could provide valuable information in terms of the memory networks being activated by this experience. Then, invite the parent to notice the emotional boundaries, mindfully noticing what it is and what it feels like to be aware of his or her own feelings and the feelings of another person, and this time noticing the clear line of where the parent's emotional space ends and the clinician's begins. Follow the same procedures to assist the parent in noticing mental and spiritual boundaries.

Next, invite the parent to visualize his or her child in the room and create space for the child. Invite the parent to choose an appropriate distance. The parent could also be instructed to bring a picture of the child to the session if visualizing is difficult for the parent. Ask the parent to physicalize the space of the child by using cushions, cords, etc. Create a circle around the picture of the child or ask the parent to visualize the child inside the circle. Notice how close or distant the parent places the child. Invite the parent to notice if distance or closeness seems easier to handle. Depending on the parent's attachment experiences, one may be easier than the other. For parents that tend to be intrusive and have difficulty seeing the child as a separate entity, invite the parent to notice mindfully what it would be like to place the child as separate from him or her while remaining connected. Use tangible objects to symbolize this connection. For instance, a cord or ribbon from the parent's space to the child's space may serve as a symbol and a tangible way for the parent to still experience the connection to the child. Once again, invite the parent to notice what the body and the heart communicate about this experience. If the emotional and somatic responses are positive, ask the parent to focus on the positive emotions, the body sensations and install them by using slow and short sets of BLS.

On the contrary, working on expanding the windows of affect tolerance resulting from interactive experiences of connection and closeness with parents that have difficulty tolerating it may be the goal. Beginning with a distance that feels appropriate to the parent and slowly moving forward into accepting greater levels of closeness may be a starting point. Based on attachment research, parents with narrow windows of tolerance for emotional connection may have the greatest difficulty right when the child explicitly exhibits the need for it. Asking for a picture of the child or inviting the parent to visualize such expressions from the child toward the parent could also enhance the experience. Create a hierarchy from what is most to least tolerable and again, take small steps to assist the parent in mindfully exploring each step and each level of closeness. Any positive moments should be studied. Identify the positive feelings associated with the experience and the location in the body and use BLS. However, as the parents bring mindful awareness to their somatic, emotional and even cognitive responses, disturbance and discomfort may be found. These are also important moments of self-awareness worth exploring, as long as the parent can tolerate the associated affect and is open to further exploration. Float backs and affect scans can be utilized to support the parent while exploring the past experiences that have laid the foundation for the current parenting reactions and responses. Potential targets for EMDR reprocessing may be identified during this exercise if the parent chooses to participate in full EMDR reprocessing sessions. If past experiences of adversity were explored and accessed during the session, state change strategies should be used to bring the parent back to psychological equilibrium. Breathing exercises, relaxation and containers may have to be utilized before ending the session. As a rule of thumb, every session where memory networks containing disturbing material have been accessed and activated should include the use of state change strategies. Always bringing the parent back to affective homeostasis should be remembered and implemented at the end of the session.

During a boundary exercise, a mother of a 9-year-old boy with extreme aggressiveness toward his siblings stated that visualizing her son in a separate "bubble" created high anxiety. She stated that she wanted to feel her child really close to her. She also had great difficulty experiencing her son's feelings as separate from her own. One of the major barriers for this mother when dealing with her son's episodes of violence was to differentiate where she ended and her son began. It is important to highlight that this information that remained implicitly encoded in the brain was not consciously available to the mother. This exercise allowed the clinician to explore in more depth the roots of her anxiety and work on creating healthy boundaries with her son while remaining connected.

Developing Resources

The use of the calm-safe place and RDI protocols can help parents expand their ability to tolerate and modulate affect. Not only is the RDI protocol (Korn & Leeds, 2002) an excellent way to help parents develop resources, but it also enhances the parents' ability to utilize them in the presence of the child's triggering behaviors. Before initiating RDI it is important to identify the parenting behaviors interfering in the development of healthy parent-child interactions. Needless to say, if abusive parenting behaviors are present, appropriate measures should be taken to correct and report this situation to child protective services. The following is a list of ineffective parental responses that need to be corrected:

- Becoming agitated and engaging in power struggles.
- Yelling and nagging.
- Giving long speeches and discourses about what the child should do or not do.
- Distancing and detaching.
- Becoming intrusive and violating boundaries.
- Not setting boundaries when necessary.
- Not following through with consequences.
- Lack of assertiveness and difficulty saying "no" when necessary.
- Judging and criticizing the child.
- Using sarcasm and teasing.
- Using "the silent treatment."
- Using the child to meet the parent's needs.
- Bringing up the negative behaviors constantly.
- Controlling and overpowering the child.

These ineffective parenting behaviors most likely are the result of how the parent was shaped by environmental and attachment experiences. In addition, the parent's response could be seen through the AIP model as the manifestation of early maladaptive experiences that are most likely encoded in the brain at an implicit level (Shapiro, 2001). As a result of the implicit nature of these memories, the parent may not have a subjective experience of remembering (Siegel, 1999) when this information is elicited by current stimuli. With this in mind, assisting the parent in identifying the current triggers and the past experiences that are setting in motion the current dysfunctional parenting responses can help the parent link the past with the present. Assisting parents in making this information available to their conscious awareness is an important step toward integration. For parents with severe affect dysregulation, appropriate stabilization should be attained before exploring triggers and experiential contributors. In addition, the presence of dissociation should be assessed and ruled out before initiating RDI and addressing attachment traumas and injuries. If extensive trauma exist, a referral to another EMDR clinician that can maintain close communication with the child's therapist should be made.

The following is an overview of the RDI procedural steps (Leeds, 2009) which I have adapted to be used with caregivers.

1. Target situation: Identify the child's behaviors, emotions, or situations that activate the parent's maladaptive material. These are the situations that tend to be challenging for the parent and where the parent fails to exhibit appropriate parenting behaviors. It may be that the parent becomes agitated and engages in power struggles, or that the parent experiences difficulty setting appropriate boundaries when needed. Questions such as: What are the emotional reactions or behaviors of your child that you find difficult to manage or that tend to push your buttons? Take a moment to reflect on the things your child does or says that you find difficult to manage what are some of the reactions you have in relation to your child that you would like to change or where you would like to feel, think or behave differently?

2. Identifying the desired parenting behavior and the supporting belief, emotions and bodily states: Assist the parent in selecting an attachment-informed parenting behavior. Once the behavior has been identified, explore the potential positive belief, emotions, body posture and state that will support this parenting behavior.

3. Exploring potential resources: Support the caregiver in selecting the resources that can be helpful in dealing with the child's triggering behaviors.

   - Mastery experiences: Identify times in the parent's life where the desired parenting behavior or quality was displayed. Identify times where the emotions or positive beliefs where present.
   - Relational resources: Select the parent's supportive figure or the role models that either embody the parenting quality or provide support and assistance to the caregiver. Having the caregiver surrounded by all the "helpers" and supportive figures could be a very powerful visualization resource.
   - Symbolic resources: Have the caregiver identify a symbol that will facilitate the parenting quality or behavior. It could also be a symbol that is associated with the positive belief, emotion or body sensations that supports this quality.
   - Somatic resource: Identify a body posture or a bodily state that supports, enhances or facilitates the desired parenting behavior.

4. Take one resource at a time and create a sensory image. Identify emotions, bodily states and postures associated with this resource.

5. Assess the validity of the resource: Ask the parent to visualize the problematic interaction with the child and check the helpfulness of this resource. Use a 1 to 7 scale. In this scale, 1 is not helpful and 7 is very helpful. If the parent establishes that this resource is not helpful in supporting the quality or parenting behavior, select a different resource. Go through different resources until the appropriate resource is found.

6. Installation: Create again a sensory image of the resource. Bring up the emotions and bodily states associated with this resource and add slow and short sets of BLS (4–6). Repeat several times.

7. Future template: Ask the parent to visualize the resource supporting the use of the attachment-informed parenting strategy or behavior. Next, ask the parent to imagine in the future being in the presence of the child while he or she is exhibiting the triggering quality or behavior. Once the parent can visualize this future event in which

the parent is able to utilize efficiently the resource and the attachment-informed parenting behavior, add slow and short (4–6) sets of BLS. Repeat it two or three times as long as it remains positive.

Keep in mind that before using the RDI protocol, the clinician should teach and practice with the parent the new parenting strategy. Role plays are very helpful in assisting the parent in fully understanding and integrating this new strategy into their parenting repertoire. After this, the RDI protocol can be used to help the caregiver access and utilize resources and parenting strategies more efficiently while in the presence of the child's activating behavior.

LEVEL III—MEMORY REPROCESSING AND INTEGRATION

When the different levels of intervention are presented to the parents, they may think that this third level may be too costly or too long. In my clinical experience, in the long run, not providing the best form of treatment in the present has the potential to end up costing more, lasting longer and being less effective. In addition, the clinician should emphasize the great plasticity of the developing brain and the importance of early intervention in promoting mental and emotional health.

This level of intervention is extremely relevant for parents of dissociative children. According to Liotti's etiological model of dissociation (see Chapter 1), a child's pathway into dissociation begins with the formation of disorganized attachment with the primary caregiver. However, even when a pattern of attachment disorganization already exists, full mental health may be accomplished if the primary caregiver achieves an organized state of mind with regards to his or her own attachment experiences. To that end, the third level of intervention with parents within a comprehensive EMDR treatment involves the reprocessing of the experiential contributors to problematic parenting. Helping the parent attain some level of integration and internal organization will in turn help the child develop unitary and more congruent models of the self and other. Appropriate stabilization of the caregiver to the point of achieving an adequate level of affect tolerance should be attained. The appropriate assessment and exploration of dissociative experiences should be carefully done. It is extremely important to stay within your level of clinical expertise. Some child EMDR clinicians may not have expertise in working with highly dissociative adults. Appropriate referrals should be provided to the parent to see a more qualified EMDR clinician. However, communication between the parent's treating clinician and the child's therapist should be maintained for best treatment outcome. Needless to say, appropriate consents to share information should be obtained. In addition, the child's EMDR clinician should review state board rules and regulations for working with parents before attempting to work directly with the child's parent. If both parents have agreed to receive treatment, they each should work with a different EMDR clinician to avoid conflict of interest, while they maintain close communication with the child's treating clinician.

Once the appropriateness of the parent and the clinician for this level of intervention have been established, the exploration of experiential contributors and past attachment experiences associated with problematic parenting interaction may be completed. Once again, it is pivotal to engage the parent's curiosity and desire to get to know the child. I usually invite parents to be my co-investigators. I invite them to do "detective work" as we learn about the parent, the child and about their implicit and explicit dynamics.

The following is a description of the steps necessary to create the parent's targeting sequence (see Figure 5.1).

1. Identify current patterned dysfunctional parenting response. These responses include but are not restricted to: Emotional and physical detachment, intrusiveness, power struggles, shutting down, nagging, controlling, role reversing, emotional dysregulation during interactions with the child, and criticizing, among others.
2. Identify the child's triggering responses and create a trigger map. Triggers could be present at different levels of human experience. The parent may find certain emotions, thoughts, behaviors, symptoms, etc., activating and triggering. Create an image of a recent event where the negative parenting response was present.
3. Identify the image that represents this event.
4. Identify the negative belief the parent holds in the present while thinking about the child's activating behavior. Say, *"When you think about the image of your child* (describe the child's activating response), *what negative beliefs do you have about yourself now?"*
5. Identify the emotional reactions associated with this image and the negative belief. Say, *"When you think about the image of your child* (describe the child's activating response) *the words* (repeat the negative belief), *what feelings or emotions do you have now?"*
6. Do a float back or, if the parent is unable to identify a negative belief, do an affect scan (Shapiro, 2001). Say, *"I would like you to think about* (describe the child's activating response), *the words* (repeat the negative belief), *and the emotions that you have and where you notice them in your body, and let your mind float back to an earlier time, where you recall having the same negative beliefs and the same emotional and bodily reactions."*

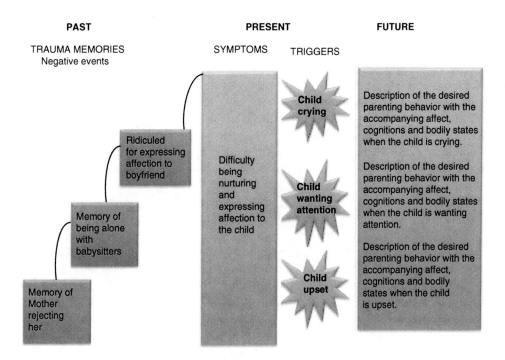

Figure 5.1 Parent's targeting sequence.

It is important that the clinician can assist the parent in floating back as early as possible to identify early attachment experiences associated with the current responses elicited by the child. Attunement to the parent's emotional state and a mindful observation of the parent's physiological reactions will guide this exercise for it to be effective. If the parent goes beyond the windows of affect tolerance, the attuned clinician should utilize strategies to bring the parent back to emotional homeostasis. Using statements of support, breathing, mindfulness, and stimulating present awareness, among others, should be used to restore emotional balance.

Once the parent identifies past experiences, organize them in chronological order to create a targeting sequence. It is important to present a picture to the parents of the presenting problems as well as a potential treatment plan. Creating a close, respectful, honoring and playful atmosphere where the exploration of such deep material can take place is critical. Good sense of humor and laughter are always wonderful tools where human beings can come together to explore who they are and what areas are in need of healing. At this point we do not want to trigger and activate the parent's defenses, but to stimulate their openness for exploration and self-awareness. The following is an example of how the picture of the current issues can be presented:

This is the story of a 10-year-old boy, adopted at birth by two high achieving parents. They brought the child to treatment because he had such low performance at school. He did not show much motivation to complete his homework or comply with any of his responsibilities at home. The parents, mostly the mother, always had to be "on top of him" in order for this boy to follow through with any of his responsibilities. A close look at the family dynamics showed a mother that was highly preoccupied with success and achievement. In fact, she was never content with the child's performance. The mother reported that she felt so hopeless to the point where she would become extremely angry and explosive at her child's lack of response. This boy started to make up stories and lie even about simple issues in his life. The lying elicited even more anger in the mother and sometimes her desire to detach from the child. These were the main responses identified by the mother: Agitation and detachment. The father would unsuccessfully try to mediate between the child and the mother. He had experienced a lot of conflict in his family of origin and as a result avoided conflict at all cost. When conflict arose between the mother and the child, he would make a few attempts to intervene, but if they were not successful he would completely distance. The father also had great difficulty dealing with this child's lies. He stated that he would become overwhelmed with the possibility of his son ending up in jail or becoming a criminal if he continued on this path. The sessions with the mother revealed the negative beliefs of "I am powerless" and "I am not a good enough mother" in association with her son lying and underachieving at home and at school. When the mother floated back to the past, she reported having images of her stepfather victimizing her. She always felt responsible for the abuse and also responsible for her mother, who she perceived as incompetent and unassertive. The mother stated that she always tried to be perfect and do everything right. She became a criminal attorney and dedicated her life to her career until she got married and adopted her child. She also stated that somehow her son reminded her of her stepfather, who was "lazy" and a "liar." On the other hand, the father reported that he had grown up in a very poor household and both of his parents had been in and out of jail. His oldest brother had always taken care of him while the parents were in prison. After identifying the memory networks his child was activating in him, he stated that he had a lot of shame around his parents' lifestyle and he feared that his son could become just like them.

It is important to highlight here that all this information was never provided during the initial intake. It is necessary to elicit it at the appropriate time, along with education about the AIP model. Since this information is encoded implicitly in the brain and remains below awareness even when activated, the parents usually do not disclose it during the intake or may not see it as relevant for the therapeutic work with their child. Once the full picture surfaced, I was able to sit down with the parents and present it along with a potential treatment plan. I said, *"Please know how honored I am to be accompanying you and your family on this journey toward healing. I know how difficult this exploration can be, but you have been such troopers! I am going to repeat back to you all the information both of you have provided, along with the information I have received from your child. I am going to put it together and formulate some hypotheses for you. Please know you are the experts of your life, so please feel free to correct me. Please try to notice what happens in your mind, heart and body when I present it and see if it resonates at some level with you. I invite you to always be my co-investigator; please feel free to add or change any of the information I will be presenting. Remember that this is not about judgment or criticism but about healing, awareness, and understanding. Okay, here I go: When your child refuses to comply with responsibilities and chores and he lies about this issue, it activates memory networks of disturbing events in your life, Mom. It activates negative beliefs such as "I am not good enough" and "I am powerless," along with emotions of desperation, anger, and sadness. These are old negative beliefs that were formed in your childhood in your experiences with your stepfather and the inability of your mother to protect you and take care of you. You learned to adapt to these negative experiences and the associated beliefs, emotions, etc., by always trying so hard to be perfect and perform. This is one of the ways you as a child found to get your needs for connection acceptance, self-worth, etc., met.*

When your child lies, does not follow through with directions and seems lazy, it triggers the old memories of your stepfather. These memories and all the beliefs, emotions and reactions in your body coming from the activation of these memories cloud the perception of your child, leading you to see a child that is lazy and a liar. When you feel the anger, desperation and sadness connected to your past memories, you become more agitated with your child and engage in power struggles with him or sometimes you just detach and lock yourself in your room.

On the other hand, Dad, you get memory networks activated that are reminiscent of the shame that you experienced with your parents. The fear that your child could become just like them causes you to detach from your child when what he actually needs is for both of you to connect even more with him. On another note, since your child was young, performance has been the way he gets the love and attention from both of you. The demands for performance have been perceived by him as so high that at times he gives up. It is easier for him not to try than to try and fail under your standards, so he stopped trying. Please know that since we are hard wired to need connection, when he does not meet your standards, he not only feels that he is losing your approval, he feels he is losing your love and connection. When any issues around performance are addressed, the memory networks containing information about him not being smart enough get activated along with the hurt and the pain. Then, when you, Mom, become angry or detached, it activates the memory networks in your child's brain that say, "I am a bad kid and I am unlovable," along with the pain and fear of feeling rejected and at times emotionally abandoned. These negative emotions, beliefs and bodily states your son experiences are connected to early experiences starting with the abandonment from his biological mother and followed by memories connected with experiences where his performance was not good enough for both of you. Please know that we are not talking about a bad child and about not-good-enough parents. We are talking about a good child and good-enough parents that when their own unresolved stuff from the past gets activated their good-enough intentions and wisdom gets clouded, making it difficult for both of you to be fully present and connected to your child and to offer true unconditional love and acceptance. Now, please take a moment to notice if this information resonates at some level. Is there something we need to modify to make this hypothesis closer to what is happening with you and your child?" Invite the parents to comment and change parts of it if it does not accurately describe the current problem. Encourage mindfulness and curiosity as you invite the parents to be co-investigators.

Notice that we are not interpreting from a psychodynamic perspective, but we are presenting back the information provided by the parents and the child. All the material gathered from doing float backs, affect-scan and history taking is presented as the parents offered it to the clinician. The clinician just puts it together and presents it back to the parents so they can make an informed decision about how they want to proceed in treatment. Once you have formulated a sound clinical picture, present the different levels of intervention as follows: *"Now that we have a clear picture of the current problem, here are the different levels of intervention:*

1. *Level one: Cleaning up a table. Your child will receive full EMDR therapy with the final goal of processing and digesting the early memories of abandonment and performance associated with the current lack of motivation and negative self-esteem. While your child is going through treatment, you will be very much involved, but at this level, we are only cleaning up the table. I will meet with you to provide just psychoeducation and specific parenting strategies you can use to help your child.*
2. *Level two: Cleaning up a room. The child gets full treatment and we do some work to help you regulate your emotions around this issue. This level will include psychoeducation as well as helping you develop resources to help yourselves regulate your emotional responses and be able to use the parenting strategies more efficiently.*
3. *Level three: Cleaning up the house. Besides the work with your child, you will also do full EMDR therapy. This way you can work on those past experiences that your child continues to activate in the present. This level of intervention will require more work in the present but less work in the long run. It will also require a team oriented approach as we will need to include two EMDR clinicians that will work with each of you. Please know I am here to accompany you, whether you want to just clean up a table, a room or the entire house. Take your time to think about this and let me know what you decide. In addition, you may want to pace the therapeutic work you and your child want to engage in. You may do one level of work and come back later on for more."*

With this method, the majority of parents that really need full EMDR therapy tend to choose to "clean up the house." If the parent does not need full EMDR treatment, there is no need to present such an alternative. Needless to say, when working with children injured and traumatized within the parent-child relationship and by abdicated caregiving systems, most likely the parents would benefit from the third level of EMDR intervention proposed in this chapter. Nevertheless, when working with highly traumatized and dissociative parents, having another therapist or therapists involved in treating the parents would be beneficial.

PARTICIPATION OF CAREGIVERS DURING THE CHILD'S SESSIONS

The question regarding the parent's level of involvement during the child's sessions remains open. Some child therapists include the parents in every session, while others rarely include the parents. Some therapists believe that inviting the parent to participate in the child's therapeutic sessions while the child is in such a vulnerable state would only perpetuate the wounding cycle of the parent toward the child. For these therapists, if the parent is included it only should happen after the parent has done sufficient therapeutic work. Clinicians of various disciplines would argue that working with just the child when the parent-child relationship is the wounding agent would compromise the treatment outcome. In this case, interventions mainly will be directed at repairing the parent-child attachment bond, which in turn will create the foundation for the child to heal. Specifically when providing EMDR therapy, different phases provide the opportunity for various levels of participation. Some EMDR clinicians may invite the parents to participate during preparation sessions, but not during reprocessing sessions. In my view, healing takes place at various levels: Individual and systemic. EMDR therapy can promote healing in the child's and parent's system, and the parent-child attachment bond. As a result, the combination of individual sessions with the child and the caregiver and parent-child sessions yields best treatment outcomes, in my clinical experience. It is of extreme relevance to always have a clear direction and purpose for every session. For example, when using Theraplay activities during the preparation phase, the goal is to start laying the foundation for connection, attunement and synchrony in the parent-child interactions. Helping the caregiver develop a mindful connection with the child and reading the child's changing affective states would be an appropriate goal for this phase. At this point, discussing any traumatogenic memories prematurely in front of the parent may obstruct rather than facilitate the therapeutic process. It is important to consider the level of self-awareness and integration the parent has achieved to be able to hold the child's mind in mind in a way that stimulates healing in the child's system. A combination of individual sessions with the caregiver, the child, and joint sessions may be used through out the eight phases of EMDR therapy. Emphasis initially in restoring some level of connection between the caregiver and the child is accomplished through the joint sessions where play, laughter and nurturing touch are used. Individual meetings with caregivers, where the tapes from the joint sessions are used to assist the parent in developing greater sensitivity to perceive and hold the child in mind, may be appropriate. Initially, the meetings with caregivers may be far more frequent than the individual sessions with the child. As the caregivers' understanding, level of attunement and self-awareness increases, the individual preparation sessions with the child will increase, followed by some joint and some individual reprocessing sessions (see Figure 5.2). By the time the child is ready to move into trauma reprocessing phases, the parent is at a place where he or she can be an active participant in promoting the integration and assimilation of such memories. Instead of continuing to wound the child, now the parent is ready to repair. Not all the reprocessing sessions may need the presence of the parent. In fact, a combination of individual and joint reprocessing sessions seems to be the best arrangement. On one hand, working individually with the therapist could be empowering for the child. Experiencing his or her own healing powers could be stimulating and exciting for the child as well. On the other hand, when working with the parent present, the child gets to feel heard and felt, as well as to experience repair during the critical moments of integration of the trauma memories. When repair is needed, the presence of the parent to provide reparative interweaves under the guidelines of the clinician could be very powerful in helping the child assimilate such information. Having a clear, thorough, initial clinical landscape laid out will greatly assist clinicians in organizing a treatment plan that truly meets the needs of the child. As a result, how and how much the parent participates in the overall treatment will depend on the needs of each individual case.

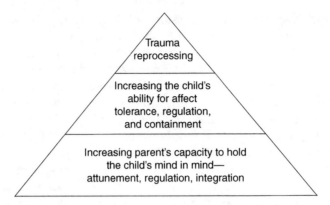

Figure 5.2 When the caregivers have been the child's wounding agents, intensive work with them may be necessary. This diagram shows the progressive work in EMDR therapy that initially concentrates more heavily on the parent and on repairing the parent-child attachment bond. This is followed by increased individual work with the child and later on the reprocessing of memories of trauma and adversity.

WHEN THERE ARE NO PARENTS

For clinicians working with children in the child protective services system, the parent may not be present or may be going through court procedures leading to severance or reunification. Some of these children may be living with foster parents or in group homes. In these cases, some level of work should still be done with foster parents to promote appropriate connection, while helping the child feel differentiated and regulated. The first two levels of work, psychoeducation and self-regulation, may be appropriate for foster parents. Group home managers could also benefit from psycho-education to help the child feel safe and regulated. In these cases, most of the work throughout the eight phases will be done with the child individually. The relationship with the therapist then becomes an important agent of change and healing. Our capacity to hold the child within our internal arms while walking through each of the phases of EMDR therapy is pivotal.

SUMMARY AND CONCLUSIONS

Many children with complex trauma have been injured within the caregiving system. They may have also experienced repetitive emotional, physical, sexual, and spiritual abuse. They have experienced enmeshment and intrusiveness in their relationship with their parents or, on the contrary, detachment and lack of connection. They may have experienced parental responses that are frightened or frightening and, as a result, they have developed memory networks containing incongruent and multiple models of the self and other. Parents with unresolved trauma and loss have the potential to perpetuate high levels of internal disorganization in the child's system. A link has been established in attachment research between the parent's state of mind with regards to his or her own attachment experiences, the parent's ability to hold the child's mind in mind, the resulting caregiving behaviors and the child's pattern of attachment with the caregiver. As long as the parent continues to be clouded by the past, the present parent-child inter-actions will be influenced and at times hijacked by the past. This will continue to per-petuate the passing and migration of the unresolved trauma and loss of the caregiver into the minds of the next generations. When the parent or past caregivers have been the wounding agents, the work with caregivers is fundamental for best EMDR therapy outcome. The inclusion of other EMDR clinicians may be necessary. Maintaining close communication among therapists will highly improve treatment outcome. This chapter presents a model to work with caregivers that involves three levels of treatment. How much the parent needs to participate and when, will be determined by the needs of each child. Developing a thorough treatment plan and a clear clinical landscape will more precisely guide the how, when, and the amount of parental involvement in the child's overall EMDR treatment.

6

Assessing and Diagnosing Dissociation in Children: Beginning the Recovery

Frances S. Waters

The first reported case of childhood dissociation by Antoine Despine in 1836 was of a 12-year-old girl, Estelle (Ellenberger, 1970). However, it wasn't until a century later that a slow resurgence of writings about childhood dissociation occurred (Bowman, Bix, & Coons, 1985; Braun, 1985; Riley & Mead, 1988; Chu & Dill, 1990; Coons, 1985; Fagan & McMahon, 1984; Kluft, 1984, 1985; Weiss, Sutton, & Utecht, 1985). Since then, there is a steadily growing literature on the topic including historical perspectives (Silberg, 2000; Silberg & Dallam, 2009) research studies (Becker-Blease et al., 2004, 2011; Kisiel & Lyons 2001; Macfie, Ciccehtti, & Toth, 2001; Shimizu & Sakamoto, 1986), comorbidity studies (Kaplowa, Hallb, Koenenc, Dodged, & Amaya-Jacksone, 2008; Malinosky-Rummel & Hoier, 1991), case studies (Coons, 1996; Dell & Eisenhower, 1990; Stolbach, 2005; Waters, 2011), theoretical (Putnam, 1997) and clinical books (Shirar, 1996; Silberg, 1996/1998; Wieland, 2011), dissociative checklists (Armstrong, Putnam, Carlso, Libero, & Smith, 1997; Dell, 2006; Evers-Szostak & Sanders, 1992; Putnam, Helmers, & Trickett, 1993; Steinburg, 1994; Stolbach, 1997), and conferences around the globe. To add to our deeper understanding of the nosology of dissociation, the recent publication by Dell and O'Neil (2009) provides a comprehensive sourcebook.

The International Society for the Study of Trauma and Dissociation (ISSTD; www. isst-d) sponsored initially the journal, *Dissociation* (which can be downloaded for free at the University of Oregon Library, https://scholarsbank.uoregon.edu/xmlui/handle/1794/1129). In 2000, ISSTD launched its own journal, the *Journal of Trauma and Dissociation*, to continue bringing scholarly works to professionals. ISSTD's website has expanded to include guidelines for evaluation and treatment of childhood dissociation and FAQs (frequently asked questions) for parents and teachers. ISSTD's professional training institute offers comprehensive courses on childhood dissociation that are taught internationally and online. ISSTD also sponsored the training DVD, *Trauma and Dissociation in Children* (Waters, 2007), to assist professionals, particularly forensic evaluators and prosecutors, in understanding dissociative signs and effective strategies in child abuse and neglect investigations.

While the bulk of the literature has continued predominately to focus on adult dissociation, these efforts shed light on how to accurately assess dissociation in children and are slowly gaining momentum in educating professionals, academics, parents, and teachers about the convoluted presentations of dissociative youth. However, because dissociative children have a high rate of comorbidity and a continuation of misinformation about dissociation, these children continue to be misdiagnosed for more popular or widely known diagnoses, such as attention deficit hyperactivity disorder (ADHD), bipolar, psychoses, conduct disorder, etc. (McElroy, 1992; Waters, 2005a).

THEORETICAL DEVELOPMENTS AND CONCEPTUALIZATION OF DISSOCIATION

Since the early 1990s, many theoretical models from different disciplines have emerged to provide a broader perspective of our understanding of the disruption of memory, consciousness, and identity. Contributions in the field of neurobiology (Bremner et al., 2003; Bremner; 2005; Stein, Koverola, Hanna, Torchia, & McClarty, 1997; Vermetten, Schmahl, Lindner, Loewenstein, & Bremner, 2006) examine how trauma affects certain brain structures and impairs consciousness and memory. The attachment and relational theories (Liotti, 1992, 2009; Lyons-Ruth & Jacobvitz, 1999; Main & Solomon, 1986; Siegel, 1999) focus on the child's traumatic relationship with the parent and the development of dissociative processes and disorders.

In the dissociative field, a number of theories have emerged. I will briefly cite some of them. Putnam (1997) views dissociation as a defense mechanism to overwhelming fear of annihilation resulting in compartmentalization of painful affect and memories and an estrangement from self.

Putnam further examines in his *Discrete Behavioral States Model* (1997) the early development of an infant's discrete shifts in response to the mother's erratic and abusive care. These discrete shifts form templates for segmenting frightening and confusing experiences from the self-beginning stages of dissociation.

van der Hart, Nijenhuis, and Steele (2006) detailed their model, *Structural Dissociation of the Personality*, based on early works of Pierre Janet, in which the traumatized self separates according to two complex action systems. One system, the apparently normal personality (ANP) enables an individual to perform necessary functions, such as work. The emotional personality (EP) is action system fixated at the time of the trauma to defend from threats. The EP contains traumatic memories and associated traumatic affect, thoughts, and behaviors. These action systems can further fragment into tertiary systems containing many ANPs and EPs that take on additional actions for the self.

Stein and Kendall (2004) present the *Global Psychological Effects of Chronic Traumatic Stress on Children Model*, based on the early works of Lenore Terr's Type 2 trauma (1991) that examines the impact of chronic trauma on the child's developing brain, alterations in consciousness and memory, disturbance in identity, difficulty in regulating emotions and level of arousal, hyperactivity and attention, relationship problems, and alterations in belief system.

The Proposed Developmental Trauma Disorder (van der Kolk, et. al, 2009) for consideration in the DSM-V focuses on the impact of multiple exposures to interpersonal trauma that causes dysregulation of somatic, affective, self and relational, and posttraumatic spectrum symptoms. This disorder lasts more than 6 months and causes significant functional impairment, including dissociation.

Waters' (1996, 2011) *Quadri-Therapeutic Model for Treating Dissociative Children* is a comprehensive model that combines the use of four theories in assessing and treating dissociative children: Attachment (Bowlby, 1973, 1980; Mahler, Pine, & Bergman, 1975; Main & Solomon, 1986), developmental (Erikson, 1968; Piaget, 1954), family systems (Bowen, 1978; Minuchin, 1974; Satir, 1983), and dissociative theory (Putnam, 1997).

The attachment theory of this model is derived from Bowlby's framework of a child's psychological responses to the loss of a parent. He describes grief and mourning stages that the child experiences as behavior directed to the lost object, hostility, appeals for help, despair, withdrawal, regression, disorganization, and reorganization of behavior directed toward a new object. My model, based on Bowlby's model of how a child copes with separation from a parent, is comparatively *a window* on how a child must survive the devastating psychological impact when exposed to frightening, confusing, or abusive parents. In my comparison model, the child, being in a devastating, helpless, untenable situation, finds a way out through dissociating affect, sensations, loss of idealized parent, etc. The child's response is to internalize the unbearable, intense affect of underlying fear, grief, mourning, and vulnerability and the associated coping behaviors into self-states, such as internalized abusive parent state, helper/friendly state, angry state, depressed state, sexualized state, etc. The states can be fragmented, less developed, or more developed as seen in dissociative identity disorder (DID).

The development theory of this model includes Erickson's Theory of Psychosocial Development (1968) that examines the formation of ego identity, a conscious sense of the self shaped by daily social interactions. The development of the self is constantly changing by new experiences. He details eight stages of relational experiences beginning at birth that, if successfully reached, build competency, capacity for intimacy, and a secure sense of self into old age. However, my model recognizes that traumatic experiences during childhood disrupt the development of identity, trust, autonomy, intimacy, etc., resulting in some degree of identity confusion and fragmentation.

Mahler's theory (Mahler et al., 1975) of separation and individuation also provides a conceptualization of developmental phases beginning at infancy to achieve a healthy identity. Mastery of each phase will help to develop a sense of individual identity. However, early child maltreatment, particularly by the mother, disrupts the child's developmental process to achieve healthy individuation. Safe exploration of emotions and the environment is then precluded. Consequently, the child may rely on dissociation and fragmentation of the self as a way to defend against feeling overwhelmed by the original trauma and subsequent traumatic triggers in the environment. This will therefore impair the child's ability to attain individuation with unified self-identity.

The family system theory in the quadri-theoretical model is based on works of Bowen (1978), Satir (1983), and Minuchin, (1974) which view the family as an emotional unit and examines the interplay among family members. Destructive interactions within the family, such as maltreatment or disruption in attachment, can cause or influence dissociative defenses. Family systems approach examines family members and their own history of trauma, unresolved attachment, dissociation, mental illness, etc. My model emphasizes the importance of engaging the entire family in assessment and treatment to improve effective communication and relationships, eliminate any behaviors that influence dissociation, and provide a safe environment.

The quadri-theoretical model provides a comprehensive and integrative perspective by examining how multiple theories intersect to provide a foundation for understanding the development and complexities of dissociative defenses in children. This conceptualization is helpful in assessment and throughout the treatment process.

All of these theoretical models–neurological, attachment, relational, dissociative–are derived from various disciplines and converge with overlapping constructs to greatly enhance the credibility and understanding of the etiology of dissociation. *These models all acknowledge the underlying cause of dissociation resulting from childhood trauma, abuse, and neglect.*

Regardless of contemporary studies, theoretical models, and training opportunities, childhood dissociation is often overlooked, misunderstood, or disbelieved today. Kluft (1984, 1985) attributes this phenomenon to the lack of recognition of dissociative behaviors in children that are expressed differently from dissociative adults, who exhibit more discrete presentations. Also, there is a disbelief or skepticism of children's reports of voices accounting for their misbehavior or children's denial of their behavior. Because caretakers will punish them for "lying" or reporting separateness, dissociative children are further inhibited to disclose such influences.

van der Hart, Nijenhuis, and Steele (2005) also postulate another crucial reason for overlooking dissociation in traumatized individuals. Professionals miss how trauma can involve some degree of division or dissociation within the self and that evaluators view dissociation as peripheral, not a central feature of PTSD.

More popular or widely recognized disorders, such as ADHD, adjustment disorders, somatization disorder, developmental disorder, and bipolar disorder, are assigned to traumatized children but dissociation is unrecognized, (McElroy, 1992; Waters, 2005a) resulting in cumulative years of emotional pain, identity confusion, memory problems, unresolved trauma, and ineffectual treatment.

ASSESSMENT PROCESS FOR CHILD AND ADOLESCENT DISSOCIATION

Conducting a thorough assessment of children with complex trauma does not occur in a single session or a series of early sessions but is an ongoing process.

As with the Adaptive Information Processing Model (AIP) in eye movement desensitization and reprocessing (EMDR) (Shapiro, 2001), each phase brings reassessment of the client's ability to move forward to effectively process trauma. Clinicians are continually gaining more information through all phases and reassessing how to intervene. Dissociative symptoms may not appear until the later stages of EMDR treatment, particularly during trauma processing. It would be advisable to assess the degree of dissociation before proceeding.

Exploring all forms of trauma, including physical, sexual, emotional, witnessing domestic violence, medical/illnesses, exposure to war or natural disasters and accidents, their chronicity, and familial responses are integral to assessing how the child defended against such experiences and whether dissociative processes were employed. Understanding these processes will assist the EMDR clinician to prepare for effectively processing the memories of trauma and adversity with children using EMDR treatment and the AIP model.

Dissociation can be nonpathological or pathological. Some signs of nonpathological dissociation are daydreaming or zoning out, fantasy, or absorption while playing a video game. These experiences do not involve any self-fragmentation and generally do not hinder the overall adjustment of the child unless there is some compulsive quality, such as hours of computer game playing that interrupts sleep or homework.

Pathological dissociation can range from moderate to severe. Moderate forms are derealization and depersonalization. Moving along the continuum of severity is the formation of self-states. These self-states may only operate internally, without taking executive control over the body, but nevertheless, they can greatly influence the child's mood, sensations, behavior, and memory. These children are diagnosed with dissociative disorders not otherwise specified (DDNOS). The most severe form of dissociation is the presence of discrete self-states that take executive control over the body, resulting in considerable memory problems, identity confusion, and more pronounced mood and behavioral switches. These children would meet the diagnosis of DID. Below is a more thorough description of these indicators.

CORE DISSOCIATIVE INDICATORS AND CASE DESCRIPTION

Peterson (1991) provides a child dissociative problem checklist, and Hornstein and Putnam (1992) examine clinical phenomenology of child and adolescent dissociative disorders. When evaluating for core dissociative indicators, utilizing valid dissociative checklists with a thorough interviewing process is warranted. The core dissociative indicators presented are often interrelated, influenced, and/or dependent on the other indicators. Dissociative symptoms can suddenly appear and disappear quickly or only appear occasionally depending on what activates them. It is because of the fluidity of such symptoms that they are often overlooked or misunderstood.

In describing each of the core dissociative indicators, I will describe a case example of a 9-year-old adopted Asian girl, Lisa, that I treated. Lisa lived with her adoptive parents and two brothers. Her mother provided extensive history of worsening, severe emotional and behavioral problems with Lisa since adoption. Lisa was only able to handle school for a half day since the beginning of her academic career and would often be sent home for frequent explosive behaviors at school and severe peer problems. At 9 years old, Lisa was still unable to open a bottle or hold silverware.

Her mother noted when Lisa came to the United States at 4 months old, she slept the entire trip regardless of being overly dressed and drenched. She was unresponsive to the heat and displayed signs of sensory processing difficulties even at this young age. The parents were not given any trauma history when Lisa was placed with them, but they noted that she had a swollen gum that appeared to be a tumor. An examination by a pediatric dentist indicated that it was not a tumor but was due to some unknown trauma to the gum. From infancy through preschool, Lisa was extremely orally defensive and feeding was a traumatic experience for her as well as her parents, as she would refuse a bottle or spoon until she was starving. She would violently swing her little arms and kick furiously if anyone came close to her. She fought having her teeth brushed. She was clearly behaving as if she was traumatized orally. Her tongue held out of her mouth, and she drooled until she was 5 years old, as she did not develop facial muscles until then. She did not recognize herself in the mirror until her mother taught her to do so at age 3. She would often have a blank look on her face.

Lisa did not bond with her adoptive mother. When Lisa would decompensate, she would display a disorganized attachment pattern of screaming and thrashing if her mother came close to comfort her. Then when her mother would walk away, Lisa would chase after her mother in fear and agony, protesting her mother's withdrawal. Lisa was utterly inconsolable, highly disruptive, and raged for hours and her mother was equally desperate for solutions. Lisa frequently would not remember these outbursts and would have a glazed look in her eyes when questioned. These sudden mood and behavior switches were often unprovoked or unpredictable. This was a common pattern repeated throughout her young life. Lisa was inconsolable and highly disruptive for hours.

Lisa's early and increasingly disturbing behavior prompted her mother to frantically search for answers by seeking various assessments. At 18 months of age, Lisa was evaluated by an occupational and speech therapists. She was diagnosed with low motor development and "splintered" physical abilities. She had significant speech and language delays. She received occupational and speech therapy since then to the time of my evaluation.

Her mother consulted with the adoption agency for advice on how to handle Lisa during her preschool years. She was advised that Lisa had reactive attachment disorder and was directed to do holding therapy (Welch, 1988), a technique of forced, prolonged holding of a child by a parent or therapist to develop attachment with the parent. This technique has met with controversy. The mother was directed to not stop holding Lisa until she began to bond with her. Lisa fought vigorously, passed out, and woke up only to resume struggling to get away from her mother, who had held her for hours. Being held down activated her stress response system, increasing her fear and consequently her dissociation. Lisa's rages increased.

A psychiatrist evaluated Lisa at 6 years of age. He reportedly was unsure of Lisa's diagnosis but gave her the diagnoses of an anxiety disorder and oppositional defiant disorder (ODD). He prescribed an antidepressant and later added an antipsychotic mediation, but her mother discontinued them due to no improvement.

Desperate, Lisa's mother sought help from a well-known and respected child guidance center that diagnosed Lisa with a developmental disorder not otherwise specified and ODD. Ruling out an affective disorder was considered. Lisa was noted to have behavioral, sensory, emotional, cognitive, and academic problems. The recommendation was behavioral therapy, which proved to be ineffective. Lisa's family had severely limited their activities due to Lisa's explosive behavior.

Lisa's mother then sought an assessment from me at the same time that she brought Lisa to a chiropractor, who provided stunning independent diagnostic impressions that were complimentary to mine, which I will explain as I highlight Lisa's core dissociative symptoms under the headings below.

Amnesia

Children can have fluctuations in their memory, including not recalling past or present traumatic and/or nontraumatic experiences. Their memory can be spotty or episodic. At one time they may remember events and at another time they may not have knowledge of those events, or they may only have a sketchy memory of the events. They may recall parts of their trauma and describe accompanied sensory distortion, such as tunnel vision or only hearing bits of the event. They may not recall their teachers, schoolwork, holidays, or even their parents, as in the case with Lisa.

In my first interview with Lisa, while she was playing with the dollhouse, I inquired about any memory problems. She simply and clearly stated, "It takes me a while to remember who my parents are." She also said it took a while to remember her brothers, as well. With further questioning, she reported not recognizing her homework when returned to her or tests she had taken, and activities she had done with her family. She also indicated that she would be accused of hitting her siblings but have no memory of such behavior.

Inconsistent memory for disruptive behavior with dissociative children can be misconstrued by parents and professionals that the children are lying or manipulating to avoid consequences. While it is exasperating for adults to manage these episodes, it is often more confusing, frustrating, and frightening for dissociative children to be accused of something for which they have no memory doing. While children may manipulate to avoid repercussions, traumatized children often have significant memory problems and dissociation should be carefully explored as a viable possibility. An empathic approach will decrease children's shame and encourage them to explore dissociative barriers and what underlying factors contribute to their amnesia.

Children's episodic memory can be dependent on many factors, such as, whether they have sufficient ego strength to handle the memory, particularly if it is traumatic, the safety of the environment, and the awareness of a trance state that contains the information of current or past events. In addition, simply asking children in an empathic manner about such experiences will often provide them the opportunity to discuss their amnestic experiences, as with Lisa, who seemed relieved to tell me about them.

Trance Behavior and Trance States or Self-States

Along the continuum of moderate to severe range of dissociation, children may stare off or "zone out" when they want to escape due to anxiety or traumatic reminders. With chronically abused children, trance behavior can become habitual even with mild stressors, which are often noted by teachers. During those times, the children may have difficulty reporting what transpired just before they zoned out or what motivated such behavior. Sometimes, because of embarrassment they will say that they were bored in school. It is important to further explore whether these periods have more significance and a pattern related to a certain affect, traumatic triggers, and/or the presence of a self-state.

A more severe form of dissociation is the presence of self-states. Young children who have auditory or visual hallucinations of people may identify them as "imaginary friends" and not distinguish them as self-states until they are older and able to assimilate their meaning. These "imaginary friends," however, may express intense affect and conflicts with each other (Frost, Silberg, & McIntee, 1996) and cause considerable distress to the child. I have treated a number of small children who have emphatically insisted that their "imaginary friends" or "angry voice" are real and not pretend.

Children can create self-states of various ages with different roles, affect, and behaviors that may directly relate to their traumatic experiences (Waters & Silberg, 1998). They may be given names that describe their function and have special significance to the child, such as hero figure, perpetrator, or mad part. They can have various degrees of influence over the child's mood, behavior, sensations, thoughts, and relationships.

Some self-states who identify with the perpetrator engage in aggressive or self-harming behaviors, such as cutting one's self, assaulting others, etc., usually attract the most attention from parents and professionals. They are often the focus of interventions and diagnosed with ODD or conduct disorder. There may also be self-states who assume identification with hero figures and who "rescued" the child when abused by "helping her fly away" or by taking the abuse for her.

Sometimes self-states are simply "reporters" of traumatic memories *without any affect*. This presentation can confuse professionals who may doubt that the trauma was really experienced, or they may minimize the traumatic impact on the child. But as Steele explained in the training DVD, *Trauma and Dissociation in Children* (Waters, 2007), "…this is a hallmark of dissociation. It didn't happen to me, or it happened to me and it doesn't really matter. There's no affect to it. There's no feeling tone to it. There's no sense of personal ownership." (This is also a sign of depersonalization, which is highlighted below.)

Because chronically traumatized, dissociative children are easily sensitized to even minor stimuli, they can rapidly switch self-states when triggered. These trance states can appear and disappear suddenly without apparent provocation and may contain only specific memories related to their own experiences. Their awareness of other self-states or their current environment may be precarious depending on protective barriers between each other. They can emerge after being hidden for years by taking executive control over the child's body or harass the child from within with degrading comments, or pressure the child to engage in self-destructive or aggressive acts. Self-states can appear, engage in aggressive behavior, and then disappear, leaving the child bewildered. These children are often accused of lying when they deny such behavior.

Lisa described a total of five self-states over several months. During the time period when she was evaluated by the chiropractor, Lisa revealed to me two baby self-states, Mary and Tommy. The chiropractor, unaware of Lisa's dissociative states, made a remarkable assessment that she had retained her primitive infant reflexes. Lisa was diagnosed with asymmetrical tonic neck reflex (ATNR) that infants display until 6 months old and then normally vanish. The signs are when eyes move in one direction, the neck moves in the same direction; when head moves in one direction, the arms and legs move in that direction, etc. Lisa's infantile reflexes were attributed to the presences of these baby states! Furthermore, they continued to influence and limit her physical adroitness and strength, as she was unable to open a bottle and effectively hold silverware.

Lisa also identified Helper, the internalized mother. Another adult helper, Shadow, was revealed after Lisa reported seeing internally a shadowy figure. Cindy, a 9-year-old angry self-state, became known during one of the explosions. Lisa appeared to switch rapidly from a helpless baby state that had extreme separation anxiety to Cindy, who would rage if her mother came close to comfort her when she was wailing. Baby's Helper and Shadow were often in direct conflict with Lisa's mothering aiming to take control. Switching from one state to another was accompanied with significant amnesia resulting in a chaotic life of fear and confusion that not only severely impaired her memory, behavior, and affect, but it also adversely affected her ability to attach to her mother.

When children have extreme and contradictory presentations, particularly severe developmental delays (regressed behavior), the existence of trance states of different ages should be considered and carefully assessed. While self-states initially helped the child survive the trauma, later some can wreak havoc on the child's life until their presence are known and their traumatic role has been processed. Resistance to interventions, denial of behaviors, and erratic presentations are critical warning signs for the clinician to explore the presences of self-states.

Extreme Mood and Behavior Switches

Rapid and extreme fluctuations in mood and behavior can often be seen as a form of bipolar disorder or ODD, particularly if they are taken at face value and not understood as a part of the etiology of dissociation. Dissociative children's mercurial presentation of sudden shifts is unpredictable, confusing, and challenging to manage. As noted above, these fluctuations are often attributed to rapid switching of self-states that have divergent affect, such as happy, mad, sad, scared, etc. They can demonstrate changeable preferences to food, dress, toys, activities, and contain contradictory thinking patterns and sudden somatic complaints, such as headaches, stomachaches, and painful extremities. While it appears confusing to the caregiver or professional, these extreme mood and behavior switches should be explored to see if they are a result of fragmentation and creation of self-states. A detailed mapping of these shifts by the parents can provide the EMDR assessor a valuable composite picture of triggers and shifts in presentation for accurate diagnosis.

Lisa demonstrated rapid switching when she felt physically threatened, was in crowds, witnessed someone at school being hurt, took long trips (her long journey to this country when adopted), and when father traveled on business (fear of abandonment, as she was closest to him). These were all traumatic reminders instigating dissociative defenses. Parts of her would either take executive control or she would internally feel their intense affect. Her moods swung from fear to aggression to despondency, in which she would wail for hours wanting to die. Her skill levels were erratic and particularly dependant on her baby states, in which she would regress to baby talk and infantile mannerisms or physical capabilities.

Auditory and Visual Hallucinations

The presence of voices and images of floating objects, faces, figures, or shadows are frequently characteristic of children with DDNOS or DID. These hallucinations originate from traumatic experiences and are indicators of fragmentation. As previously reiterated, the voices can be antagonistic, friendly, helpful, or destructive.

Teens may be hesitant to report voices for fear of being seen as "crazy." Asking children in an empathic way about their hallucinations, while explaining that other children with similar trauma histories have reported these types of experiences, can minimize their resistance to reveal them. I will often explain that the voices are part of them that helped them in some way with "the bad things that happened to them, even the voice that seems angry." This approach has helped children to begin to understand the meaning of the voices and reduce their anxiety and phobia toward that state. It will also increase the angry state's willingness to cooperate in therapy.

So that I may be able to understand the child's perception of the visual hallucinations of the "scary figures," etc., I will ask the child to draw a picture of them during the initial phases of EMDR treatment in order to assess dissociative responses more thoroughly. Their drawings will diagnostically provide much data about the child's perception of their voices or self-states, such as how well their identity is developed, how powerful they are, and how scary the child perceives them. Some children may draw a head or a complete body that is large with oversized arms and scary-looking faces.

In the preparation phase of EMDR treatment, I will provide further psychoeducation about these parts containing feelings that the child was unable to handle alone and how the parts also need help to learn to express themselves in appropriate ways. Helping to demystify these hallucinations can help to engage the children to express their inner experiences.

Lisa was very open to reporting about her auditory and visual hallucinations. It was a relief to her to be able to understand them and to begin to have some control over their influence. Her mother was often present during these sessions and was very nonjudgmental, empathetic, and supportive, which greatly helped Lisa to overcome some shame about them, particularly associated with embarrassing behavior.

Once children understand that their frightening voices or images were originally formed to help them survive, their fear and resistance to disclose them is lessened.

Depersonalization and Derealization

While depersonalization and derealization were mentioned above, it is worth highlighting here in depth.

Steele, Dorahy, van der Hart, and Nijenhuis (2009) eloquently describe depersonalization as: (1) the existence of an observing and experiencing ego or part of the personality (Fromm, 1965); (2) detachment of consciousness from the self or body (i.e., feelings of strangeness or unfamiliarity with self, out-of-body experiences); (3) detachment from affect, such as numbness; (4) a sense of unreality, such as being in a dream; and (5) perceptual alterations or hallucinations regarding the body (Noyes & Kletti, 1977). Derealization involves a sense of unreality or unfamiliarity with one's environment, and distortions of space and time (Steinberg, 1995,p. 162).

Steele et al. (2009) believe that many forms of depersonalization and derealization are alterations of consciousness and memory.

Shimizu and Sakamoto's (1986) research describes 16 cases of depersonalization that developed before the age of 15. The majority of dissociative children that I treated who described depersonalization and derealization experiences also had self-states present at that time. However, I worked with an adoptive teenager who did not disclose any self-state related to his feelings of depersonalization and derealization.

Regarding Lisa, she had considerable depersonalization predominately related to her mouth, but also to other parts of her body that would become activated when she ate. For example, Lisa did not feel her mouth, did not taste or smell her food, and was unaware of how she was chewing her food. She was desensitized to food that drips on her arms, lap, and legs. Upon further exploration, while Lisa's baby states did not take executive control over her body, they were internally influencing her sensory losses. This example demonstrates the complexity of tweaking what is affecting the prolonged symptoms of children who may appear to parents to be careless, sloppy, and resistant to correction, but truly are numb to their bodily senses.

ASSESSMENT TOOLS

Along with a thorough interview process, there are some gold standard dissociative assessment tools for children and adolescents that are valid and reliable. These tools can further aid the EMDR evaluator in diagnosing as part of a complete assessment.

A common caregiver checklist is the *Child Dissociative Checklists* (CDC, Putnam et al. 1993) that has been used also by teachers to rate children's behavior. It is geared for children from preschool to 12 years old.

The most widely used standardized measurement for caregivers and teachers is the *Child Behavior Checklists* (CBCL, Achenbach, 1992). The CBCL evaluates children's internalizing and externalizing behaviors and is often used for diagnosing ADHD. However, this checklist has the following items that overlap with dissociative symptoms: acts too young for age, can't concentrate, can't pay attention for long, confused or seems to be in a fog, daydreams or gets lost in his/her thoughts, stares blankly, sudden changes in mood or feeling. Studies (Malinosky-Rummel & Hoier, 1991; Sim et al., 2005) have included the CBCL in effectively detecting dissociation in children.

There are a number of dissociative self-report checklists. A commonly used one is the 30-item questionnaire, *Adolescent Dissociative Experience Scale* (ADES) (Armstrong et al., 1997). The more comprehensive 218 questionnaire, *Adolescent Multi-Dimensional Inventory of Dissociation v.6.0* (Dell, 2006), rates 14 major facets of dissociation. It can be obtained by contacting Dr. Dell at pfdell@aol.com.

Stolbach's (1997) *Children's Dissociative Experiences Scale & Posttraumatic Symptom Inventory* (CDES-PSI) is a self-report for children designed for 7- to 12-year-olds, but the author has communicated that he has found it helpful with adolescents, as well (Stolbach, personal communication, May 2006). This checklist is valid for differentiating traumatized children from nontraumatized children and is easy for children to fill out. While there are no valid norms for dissociation, I have found this helpful in detecting dissociative symptoms with traumatized children. For those younger children who do not read, I have read the questions in a matter-of-fact way so as to not skew the results.

The *Children's Perceptual Alteration Scale* (CPAS, Evers-Szostak & Sanders, 1992) is a self-report measure of dissociation for children 8 to 12 years old. It was derived from the Perceptual Alteration Scale for adults (Sanders, 1986) and is a helpful measurement for childhood dissociation as well as normal development and childhood psychopathology.

Briere's (1996) self-report, *Trauma Symptom Checklist for Children* (TSCC), has six clinical scales: Anxiety, depression, posttraumatic stress, dissociation, anger, and sexual concerns. There are three dissociative questions that can be used to signal a need for a more thorough evaluation with one of the specific dissociative checklists. Even if a child doesn't endorse dissociation on the TSCC, I also administered one of the dissociative checklists, particularly when the child displays dissociative symptoms.

Steinburg developed the *Structural Clinical Interview for DSM Dissociative Disorders* (SCID-D) (1994), which requires training, and can be used with adolescents who can maintain sustained attention and have an average or higher level of cognitive functioning.

When caregivers and children significantly endorse items on the checklists, I will follow-up with a request for clarification.

DIFFERENTIAL DIAGNOSES AND COMORBIDITY

Shapiro's (2001) Adaptive Information Processing Model explains that when an individual is under high arousal as a result of trauma, the information processing is thwarted. Consequently, the traumatic experience is maladaptively stored, resulting in symptoms. Traumatized children and adolescents often have a high level of comorbidity as a result of unprocessed trauma. These symptoms can confuse or mask their traumatic origin and the sequelae of dissociation. It is the myriad of symptoms that are seen with traumatized children, such as extreme mood swings, inattention, and oppositional behavior that are given more commonly known or accepted diagnoses, such as bipolar disorder, oppositional defiant disorder, and attention deficit hyperactivity disorder (ADHD). Even when recent reports of traumatic experiences were provided, unfortunately, clinicians will disregard their significance and diagnose according to the most florid or disturbing symptom, thus ignoring any dissociative phenomenon (Waters, 2005a). This is particularly serious, as early detection and proper processing of the trauma, including the use of EMDR, can save children from years of escalating symptoms that have been resistant to previous treatments and medication regimens.

Overarching complexity of co-morbid symptoms in dissociative children is that these symptoms can be brief and intense, or lasting for days, months, or years, and then suddenly disappear. Because these erratic symptoms are often contained in self-states of children with DID or DDNOS, as highlighted previously, it is often confusing to the diagnostician to see the correlation between sudden, sporadic symptoms contained in brief presence of self-states. Self-states can have specific behavioral or emotional problems that stem from how they were affected by the trauma. *Consequently, there can be an exhaustive list of co-morbid symptoms and diagnoses ascribed to dissociative children.*

Frequent co-morbid symptoms or diagnoses commonly seen in dissociative children are PTSD, ADHD, ODD, bipolar disorders, psychotic disorders, substance abuse, obsessive-compulsive disorder, sexual problems, conduct disorder, somatoform disorders, anxiety, depression, and eating disorders.

Lisa's mother was an excellent reporter of Lisa's symptoms and kept copious notes describing her daughter's convoluted presentation in detail. Nevertheless, Lisa was diagnosed with an anxiety disorder and ODD by the psychiatrist and later by a child guidance clinic. Neither considered her early history of infant trauma and dissociative symptoms.

To assist the EMDR evaluator, I will address three common misdiagnoses ascribed to dissociative children that have overlapping or similar presentations but contain distinctive differences that are ignored.

Attention Deficit Hyperactive Disorder

There are many overlapping symptoms with ADHD and dissociation that often mask the dissociation. Clinicians who are unfamiliar with dissociative signs of trance states will ascribe traumatized children's inattention or daydreaming to ADHD. Research by Malinosky-Rummel and Hoier (1991) cite these similarities with traumatized children who scored in the significant range on dissociative checklists as well as on the CBCL's dissociative symptoms. As noted before under *Assessment Tools*, common signs on the CBCL for dissociation that are particularly seen with children with ADHD are inattention, feeling in a fog, staring, and daydreaming. It is crucial for proper treatment that trauma and dissociation be evaluated before assuming that it is ADHD-Inattention type.

Bipolar Disorder

Bipolar disorder is a dysregulation of the affective system in which there are swings in mood from hypomania to depression, usually lasting weeks or months. In the last decade, there has been a dramatic change in a more permissive, less rigorous standard in diagnosing children with bipolar disorder, and 90% of those diagnosed are receiving medication with little testing for effectiveness or safety (Moreno et al., 2007). The rate of diagnosis of pediatric bipolar disorder has increased 40 times in the last 10 years (National Institute Mental Health [NIMH], 2007). Diagnoses of bipolar disorder in children and youth increased 4,000% from 1994–1995 to 2002–2003. This has resulted in considerable controversy over this diagnosis.

One of the hallmarks of dissociation is the rapid, extreme mood and behavioral switches that can last from seconds to hours, and are sometimes accompanied by amnesia. As explained above, these extreme switches can be attributed to self-states with intense affect, but all too often dissociation is not diagnostically considered.

A seminal article by Parry and Levin (2011) critically examines multidimensional factors that influence the overdiagnosis and misdiagnosis of pediatric bipolar disorder, including the impact of popular books, the media, and pharmaceutical industry, and the lack of examining developmental trauma and attachment factors on affect dysregulation.

Janet Papolos, co-author of *"The Bipolar Child: the Definitive and Reassuring Guide to Childhood's Most Misunderstood Disorder"* (Papolos & Papolos, 2000), in an interview on National Public Radio's Infinite Mind (Lichtenstein, 2005) related parents describing their children as,

> Dr. Jekyll and Mr. Hyde ... the child has the LOOK [in capital letters per her report]. Their eyes get very glazed and the child gets a feral look like he is fighting for his life... after it is over, the child doesn't remember it. They often sleep and don't even remember it and if they do remember, they feel so badly.

This is a classic verbatim of dozens of parents' descriptions of their dissociative preschool and older children that I (Waters, 2005b) and others (Silberg, 1998; Wieland, 2011) have described.

There is a paucity of bipolar studies that note a history of childhood physical and sexual abuse (Blader & Carlson, 2006; Hyun, Friedman, & Dunner, 2000; Levitan et al., 1998; Mueser et al., 1998; Wexler, Lyons, Lyons, & Mazure, 1997). There is a need for more professional education on discerning the difference between overlapping symptoms of bipolar disorder and the relationship between trauma and dissociation in children and adults. There have been presentations addressing this issue at conferences (Levy, 2009; Waters, Laddis, Soderstrom, & Yehuda, 2007).

There is one refreshing article in which Harris (2005) describes a case example of a 10-year-old boy previously treated for bipolar disorder with escalating series of medications. Upon a careful case analysis, the boy described severe beatings by his grandparents and clearly described dissociative symptoms of depersonalization and derealization when triggered. He reported, "I just see red...I don't really know where I am or what I'm doing...I don't really feel in my body." (Harris, 2005, p. 530). More research is required to understand the correlation between traumas, affect dysregulation, and dissociation.

The child guidance center that evaluated Lisa had considered Lisa having an affective disorder, but seemed confused as to what attributed to her affect dysregulation. Dissociation was not discussed.

Hallucinations, Psychosis, or Schizophrenia

Moskowitz (2011) offers a valuable historical description of two opposing paradigms when examining hallucinations and how auditory and visual hallucinations have been predominately viewed as psychotic with primarily a biological origin (brain disorder) rather than being influenced by psychological factors, such as traumatic experiences. This staunch, enduring position of hallucinations being psychotic has greatly influenced the DSM and overshadowed the pioneering work of Bleuler's (1911/1950), who described schizophrenia as "split off" of the personality.

Because of this "split" in the paradigms and the strong focus that hallucinations are a brain disorder, the recognition of overlapping dissociative symptoms of auditory and visual hallucinations has greatly contributed to misdiagnosing dissociative patients with a psychosis or schizophrenia (Bliss, Larson, & Nakashima, 1983; Rosenbaum, 1980; Ross, Joshi, & Currie, 1990; Ross, Norton & Wozney, 1989).

A major distinction between psychosis and schizophrenia and DDNOS or DID is that dissociative clients' reports of auditory or visual hallucinations are attributed to *self-states* that formed as a *result of traumatic related experiences* (Kluft, 1987a; Ross, Joshi, & Currie, 1990). Furthermore, Sar and Ozturk (2009) explain,

> The dissociative patient's reported claim of containing another person's existence, or of having more than one personality, cannot be considered a delusion. Such claims do not originate from a primary thought disorder, but rather from experience itself-the actual experience of the other as "not me" (Sullivan, 1953). In contrast, the delusions of a schizophrenic patient are thought to be the result of a primary disturbance of thought content. (pp. 536–537)

I have encountered in my practice many traumatized children and adolescents who reported auditory and visual hallucinations derived from self-states but were given a previous diagnosis of a psychotic disorder. Their treatment modality was a psychopharmacological approach without any efficacy and attention to the meaning of the voices and their traumatic origin.

Numerous studies and clinical vignettes have described hallucination in dissociative children and adolescents with DDNOS and DID (Coons, 1996; Dell & Eisenhower, 1990; Hornstein & Putnam, 1992; Putnam, 1997; Silberg, 1996/1998; Shirar, 1996; Waters, 2005b, c; Wieland, 2011).

It is crucial for dissociative children's recovery that EMDR diagnosticians become familiar with trauma-related hallucinations within self-states so that these symptoms are not misdiagnosed as psychotic or schizophrenic and prescribe a treatment regime that is antithetical to effective, integrative therapy of a fragmented traumatized youth. For a more comprehensive analysis of differential diagnosis of hallucinations, I encourage the reader to see *Part X: Dissociation and Psychosis* by Dell and O'Neil (2009, pp. 519–568).

COMPONENTS IN THE INTERVIEWING PROCESS

As in other assessments, many factors determine how to proceed with interviewing the child and family members. Relevant factors to consider are professional standards, clinical judgment and style, purpose of the interview, child's age, and how comfortable the child is to being seen alone or with the parent. I usually see the child or adolescent initially with the parent or caregiver, unless the teen wants to be seen alone, to gather basic referral and identifiable information and some developmental history. I note particularly how the parent(s) and child interact with each other and define the problem. At some point, I will talk to the parent alone to gather more detailed developmental and trauma histories and symptoms. I will interview the child alone to assess his overall functioning, his relationship with his family members and peers, trauma and academic history, and symptoms. As deemed necessary, I will request to interview other family members.

When Lisa's mother requested that I evaluate her daughter, she was desperate and fraught with concern. Her brief description of her daughter's history on the phone was clear to me that I needed to gather a detailed history from her mother prior to seeing Lisa so that I could intervene quickly and effectively with Lisa. I met with her mother for 2 hours and gathered a chronologically well-organized description of Lisa's symptoms from her placement with them at 4 months old to present including a developmental, academic, social, and family history, and I reviewed previous evaluations and interventions. My hypothesis was that the origin of her symptoms was oral trauma of unknown cause that occurred sometime during her Asian foster home placement, and that she was exhibiting dissociative defenses.

Lisa's had severe emotional dysregulation. Included in phase one of EMDR treatment is an evaluation of emotional regulation capabilities. Adler-Tapia and Settle (2008) stress the importance of developing affect regulation skills particularly with dissociative children so that they can stay connected to the therapy. That was also my goal as Lisa identified self-states that accounted for her labile mood.

Assessing the Family Environment

The impact of the family environment on the development of childhood dissociation cannot be understated, nor can the reliance on previously formed dissociative mechanisms. It is well accepted that in order for children to be treated, they need a safe environment. As Silberg points out, "I believe increasingly hostile and lonely environments that make real connections and relationships impossible further encourage the consolidation of dissociative symptoms" (Silberg, 2001, p. 1). Others have described negative environmental influences on shaping dissociative defenses in children, particularly with parents who also display dissociation (Benjamin & Benjamin, 1992; Benjamin, Benjamin, & Rind, 1996; Mann & Sanders 1994; Peterson & Boat, 1997; Yeager & Lewis, 1996). These children are particularly vulnerable to reoccurring abuse. However, Kluft (1987b) discusses the parental fitness of mothers with DID.

I have treated dissociative parents on both ends of the spectrum, from providing a safe environment to abusing their children, necessitating a child protection referral. The dissociative adults who seemed to provide a stable environment for their children were those who actively sought treatment and processed their pain. In turn, they were able to be sensitive, empathetic, and protective parents.

A thorough parental history that includes any trauma, attachments to their own parents, dissociation, and legal, financial, medical, and other mental health conditions will help the evaluator to determine their relevance to the dissociative child's symptomatology.

I have worked with dedicated foster and adoptive parents who also had significant trauma, unresolved attachment issues, and dissociation who became triggered by their demanding, dissociative children. Some abused their children. Referring parents to therapy, support groups, and respite care can prevent maltreatment or reinstate a safe environment.

Fortunately for Lisa, her parents came from a stable environment with healthy attachments to their parents who provided support. Both parents appeared to have a healthy, traditional marriage in which the mother stayed at home while the father was gainfully employed. There were no significant problems noted. Mother did have a high-risk pregnancy after Lisa was adopted, necessitating that she maintain bed rest for the latter part of her pregnancy. This mostly exacerbated Lisa's symptoms. Their other two children were healthy and well adjusted. They tolerated Lisa's acting out, but it did put stress on them.

History Gathering From the Parent Regarding Their Child

It is important to ask questions about trauma and dissociation, even when the presenting problem is nontrauma related. Parents often seek services for the most disturbing symptom, such as oppositional behavior, attention problems, and anger issues, and may be unaware of the underlying causes. If parents do report some form of trauma that their child incurred, they may not understand the relevance to their child's symptoms.

Gathering from the parents a thorough developmental history from pre-birth to the child's current age will assist in assessing any causal relationships to the presenting symptoms. Questions should include all forms of interpersonal trauma, separation from parents, painful medical conditions and interventions, accidents, war exposure, natural disasters, as well as relationship with parents, siblings and peers, academic performance, extracurricular activities, and any court/legal involvement. Building a time line of significant events correlated to the child's age and onset of symptoms will assist in developing a causal relationship.

Particular attention in history gathering of trauma should include whether the child's parents were available to assist the child to cope. Any signs of dissociative symptoms should be explored. Since parents often do not know what dissociative signs are, educating them about indicators will elicit a more accurate and complete response. The issues to be covered are signs, frequency, and duration of any trance behaviors; persistent denial of disruptive or explosive behavior even after disciplined; extreme mood and behavior switches activated by minor stimuli or for "no apparent reason"; and other memory problems beyond ordinary forgetfulness of significant and/or daily events, particularly after an explosive incident. It is easy to perceive the child's denial of such behavior as avoiding responsibility, but memory problems are common with dissociative children. Requesting details of an incident will help to track gaps in the child's memory.

The following is a list of questions that will assist in identifying dissociative symptoms. Depending on the parent's response, some questions may not be necessary. This is a guide for the clinician to use with discretion. Many of these questions correlate with ISSTD's Frequently Asked Questions for Parents (www.isst-d.orge). (While questions apply to both males and females, for simplicity, male gender is used below.)

List of Questions to Ask Parents

- Do you see your child staring, unresponsive, or in his own world (not including when playing video games or watching television)? How often and how long?
- Does your child have extreme mood and behavior switches, and if so, describe those times and what you notice about his behavior and affect? Does he seem different at those times, and if so, in what ways?
- Does your child have a favorite food, activity, clothing, etc., but then hates it another time?
- Do you notice any changes in the child's eyes, such as blinking, fluttering, eye roll and/or change in voice, mannerisms during these times?
- Does your child deny his aggressive/disruptive behavior even when you witnessed it? How does he respond to you at those times? Does he continue to deny such behavior even after he was disciplined? Does he deny other behaviors or situations that are not problematic, i.e. conversations or activities?
- Has your child ever said he hears voices or sees things/people, but no one was around? Describe those times.
- Have you heard your child talk to himself and/or refers to himself in the third person? Does he sound like he is using a different voice during those times? Does he seem younger or older?
- Does your child have an imaginary playmate (beyond 8 years old)? Describe what you notice.
- Does your child look and behave differently at times that are not attributed to illness? Describe those times in detail.

- Does your child have memory problems to events that he should recall, such as holidays, birthdays, etc., past and present?
- Does your child adamantly deny you told him to do his homework, or chores when you were facing him, engaging with him in the conversation, and he wasn't engaged in any other activity, such as computer, TV, etc.?

These questions, which were described earlier, were asked of Lisa's mom, which laid the foundation for my interview with Lisa.

Interviewing the Child

Dissociative children can often display subtle shifts when switching from one state to another, particularly if the self-state's age is close to the biological age of the child, making such shifts challenging to detect. Shifts can occur with children who have DID as well as DDNOS. Those with DDNOS can have internal states that influence shifts in the child without taking executive control of the body. Shifts can occur rapidly, making the occurrence difficult to detect and can be subtle.

The following are some signs of shifts:

- Sudden staring or glazed look when talked to
- Rapid blinking, fluttering, or eye rolling without any warning
- Other facial changes–biting lip or a burrowed frown
- Voice changes in tenor, inflection, or language, such as baby talk or demanding adult tone
- Body posture, from relaxed to stiff or from coordinated to clumsy
- Contradictory thoughts noted in the same sentence, such as "I don't get along at all with my mom. We get along alright," or, "I hate soccer. I like playing it"
- Dramatic changes in behavior preferences, such as enjoying drawing in office to hating it
- Shifts in awareness of what was just said by the child or therapist or confusion, discrepancy, or denial of earlier report of traumatic and nontraumatic events

It important to be aware that even common questions can be triggering to traumatized children. These questions may spontaneously cause dissociation and shifts in self-states, particularly when they pertain to traumatic reminders, such as name of the perpetrator, events or symptoms related to the traumatic event. Exploring what precipitated such shifts is a crucial step in untangling the onset of the dissociative processes. Because dissociative children are often unaware of what prompted sudden changes, meticulous questioning is required to find out what transpired *just seconds before the shifts* (Silberg, 2012). Questions related to what transpired within the child's mind, what bodily sensations are felt, any internal conflicts, internal voices, or any upsetting reminders will provide valuable information about what instigated these shifts. If the child is not aware after questioning, cataloguing these moments and coming back to them later, particularly when a similar shift occurs, may provide illumination. Once the interviewer spends more time with the child, a pattern of such shifts becomes more observant and a complex picture emerges.

These shifts in affect and thought processes can show some evidence of internal confusion or conflict that may relate to some self-states for which the child may or may not be consciously aware. Self-states can have varied preferences to food, dress, activities, and relationship disparity with parents, siblings, friends, teachers, etc. They can have divergent skill levels in academic and social performances, depending on their age and how they were formed, and their purpose. Some of the shifts may be subtle while others may be more extreme. Dissociative children can switch so rapidly that it is easy to overlook the shifts or attribute them to other reasons, such as the child is nervous, or just has a cognitive impairment. However, it is these shifts that can be clues to dissociation. Questions should be geared to exploring shifts that occur in the session as well as a general exploration of sudden changes or shifts that the child experiences.

Auditory and visual hallucinations should be asked about, as in any mental status exam. If endorsed, then follow-up questions about the details of the hallucinations are recommended that cover frequency, triggers, details of what is said and seen, and impact on the child. When I specifically inquire about dissociative symptoms, I will present these questions in a nonchalant manner, explaining that I have worked with many children that have described similar experiences. I will explain that these experiences occur because of stress and upsetting events. This normalization helps to put them at ease to talk about their hallucinations.

I will often see the child with the caregiver initially to learn what the concerns are and to begin rapport building. It is important to begin on more neutral ground by asking about the child's interests, hobbies, favorite games and television programs, any heroes, or people they admire (Adler-Tapia & Settle, 2008).

At some point in the evaluative process I will ask the child and caregiver to fill out the appropriate dissociative checklists. I will ask the youth to explain items that he significantly endorses.

Silberg (1998) discusses interviewing strategies that can help children reveal their internal experiences. Because it is less stressful for younger children to be engaged in a play activity when interviewed, I will ask them questions about dissociative experiences as they play with toys, dolls, etc. With adolescents who are fidgety, I will provide a squishy ball to hold, drawing supplies, or some other activity that helps the youth feel calmer and more comfortable. Some of the questions are similar to the questions on the dissociative checklists.

The following are suggested questions to explore dissociative symptoms with children and adolescents. Depending on the age and developmental level of the child, modification or reframing of the questions will need to occur. Pace the questions according to the child's ability to manage them.

Some Suggestive Questions to Ask the Youth

- Have you ever had or have imaginary friends? Do they seem real to you? If so, in what way?
- Some kids who have been through similar situations have reported hearing voices either inside or outside of their minds. Have you had that happen to you?

If the answer is affirmative, follow up with these questions:

- Do they seem friendly, angry, sad, scared, etc.? What do they say? How often do you hear them? What is happening just before you hear them? What feelings do you have when you hear them? What thoughts do you have when you hear them? Do you talk to them?

■ Do you ever see things, objects, or people and later realize that what you saw wasn't there or you weren't sure if they were there?

If the answer is affirmative, follow up with these questions: Did you hear voices at the time and, if so, what were they saying? Please describe what you saw? When do you see them? How often do you see them? What were you doing, feeling, or thinking at the time?

■ Do you find yourself zoning out and not aware of what is happening in the here and now?

If the answer is affirmative, follow up with these questions:

■ How often does that happen? What is going on just prior to zoning out? What are you feeling or thinking just before you zone out? For how long does it happen? What is the shortest and longest amount of time? Where do you go in your mind? (Child may not know.) Do other people notice this, like parents or teachers and, if so, what do they say to you? Do you have control over it or does it just happen?
■ Do you ever have a hard time recognizing or remembering your parents, siblings, friends, teachers, etc.?

If the answer is affirmative, follow up with these questions:

■ When are those times (when wake up in the AM, bedtime, stressful times)? Who do you have a hard time remembering or recognizing? Do you hear voices at that time? What are you feeling and thinking then? How often does this occur? Do you tell anyone about those times?
■ Do you have a hard time remembering what you did, like homework? Do you get homework back and not remember you did it? Or not remembering drawing, playing games, doing chores, or doing other activities, but others indicate you did those activities?

If the answer is affirmative, follow up with these questions:

■ Can you please tell me about those times? How often? What seems to be occurring at those times that may have something to do with not remembering? Are you mad, under stress, having a conflict? Do you hear any voices or see things inside of your mind or outside of your mind that may not be there later when you are having problem remembering?
■ Do you have a hard time remembering scary or bad things that happened to you?

If the answer is affirmative, follow up with these questions:

■ Can you tell me about them? (Be aware that you may not want to pursue too many details about trauma, as the child may not be ready to disclose or be strong enough to handle the disclosure. You may witness some dissociative shifting, which is diagnostic. Notice the child's reactions and follow sound therapeutic guidelines and principals.)

Keep in mind that these questions can be asked throughout the evaluation process and also during the treatment phase as indicated. They are only a starting point to further explore amnesia, trance states, and other dissociative experiences.

When I first met Lisa, we sat on the floor and played with the dollhouse while I asked general questions about what she liked to do, etc. Then I asked about memory problems. She reported that it takes a while for her to remember her parents and siblings and that she is accused of doing things that she does not have any memory of doing. She endorsed hearing voices that sounded like a baby and another one that was garbled. I reassured Lisa that other children have reported similar experiences and that I knew how to help them with those experiences. The next morning, I received a phone call from her mother. She excitedly told me that after the session, Lisa went back to the waiting room, sat down next to her mother, and for the first time, looked at her mother's eyes and smiled. Her mother was thrilled that Lisa did not have "that blank look" on her face! Mother hugged her daughter. This report confirmed that my questions and reassurance had opened a door for Lisa to begin to heal. She appeared relieved to finally have someone who understood her.

OTHER COLLATERAL INTERVIEWS AND COLLATERAL REPORTS

With appropriate releases, it is invaluable to contact teachers, school and past mental health counselors, medical and legal personnel, child protective services, and other professionals to garner pertinent information regarding traumatic history, previous diagnoses and failed treatment experiences. Traumatized children, who have a lengthy history of ineffective psychopharmacological and clinical treatment episodes, often have underlying dissociative processes that impact their resistance to standard therapies.

Principals and teachers are frequently the first to detect clear signs of dissociation with their students, which is critical to my diagnosis and treatment design (Waters, 2011), noting amnesia, trance behaviors, and extreme mood switches. When I have a child displaying dissociative symptoms, I will refer educators to the website of The International Society for the Study of Trauma and Dissociation's Child and Adolescent FAQ for Teachers (http://isst-d.org/education/faq-teachers.htm). I will then follow up with further consultation with teachers and school counselors to discuss the signs and effective strategies to decrease children's dissociative behaviors in the classroom.

Consulting with child protective services and police and receiving their investigative reports can provide a chronology of trauma and related anniversary reactions. Explaining signs of dissociation to investigators can assist them to formulate a more accurate understanding of the child's trance behaviors or inconsistent reports. I will refer child protective service workers, forensic evaluators, and lawyers to a training DVD (Waters, 2007) for further understanding dissociative children's responses.

I collaborated with Lisa's chiropractor, informing her of my assessment of Lisa's infant self-states and our complimentary work. She was intrigued and receptive. She had Lisa do a series of core strengthening and bilateral integrative exercises that helped Lisa cross over her midline in opposite directions with her head and arms. When I worked with Lisa on age progressing the infant self-states, there was a dramatic improvement in her ability to do these exercises. She was finally able to open bottles and adequately hold silverware.

I consulted with the adoption agency about Lisa's complex presentation that required specialized treatment for dissociation and requested their financial support for her intensive treatment, which was granted.

Because Lisa was no longer acting out at school and being sent home, I did not need to consult with her teacher. I monitored Lisa's academic progress through regular reports from her mother.

CLINICAL SUMMARY AND CONCLUSIONS

This case highlights how trauma can have a profound impact on a helpless baby who has no recourse but to escape by dissociating (Liotti, 2006, 2009; Solomon & George, 1999). During evaluation, EMDR clinicians need to gather extensive early history of any trauma and recognize that infants are "not too young to feel," and reliance of dissociation is an effective escape for them.

When assessing children, examining the efficacy of past treatment episodes can provide a clue to any dissociative processing that may account for treatment failures. In Lisa's case, standardized, acceptable, or questionable therapeutic interventions unwittingly increased her dissociation. Her medication was ineffective in affect regulation due to her dissociative mechanisms. Holding therapy had an adverse impact on Lisa's ability to build attachment with her mother and appeared to escalate her dissociative responses. Behavioral therapy was ineffective as her dissociative states controlled her behavior. Without identifying their presence and roles, behavioral consequences or rewards had little meaning in rectifying her disturbing behavior.

As in Lisa's case, dissociation should be considered when traumatized children display splintered abilities, regressed or developmental delays, trance behaviors, extreme mood switches, and memory problems. Past treatment failures warrant further exploration of underlying dissociative mechanisms that may be thwarting progress.

Finally, but critically important, Lisa's safe environment and her astute, empathetic, and conscientious mother, who kept copious notes tracking Lisa's mercurial presentation, were instrumental in evaluating the presence of her dissociative states.

Early unrecognized and untreated dissociation can be devastating. Children and adolescents who dissociate can be prone to a lifetime of debilitating symptoms. While traumatized children present a convoluted picture that can easily be misinterpreted and misunderstood due to a plethora of shifting symptoms, it is such complex, mercurial presentation that is characteristic of dissociation. EMDR professionals should not be sidetracked by the symptoms alone and miss the underlying dissociative processes that play a central role in maintaining the symptoms. Otherwise, dissociative children will continue to experience impairment in identity, memory, and perception of the environment that will hinder their ability to reach their potential.

Early identification of dissociative processes is a paramount step to design an effective treatment course, along with a safe environment, that will nourish the child's ability to release dissociative mechanisms. This will pave the way for the dissociative child to become a unified self who is able to pursue a fulfilling life.

After Lisa suffered nine turbulent years of severe depression, confusion about herself and her surroundings, constant triggers of early traumatic reminders, several assessments and failed interventions, her dissociative symptoms were recognized. Asking simple but potent, relevant questions were critical to uncovering her dissociative defenses that severely contributed to her persistent and debilitating symptoms. Lisa's recovery can now begin.

7

Advanced Preparation Strategies for Dissociative Children

TALKING TO CHILDREN ABOUT DISSOCIATION

Oftentimes, children with mild, moderate, or severe forms of dissociation will need extensive preparation in understanding dissociation, learning how to communicate about dissociation, and getting familiarized with dual attention strategies. After a thorough assessment of the child's dissociative experiences has been attained, children should be educated on the meaning of dissociation: What it is, how it happens, why we believe it happens, and how we can communicate about it. The book, *The Different Colors of Me* (Gomez & Paulsen, in press), is one of the first books that explains dissociation to children. This book covers not only what dissociation is, but it explains to children the different levels of dissociation using child-friendly metaphors and analogies. This book can also be used as a tool to establish a first line of communication with children about what they do when they dissociate. Many children that dissociate have come to make sense of these experiences on their own. The following are the reflections of a 20-year-old woman diagnosed with dissociative identity disorder (DID) on her own dissociative responses as a child:

"We had names for things, even names for things they did to us, but in terms of things we did to cope…I had different names for things, depending what it was I was doing or trying to do. I'd do what I called "becoming a doll," when I'd numb out, I just didn't have words or understanding for "numb" yet, but I had my own name for it. I even understood the different levels of dissociation that I had. "Floating," "Folding up," "Going away," "Getting small"… When I'd completely dissociate to the point of blacking out, I called it "my world" game, I'd go off into my own world, leaving the real one behind. I also did what I called "hiding." I focused on things like walls or doors, something with bumps, a texture, or a grain and I'd find shapes in them. I have uncanny memory of many different walls and ceilings that were in my lifetime. This was something we did from a very, very early age. It started with fixating on things. There are memories of counting the slats in our crib. Not really "counting" but…going from one end of the rail to the next, over and over methodically."

It is important to highlight how at such a primal level this woman was able to have some level of awareness, even as a young child of what her mind and body were experiencing. Even though her capacity to reflect on these experiences at a conscious explicit level was not developed until later as she mindfully studied her own dissociative responses, as a child she was able to give some meaning to them. An important quality that clinicians working with dissociative children need is curiosity. Looking at children with a genuine interest in understanding the distinctive and exceptional ways they each have come to organize their own subjective perception of the world will highly enhance the process of evaluating and assessing the presence of dissociation. With this in mind, when talking about dissociation, invite children to share how they have come to understand and name the different levels of dissociation. Ask if they have names or ways to call such experiences or if they have shared these exceptional experiences with anybody in the past. Some children that dissociate may not have much explicit conscious awareness of such responses. If they have some awareness, they may think that every other child engages in dissociative behaviors. If they have ever disclosed such experiences to others, they may have been shamed or dismissed. As a result, they may not be open to sharing these experiences in therapy. It is important to emphasize the ultimate positive and survival nature of dissociation. Start by helping children see for the first time how they survived and how this actually makes them "heroes." Seeing themselves for the first time through the eyes of acceptance and admiration begins to build new internal working models of the self. Several strategies, analogies, and metaphors will be presented in this chapter to address dissociation from different angles and perspectives. Clinicians will have a wide range of methods of introducing and explaining dissociation to children. I encourage you to use the strategies that better meet the needs of each client, while honoring your views and style as a therapist.

THE DIFFERENT PARTS OF THE SELF

Using a language that reaches both brain hemispheres, especially the right with dissociative children is always helpful. Analogies and stories that help children understand the multiplicity of the self may be presented during the preparation phase of eye movement desensitization and reprocessing (EMDR) therapy. A wonderful analogy inspired by nature can help children understand the different parts of the self. The rainbow analogy used in the book developed by Gomez & Paulsen (in press) can help children understand dissociated states using child friendly stories. These preparation strategies and analogies are helpful for children over six years of age.

THE RAINBOW ANALOGY

The rainbow analogy may be presented as follows: "*When we are born, we all have a 'shiny me' and all the colored pencils to create the rainbow inside of us. As we start to touch, hear, smell, taste, and see the world, we start to paint our own special rainbow. Our internal rainbow has different colors. Sometimes we are red and sometimes we are blue. It is like an inside family of colors. For example, some kids have an inside color that loves to dance or play sports. Some kids may have a color that gets really mad when things don't go his or her way. All the colors get to know each other and work together when things go well. Sometimes, when we have negative or yucky things happen to us, we get colors with mixed-up feelings and thoughts. When that happens, the colors have trouble connecting with each other and with the 'shiny me.' Some colors have all the mixed-up feelings and thoughts from yucky things that may have happened to us. These colors also have all the things that we do to protect ourselves from the mixed-up stuff. For example, we may have learned to always be a chameleon (blend in) and please everybody, or we may have learned to go away and dissociate. We may have learned to just numb ourselves so we don't have to feel. These colors just get really freaked out when we remember the yucky things that happened and the mixed-up feelings and thoughts. When these colors freak out, they may want to take off and run, fight, or they may just freeze. They may do things that can be hurtful to themselves and others. Sometimes they just do a lot of dangerous spine-tingling things so they don't get to feel the other colors that have mixed-up stuff. It is always important to remember that, even though we have many colors, we are one beautiful rainbow with only one 'bright shiny me.'"*

Sometimes these colors get so far apart that one color may not notice or know what the other color did. This could be very confusing for kids when they get in trouble and they don't remember which of their colors did it. When the mixed-up stuff is no longer there, all the colors can connect with the "bright shiny me" and work together so kids get to enjoy their own rainbow.

You may invite the child to draw a picture of the "bright shiny me" and the different colors of the self or wait until the "color" surfaces during a session and invite the specific color to be heard, seen, etc. Another approach may be to assist the child in creating a map with the colors of the rainbow. Each color will represent a part of the self. It may be the part that gets angry and gets violent when the child does not get what he or she wants, or the part that pleases people and wants to meet their needs, especially caregivers. Once each color has been identified, you could use ego state interventions or Internal Family Systems (IFS) interventions (see Chapter 13). If you choose to create an initial mapping of the system, using microphones, interview each color or part. You may want to have hats of different colors so the child can wear a hat or something of the colors being interviewed. Invite the child to draw the rainbow with the different colors of the self. Invite each part to come in and pick its own color. Say, "*I wonder if we can get to know the different colors of your rainbow. I notice that there is a part that has a hard time when things do not go its way. I would like to invite this part to choose its own color to represent it.*" Once the part has chosen a color and has given permission to be interviewed, the clinician can invite the child to witness the part in any way this color or part would like to be seen and known. Ask the part to show the child what it needs the child to know about itself. What does the part want the child to know about what makes it want to come out? This is information that can be recorded in the child's targeting sequence. In addition, finding out about the work this color or part has been doing for the child is important. Honoring and appreciating the work the parts have been doing is an important initial step. Be aware of how much exploration the child can tolerate. The ability of the clinician to be aligned with the child's internal states will serve as the main foundation of any therapeutic activity. Be aware of any physiological changes or behavioral changes that tell you that other parts or colors are present or that strategies to bring the child back to emotional equilibrium should be used. Get the rhythm and the pace of the child's energy flow. The rainbow analogy helps children get in touch with diversity and multiplicity that exist in them. It also helps children that over identify with the negative aspects of the self to have a broader and expanded perspective of who they are and the existence of their "bright shiny me." They learn that they are so much more than their injured parts. In addition, it promotes and encourages acceptance, understanding, and, ultimately, compassion toward the wounded parts and the work they have been doing to help and protect the child.

As the child learns about multiplicity, wholeness is also emphasized. Even though the child has different colors, there is only one person and one "shiny me" in each of us. See Chapter 13 for more IFS strategies within EMDR treatment.

THE DISSOCIATION KIT FOR KIDS

A good way of introducing the concept of dissociation is by using "The Dissociation Kit For Kids." (A box of at least three drawers that can be used to create the kit.) Information on dissociation, illustrated cards describing a wide range of dissociative responses, and tools to help children maintain dual awareness are placed inside the kit. This kit provides a more tangible and concrete experience of what dissociation is. The items inside the kit are placed in three categories: Items that assist the child in understanding dissociative symptoms and dissociation, items that assist the clinician and the child in assessing present awareness, level of energy and consciousness, and items that are directed to helping the child in restoring dual awareness.

TOOLS TO EXPLAIN AND ASSIST CHILDREN IN UNDERSTANDING THE DIFFERENT LEVELS OF DISSOCIATION

1. Children's books on dissociation.
2. Laminated cards with drawings or art clips showing different dissociative experiences. Experiences such as floating, depersonalization, derealization, feeling numbed, hearing voices, or having memory lapses, among others, can be illustrated. Art clips downloaded from the Internet can also be useful.

TOOLS TO EXPLAIN, MAINTAIN, AND RESTORE DUAL AWARENESS

1. Geometric shapes in various colors.
2. Different textures or a children's book with textures.
3. Small containers with basic scents that children can easily identify. Fruit scents, bubble gum, cookie dough, vanilla, and lavender are some of the scents that might be suitable for children. The use of scents with children with allergies may not be appropriate.
4. Gum of different flavors.
5. Finger puppets or small stuffed animals.
6. Cards with art clips of children standing up, jumping, etc.

TOOLS TO ASSIST CHILDREN IN EXPLORING AND ASSESSING PRESENT AWARENESS

1. Cards with a wide range of animals that represent different levels of internal energy, present awareness, and level of arousal.
2. Signs. These signs are made of green, yellow, and red construction paper. Cut three squares and glue a wooden stick to the back of each. Write the word "IN" on the green square, the word "OUT" on the red square, and the words "HALF and HALF" on the yellow square. These are the three signs the child can use to report how present he or she is. The child will use the green square when feeling completely present, the red square when not feeling present at all, and the yellow square when feeling moderately present.
3. Hand fans that open up to form a circle or semi circle.

4. Figures or wooden marionettes that have flexible bodies that can be moved from stiff and stern to completely collapsed postures.
5. Laminated cards that show children singing.

The kit should be decorated with stickers to make it more appealing to children. The following is the order in which the kit and the concept of dissociation may be introduced:

Step One: Using the book or the cards, go over what happens when children dissociate. Explain why people dissociate and emphasize the adaptive aspects of dissociation. However, talk about how dissociation now may create difficulties for the child. Assist the child in identifying the specific and special ways in which he or she may dissociate. Use analogies presented in prior chapters that present dissociation as a survival resource. Create a list and put these experiences on a card, so a common way of communicating about these experiences can be developed. This card will remain in the child's clinical chart, but will be accessible to the clinician during EMDR reprocessing sessions.

Step Two: Identify the words that should be used when talking about dissociative experiences. Invite the child to share how he or she has been calling different dissociative responses. If the child does not have specific names, ask the child how you both should refer to these experiences, so a common vocabulary can be developed.

Step Three: Encourage awareness at the different levels of human experience: Cognitive, emotional, and sensorimotor. Let the child know of the different languages human beings speak. You can also use the analogy of the different channels we tune in to when we listen to the radio or the television. Introduce the language of the channel of the mind. Let the child know how the mind speaks the language of thoughts and words. Follow with the heart and the language of feelings. Next, talk about how the body speaks the language of sensations and movement. Once dissociative experiences have been identified, invite the child to explore or notice what the mind, the heart, and the body communicate about each experience. Invite the child often to tune in to each channel one at a time. Keep in mind that at this level we are helping the child take the initial steps into developing awareness, mindfulness, and an understanding of how and when dissociation occurs.

Step Four: Use the following strategies to evaluate the child's present awareness and field of consciousness:

IN, HALF and HALF, and OUT signs: These signs are designed to assist the child in understanding and identifying different levels of present awareness. When using these signs, start by explaining how these signs are like an internal compass that let us know how much we are IN the present. These signs allow us to check our internal experience of being completely IN the present, HALF and HALF, or completely OUT of present awareness. The following exemplifies a way of introducing the signs: You may say, "*I have these really cool signs that help kids understand how present they are. Sometimes children can be here with me, but they are not necessarily present. Sometimes their bodies are here, but in their minds or hearts they are somewhere else. Sometimes they may think their bodies are present, but they do not feel their bodies that much. I have three signs, one that says IN, another that says HALF and HALF, and the last one that says OUT. When you are IN you can hear me well, see me well, you know very well that you are here in my office, and you feel fully awake. When you feel OUT, you hear me really, really, far away.*

You may feel very sleepy and even though you are in front of me, you feel like I am really far from you. You may start to feel really small and you may feel only parts of your body, or may not feel your body at all. You may also go to a special place in your mind where you go when things don't go well or you are not feeling good. When you are HALF and HALF, you hear my voice a bit far. You can see me, but I may look a bit away from you. You may feel just a little bit of your head floating or may feel a bit sleepy. Let's practice! I want you to notice how present you are now and hold either the IN, HALF and HALF, or OUT sign." If the child is dissociating, practice with some of the tools included in the Dissociation Kit for Kids. This is done with the following purposes: (1) Helping the child get acquainted with dual awareness tools. (2) Identifying the strategies that are more effective in restoring dual awareness for the child. (3) Making the process predictable, so when these tools are used during the reprocessing phases, they are familiar for the child. Once the child has practiced with each of the dual awareness tools and is reporting sufficient awareness of the present, invite the child to notice it and provide slow and short sets of BLS. This is done with the purpose of enhancing the child's capacity to stay present. In addition, it is helping the child recognize these moments of feeling grounded and present. The following are additional tools that can be used to enhance the child's understanding of the different levels of consciousness and awareness.

Hand fans that open to form a circle or semi circle: Hand fans are great tools to explain the different levels of dissociation as well as to assist the child in understanding the field of consciousness. A half, 180° open fan represents a mind, heart and body able to fully embrace a wide range of stimulus and able to stay present, while accessing different elements and aspects of the disturbing material. It also means that the mind, heart, and body are still able to contain information that could be distracting and stay within appropriate levels of arousal. A completely open, 360° fan represents a mind, heart, and body that may be overwhelmed with disturbing information. It also means that the child is moving into states of hyperarousal and is losing dual awareness due to the accessing of too much disturbing material. A completely closed or a quarter-closed fan represents the total loss of dual awareness. It means the partial or total restriction of the field of consciousness. I assume the child is still somewhat present if he or she is able to show the clinician with the fan the level of present awareness. Ask the child to use the "fan thermometer or fanometer" or the "dissociation fan" and show you how present he or she is now. Once again, this special fan should be introduced with or in place of the in, half, and half and out signs. It serves the same purpose while providing a wider range of possibilities when assessing the field of consciousness and dual awareness.

Wooden figures or wooden puppet strings with flexible bodies that can be moved from stiff and stern to completely collapsed postures: The same as the dissociation fan or "fanometer," wooden puppet strings can assist children in expressing different levels of arousal and dissociative states. By pushing in the center of some wooden animals and figures, the animal may become really straight and stiff or it may collapse as the pressure of the cords holding the animal is reduced. Ask children to use the figure to show how they are currently feeling in their bodies. A straight figure would represent an appropriate level of energy and arousal. A figure that shows a flaccid, limp body would represent dysregulation of the affective system to the point of falling into complete collapse. The dissociation fan and the dissociation puppets (Figure 7.1) are playful and developmentally appropriate tools to help children understand different levels of consciousness, energy, and present awareness.

Step Five: Practice with the child using tools to restore dual awareness. Identify the ones that the child finds especially helpful and effective. One of the main goals of utilizing these tools, in Pierre Janet's terms, is to expand the field of consciousness and restore present awareness. Considering how the right-brain harbors our emotions and is more connected to subcortical areas of the brain (Siegel, 2010), when processing memories of attachment and adversity, the right hemisphere will be highly involved and activated. When the child has moved out of the windows of affect tolerance, in order to modulate arousal and balance right-left brain activity, stimulating the left-brain may be beneficial. Since the left-brain is involved in labeling, listing, logical, and linguistic tasks (Siegel, 2010), using activities that invite the left-brain to participate may help the child restore dual awareness and come back to appropriate windows of affect tolerance. Moreover, stimulating the frontal lobe with its integrative capacity as well as jump-starting thalamic activity (Lanius, 2005) may also assist children in restoring dual awareness. The following are some examples of dual awareness tools that can be used with children.

Using geometric shapes: Geometric figures of different colors are designed to have the child engaged in the process of describing, labeling, or selecting shapes and colors. Have geometric figures of different colors already cut out inside the Dissociation Kit for Kids. The clinician may ask the child to describe a geometric shape or to select a figure of a specific color.

Using textures: Textures can be used in various ways. The child may be asked to identify a texture by touch. The child may also be asked to identify objects or animals that have the texture the child is touching.

Using scents: Some studies have suggested the potential role that thalamic activity plays in dissociation. Reduced levels of thalamic activity may be associated with dissociative responses (Lanius et al., 2002; Lanius, Blum, Lanius, & Pain, 2006). In addition, it is known that olfactory information is the only form of sensory stimulation that bypasses the thalamus. All other incoming sensory information is routed through the thalamus. Lanius (2005) has suggested that the use of olfactory stimulation may be an effective way of jump-starting thalamic activity. With this in mind, in order to re-establish dual awareness by stimulating thalamic activity, the child is invited to guess or identify scents. These scents are part of the Dissociation Kit for Kids and contain basic, child-friendly scents. Once the child has identified two or three scents, the clinician uses again the in, half and half, and out signs; the dissociation fan; or the marionettes. This is done with the purpose of assessing how

Figure 7.1 The dissociation puppet.

present the child currently is, as well as to assess the effectiveness of each strategy in restoring dual awareness.

Using gum: During the reprocessing of memories of adverse events, the social engagement system should be activated for the integration and assimilation of such memories to take place. When using gum, the activation of the parasympathetic ventral vagal system is accomplished through the stimulation of the digestive system, salivation, and the facial muscles involved in mastication. For highly dissociative children, they may be given gum at the start of trauma reprocessing sessions. The clinician may also choose to give the child gum only when the child starts to exhibit states of hypoarousal that may potentially develop into dissociative states.

Using stuffed animals or finger puppets: Another way of expanding the field of consciousness is by asking the child to describe a stuffed animal or an object. Different small objects and stuffed animals can be placed inside the Dissociation Kit For Kids. When the child shows physiological signs of hyper- or hypoarousal such as changes in breathing, skin tone, voice, pupil size, or muscle tone, the clinician may ask the child to hold the object and describe it. Once the child has finished describing the object, the clinician should again assess the child's present awareness with signs, the fan, or the marionette. In addition, playing catch and tossing the puppet or stuffed animal back and forth to the child can help the child stay grounded and restore present awareness (Knipe, 2010).

Using cards with pictures of children in different body postures and positions: One of the best and quickest ways of restoring dual awareness and bringing the child back into the present is movement. Create laminated cards using art clips from the internet or simple drawings of children in different positions: Children in a straight up position, children standing up, children with their arms up or down, etc. Ask the child to look at the picture and imitate the movement. Once the child has executed the first movement or body posture, assess the energy level and present awareness and invite the child to notice the change.

Imitating facial gestures: Involving the facial muscles and facial contact with the therapist can assist the child in restoring present awareness through the stimulation of the social engagement system. Have laminated cards with just a sentence to remind you and the child of this strategy. A sentence like "mirror facial gestures" can prompt you or the child to use it. Use your face to execute gestures or feeling faces, and then invite the child to mirror and imitate the facial expressions. Once the child has been successful in mirroring the facial gestures, ask the child to notice what happens with his or her internal level of energy.

Singing and using our voices: Singing and chanting, according to Levine (2010), opens up the chest, lungs, mouth, and throat, stimulating *"the many serpentine branches of the Vagus nerve"*(pp. 125). Singing songs or just humming together with the child could be very powerful. As Levine beautifully states it, *"face-to-face, eye-to-eye, voice-to-ear, I-to-thou contact . . . make it possible for the client to negotiate a small opening into the social engagement system"* (p. 127).

Using cards with pictures of animals: Have laminated art clips of different animals. The different animals represent different body postures, arousal levels, and internal states. For example, a giraffe has a straight-up position and is in a calm state, a gorilla walks with a bent torso, a turtle is really slow, and a horse may be really fast. Asking the child what animal best represents their energy level and body posture will yield the child's level of arousal and present awareness. Go through the cards with the child and explore the different animals while explaining what each animal may represent. For example: Say, *"When we feel like a giraffe, we feel big and tall and inside we feel strong and calm. This feeling does not have anything to do with our real size. We can be small and have tall and big strong feelings inside and we can be tall and big and feel really small and bad inside. When you feel like a giraffe, you can see me and hear me and know you are safe in this place. When we feel like a turtle, we feel scared and may need a lot of protection; this is why we need a nice shell that can keep us contained and sheltered. We move slowly because we feel slow inside and everything around us seems to go really slow. When we feel like a mouse, we feel really small and not seen by anyone, even if we are big. We don't feel very strong, and inside we feel really scared, so we try to move really fast or freeze and not move. When we feel like a mouse we feel like things are going really fast inside of us even if we can't move."* After you have gone through all the cards and animals, invite the child to notice what animal represents best how he or she feels right now. Then, practice with the different tools of the Dissociation Kit For Kids to bring the child back into the "giraffe state." Once the child reports being back into the "giraffe state," ask the child to notice how it is to feel like a giraffe. Invite the child to notice all the good things about being in a giraffe state and where the good stuff is felt in the body and use slow and short sets of BLS.

Using exercise balls: Having the child sit on an exercise ball during the reprocessing of disturbing memories may assist the child in preserving interoceptive and body awareness at all times. Considering how balancing on a ball involves muscle awareness, grounding, centering, as well as being in touch with internal sensations (Levine, 2010), it constitutes a great tool to maintain dual awareness during the exploration and reprocessing of disturbing material. However, in my clinical experience, it only should be used with mild to moderate levels of dissociation in order to prevent potential physical injuries if the child falls off the ball.

The Dissociation Kit For Kids should always be near the child and the clinician during reprocessing sessions. In addition, all these strategies should be utilized initially during the preparation phase so the child is familiarized with them. These strategies can assist the child in enhancing his or her capacity for social engagement and interoceptive awareness. Later on, during trauma processing, they may be used to restore dual awareness. To better utilize these strategies during the reprocessing of trauma, clinicians should be attuned to the subtle physiological changes that signal the presence of dissociation and the resulting loss of present awareness.

ENHANCING THE BRAIN–BODY CONNECTION: SENSORY-FOCUSED EMDR STRATEGIES

When children experience trauma, neglect, and hardship, their relationship with their bodies become thwarted and chaotic (Levine, 2010). These children exhibit great difficulty learning from experience due to their bodies' inability to take the totality of their experience and learn from it. As a result, according to Levine, they engage in inefficient and ineffective strategies to manage and adapt to their environments. Stimulating interoceptive awareness is a fundamental aspect of the work needed during the preparation phase of EMDR therapy with dissociative children. Visceral, proprioceptive, as well as kinesthetic-muscle awareness should be stimulated. Helping children experience a "whole world" instead of a "fragmented world" requires children to find integration at a sensorimotor, affective, and cognitive level. Stimulating sensorimotor integration and processing during the different phases of EMDR therapy is also pivotal, especially with children that have disconnected from their bodies. The following are EMDR advanced strategies to stimulate present as well as interoceptive awareness.

ENHANCING THE CHILD'S PRESENT INTEROCEPTIVE AWARENESS

This Strategy is intended to strengthen the child's interoceptive awareness of the here and now reality. It is extremely helpful for highly dissociative children. Emphasize a here and now approach and invite the child to engage without judgment of good or bad or right or wrong. This strategy should be introduced during the preparation phase, but could be used during reprocessing sessions if the child starts to dissociate.

Start by enhancing the child's awareness of the HERE and NOW by saying, "We *are going to start practicing with things that you see, hear, smell, touch, and taste here in my office. Let's start with the things that you are SEEING right now. What are your EYES telling you about where you are now?*

> Child: *My eyes are telling me that I am in your office.*

> Therapist: *I want you to notice what it is like to SEE where you are now with your eyes.* Provide short and slow set of BLS.

> Therapist: *Notice what you are TOUCHING with your HANDS and your body. What are your hands and your body telling you about where you are right now?*

> Child: *My hands are telling me that I am sitting on a couch that is in your office.*

> Therapist: *I want you to notice what it is like to listen to your body and your hands telling you that you are here in my office sitting on a couch.* Once again, do a slow and short set of BLS. If the child reports disturbance or negative reactions, do not use BLS. However, if the child can tolerate it, explore the disturbance by doing "detective work" with the child. Explore what the eyes or the ears are reporting to the child that is experienced as disturbing. What the mind, the heart, or the body is informing about this experience may be inquired. You can also use microphones to interview the eyes or the ears to make it more playful.

> Therapist: *I want you now to use your NOSE and notice what the smell is telling you about where you are right now.* Having a usual scent in your office may help children create an olfactory association to your office.

> Child: *Your office usually smells like something sweet, so my nose is telling me that I am in your place.*

> Therapist: *I want you to notice what it is like to get this information from your nose and to notice the smells of this place.* Provide slow and short sets of BLS.

> Therapist: *When you pay attention to your ears and the noises that you hear, what are your ears telling you about where you are right now?*

> Child: *I hear birds and I hear your voice, so I know I am in Ana's place.*

> Therapist: *I want you to notice what it is like to get this information through your ears and to notice through your ears the birds and my voice.*

Therapist: *I am going to give you a piece of gum. I want you to chew it and notice what your taste is telling you about what you are doing and where you are right now.*

Child: *My mouth is telling me that this is a strawberry-flavored gum and that I am chewing the gum in Ana's place.*

Therapist: *Very good! Now continue to feel the strawberry-flavored gum and notice that you are chewing the gum in Ana's place.* Provide slow and short sets of BLS.

These presently oriented, sensory-focused interventions have the capacity to enhance the child's ability to stay present and mindful. These strategies can also be used during the reprocessing phases of EMDR therapy if the child loses dual awareness and shows signs of dissociation.

ENHANCING KINESTHETIC AWARENESS: MUSCLE TALK

Teaching children how, when, and what our muscles communicate can enhance their capacity to connect with their bodies and the important messages they have for us. Without these messages, we could get lost and respond to safety as if we were in the face of danger, and respond to danger as if we were in the face of safety. Survival and adaptation requires the appropriate integration of the information received in the brain from our friends, "the muscles."

Using the wisdom of nature, we can convey the importance of listening to how our muscles talk. Helping children experience and integrate kinesthetic information such as firmness, limpness, flabbiness, softness, stiffness, and inelasticity may be done by the use of animals and nature. For instance, different trees offer different levels of rigidity and flexibility. Inviting the child to experience what it would feel like to become an Oak tree and then changing to becoming a long, flexible palm tree can give the child the experience of tensing and relaxing muscles. Pendulating as we move from experiencing a hand or a leg or the entire body as if they were made of wood, to experiencing the same parts of the body as if they were made of spaghetti. Invite the child to notice which one feels better or worse and/or what messages these bodily states usually have for him or her. This exercise may also yield important information about the child's current and past experiences. Different roads and avenues may be followed as we engage in these exercises. More cognitive tasks may be stimulated as the child learns to connect and listen to the body. As we access procedural memory, we may inquire about when these muscle responses are usually present. Negative cognitions are also accompanied by specific body postures and somatic reactions; so once a channel is accessed, others may be open as well. The different protocols and exercises are used depending on the specific goals, needs of the child, and the phase of EMDR therapy we are in. Specific somatic interventions that can be used throughout different phases of EMDR therapy will be covered in further chapters.

BREATHING AND GROUNDING EXERCISES FOR CHILDREN

Helping children grow roots and wings can promote balance, integration, and healing. Connecting with the earth and the sky gives us security and a foundation, but also freedom and possibilities. Encourage the child to engage in mindful observations and awareness focused in the here and now. In addition, promote awareness without judgment of good or bad or right or wrong. Start by inviting the child to notice the earth and the ground. Talk about all the nutrients plants get from deep within the earth. The Oak tree, after undergoing a level of growth, goes deep into the earth and within itself before going into another growth cycle. Invite the child to connect with the earth so he or she gets to feel how the earth can feed us and support us. Invite the child to grow roots to feel connected to the earth and find balance just as the trees do. Another analogy may include animals. For instance, invite the child to imagine what it would feel like to possess the powers of having legs like frogs do, which have the special power to stick to the ground in such a balanced way. Ask the child to notice how his or her legs can feel the earth. Invite the child to just notice and stay with the sensation of connecting with the ground and the earth. Ask the child to feel the firm, and at the same time, flexible legs like frogs do, which allows them to jump and land in such a perfect synchrony and alignment. If the child reports positive emotions and bodily states, enhance this new awareness by using slow and short sets of BLS. Practice with breathing as well and invite the child to notice how breathing can go fast and slow and ask the child to notice which one feels better and more familiar, but at the end, stay with the most comfortable and relaxing rhythm. Once the child finds the right tempo and pace, use slow and short sets of BLS. If at any point negative material is activated, gently explore it, if appropriate, or change the activity to bring the child back to a state of homeostasis. In addition, keep the child grounded in reality, knowing that we are just allowing ourselves to have different experiences in our bodies.

Another fun exercise inspired by London (2004) consists of inviting the child to notice his or her breathing while rocking a baby to sleep. For this exercise you need a small stuffed animal or baby that is placed on top of the child's belly. The child should be laying down as he or she experiments with different breathing rhythms, from slow to medium to fast. The child is invited to notice how different rhythms may feel to the baby. The ultimate goal is to have the baby feel so good that the baby can fall asleep. The parent can also be present, as it is with all the exercises presented in this chapter. As the child experiments with different cadences and tempos, invite him or her to notice and enhance it with BLS. Once again, BLS at this level of EMDR therapy should only be used when the child is in a neutral or positive state. If negative material arises, gently explore it. If the child becomes agitated or dysregulated, bring the child back to balance and equilibrium by using any of the state change strategies described in previous chapters.

Using Bubbles

Playful strategies to help the child learn breathing strategies and notice the rhythm of the air and lungs can be used with bubbles. Blowing bubbles using different speeds and rhythms can be really fun and enjoyable for children. "Fast bubbles" as the child blows fast, and "slow bubbles" as the child is invited to blow really slow may be used during different phases of EMDR therapy. During the preparation phase, parents can be invited to witness these exercises during therapy sessions so they can continue to practice them with the child on a daily basis.

HELPING CHILDREN RECLAIM THEIR BODIES

Children with high tendencies to dissociate have very poor awareness of their own bodies. They feel numbed or feel a body that is disjointed and fragmented.

Many children, in their attempt to feel their bodies and to have some sense of containment, may use strategies that are usually misunderstood by parents and mental health professionals. In an effort to have some sensory connection to their bodies, children may do things that could be at times confusing for parents. I have come across children that insist on wanting to wear really tight clothes or wear tight undergarments. Other children have insisted on carrying extra heavy backpacks every day to school without an apparent reason or need. When asked about the reason behind it, they stated that they just liked the feeling of it. A 6-year-old presenting with moderate dissociative symptoms made every morning a request that seemed strange to her mother. When it was time to do her hair, she asked her mother to repeatedly pull her hair very tightly into a ponytail to the point, according to the mother, of potentially causing pain. However, the child never expressed any pain and would get mad at her mother if she did not honor her requests. For many dissociative children, the inability to feel their bodies might lay at the bottom of self-injurious behaviors. Helping children reconnect with their bodies is fundamental, but it should be done gradually. Connecting to the body too fast too soon may potentially cause dysregulation in the child's system. When the clinician has identified the lack of interoceptive awareness, steps toward reconnecting with the body should begin during the preparation phase. Mild, moderate, and severe forms of dissociation and detachment from the body may be found in children. How much of their bodies they feel should be assessed. Bringing mindfulness to the body and bodily states should be an important aspect of the preparation phase with dissociative children. The following represents strategies that can be used with children at different developmental stages and age ranges.

STRATEGIES WITH YOUNG CHILDREN

Playful strategies that use the magical thinking ability of young children may be very beneficial. When the parent is available, the parent-child relationship provides the perfect climate for the body to come alive. Nurturing touch and play constitute very powerful ways to awaken the body. Theraplay activities that combine play, connection, and touch are great avenues to stimulate body awareness. Considering how the sense of self does not develop in isolation, but through the repetitive parent-child interactions, the repair and reconnection to the body for young children should happen in connection with the caregiver. Helping children feel "felt" (Siegel, 1999) creates the appropriate stage for the development of healthy body awareness. Play activities such as body outlines, hand and foot prints, and face painting, among others can create the appropriate environment to reconnect or connect for the first time with the body. See Chapter 12 for the use of EMDR and Theraplay.

STRATEGIES FOR SCHOOL-AGE CHILDREN

School-age children can also benefit from playful activities that involve the body. In addition, stimulating brain activity and neurogenesis through mindful awareness of the body could prove to be very powerful. For some children, their attachment experiences have shaped their brains in such unique ways. Depending on the strategies developed by the child to deal with attachment needs, right or left brain activity may be more prominent or reduced. Individuals with avoidant and dismissing patterns of attachment have reduced the participation of the right hemisphere in order to evade dealing with the pain of not having their needs for connection met. On the other hand, anxious, ambivalent, and preoccupied individuals may have a right hemisphere that is flooded and chaotic, affecting the capacity of the frontal regions to cope (Siegel, 2010). Moreover, children that experienced trauma and hardship when lower regions of the brain were developing will experience greater difficulties regulating fight, flight, and freeze responses. These responses may be activated by minor environmental stimuli in the present (Perry, 2006). "Vertical" and "horizontal" integration (Siegel, 2010) should be stimulated throughout the different phases of EMDR therapy. Integration is fostered during the preparation phase, but it is more rapidly attained during the reprocessing phases. Stimulating the child's lower and subcortical areas of the brain so they can work in sync with higher brain regions is a goal of many of the exercises proposed in different chapters of this book. In addition, it is equally relevant to promote "horizontal" integration so the right and left hemispheres can synchronically work together. The use of activities, such as the one described below, are designed to stimulate mindful awareness of the body and promote the linkage of differentiated systems. (see Chapter 11 for the use of more somatic interventions.)

For this exercise, you could use microphones to engage each part as the child is invited to mindfully notice different parts and organs of the body. The following script exemplifies how to introduce this activity.

> Therapist: *We are going to learn about our bodies and how our bodies talk and sing to us. Let's check how your body talks and sings to you. Let's just start by noticing your right hand. Can you feel your right hand? Does it feel cold, warm, or really hot?*
>
> Child: *It feels kind of warm.*
>
> Therapist: *Does the warm feeling in your right hand feel good or bad?*
>
> Child: *It feels good.* If the child reports negative sensations, invite the child to notice it and use it as an opportunity for exploration. Interview the hand. Have a microphone and engage the right or left hand into a conversation. Invite parts to talk to each other. If the right hand has positive feelings and the left hand has negative feelings, ask the hands to dialogue. What would the right hand say to the left?
>
> Therapist: *Okay, I want you to just notice or pay attention to your right hand and the warm feeling.* Provide slow and short sets of BLS.
>
> Therapist: *Do you feel all your fingers and your right palm or only a bit of them?*
>
> Child: *I feel all my fingers.*
>
> Therapist: *Okay, let's just feel all the fingers of your left hand and just notice what is like to have all your fingers.* Provide slow and short set of BLS.
>
> Therapist: *Does the right hand want to move, or it wants to stay still?*
>
> Child: *I feel like it wants to move.*
>
> Therapist: *What movement do you think the right hand would like to make? Does the right hand want to move up and down? Shake? Squeeze? Make a fist? Or does it want to do something else?*

Child: *The right hand wants to make a fist.*

Therapist: *Okay, let's make a fist and just notice what your right hand is doing.*
Provide slow and short sets of BLS.

Depending on the child, you may want to stimulate initially one side of the brain
more than the other. In addition, after you bring awareness to both sides of the body,
invite the child to notice both hands or both feet at the same time. In addition, involve
organs such as the heart, the stomach, and the lungs. If the child does not report any
awareness, sensations, or feelings in the hands or any other part of the body say, "*Okay,
we are going to work on helping you feel your hands one bit at the time. Let's start by putting
some lotion on your right hand and making a hand print.*" The child can put the finger
paint or lotion on, or the clinician can instruct the parent to put lotion on the child's
hand and then place it on a piece of paper to make a hand print. Once the handprint
has been made, put powder on top of it to make the print more visible. The handprint
will begin to make the existence of the hand more real and tangible for the child. Invite
the child to notice the hand printed on the paper and the feelings associated with it.
Provide a slow and short set of BLS as the child is noticing the handprint. However, if
the child reports negative responses or feelings, instead of using BLS, take the opportunity to explore it. Interview the hand or the pain or the uncomfortable sensations.
Remember that any response, whether positive or negative, represents an opportunity.
If the response is positive or neutral, it is an opportunity to enhance this awareness or
positive response by using BLS. If it is negative, it is an opportunity for exploration. If
the responses continue to be neutral or positive, do the same with the other hand and
both feet. You can also use aluminum foil to make the complete hand shape. Create
the shape of both feet, legs, hands, arms, head, and torso using aluminum foil. When
creating the prints, the clinician instructs the parent to wrap the aluminum foil around
the body parts. The clinician may assist the parent with wrapping the hands or feet.
However, appropriate consent from the parent and the child to use touch should be
obtained early in treatment.

It is fundamental that the clinician remains attuned to the child's internal states
as he or she engages in these activities. Some children may be able to fully engage in
this activity while others may only be able to tolerate a portion of it. Be aware that
at any point during the preparation phase, any work, even if it is positive information, may become potentially negative. If the child becomes agitated or reports negative emotions, work on helping the child feel contained and regulated by using other
preparation strategies described in this book. In addition, use your own system to
resonate with the child to bring him or her to emotional homeostasis. Use what nature
has given you: Your internal states, eye contact, the tone and quality of your voice,
and your nurturing regulating touch. If the child is experiencing negative affect, the
clinician's ability to tolerate and modulate his or her own affect will influence the
child's experience. The full experience of becoming agitated or fearful followed by
the effective use of regulatory strategies becomes a mastery experience for the child.
If the clinician is able to have an attuned presence and gently reestablishes emotional
balance, this experience will become an act of triumph for the child. However, if the
clinician also becomes dysregulated and fearful, or frustrated, the overall experience
may reinforce the child's sense of hopelessness and phobia of the negative affect. If a
strategy being used is not effective in bringing the child back to balance, keep in mind
that there is always an opportunity for repair.

How well the clinician can resonate physiologically with the child is of a great importance. According to Siegel (2011), individuals with increased body awareness have been found to have more empathy toward others. "When we can sense our own internal state, the fundamental pathway for resonating with others is open as well" (Siegel, 2011, p. 62). Helping children develop interoceptive awareness will require clinicians that are able to fully feel and experience themselves and their bodies.

WHEN THE BODY IS NONEXISTENT

Some children may actually report no awareness or recognition of any sensations in their bodies. Slow steps should be taken to help the child reconnect to the body. Children diagnosed with DID may have a confusing and distorted sense of the body. Different parts, alters, or ego states may have come to believe that they have different bodies. In my clinical experience, however, these dissociative barriers are not yet as consolidated and rigid as the ones found in adults with DID. As a result, the integration of different parts can happen faster.

Meeting the Body for the First Time

Creating curiosity and a genuine desire for getting to know the body could create a solid foundation. Meeting the body parts and organs as if we were meeting them for the first time could incorporate some playfulness to the process of embracing the body. Many children, when they are asked what they are experiencing in the body, may respond with the usual "I do not know." The following strategies do not require that the child have previous awareness of body sensations, only curiosity to meet the body for the very first time. These strategies are a good way to begin the process of learning the language of the body while being in playful states.

Therapist: *We are going to learn about how the body talks to us. Sometimes, we stop listening to the body because we had too many mixed-up feelings inside the body. Now we are going to start working on just getting to know our bodies little by little. Let's take a moment to just listen if the body is communicating something to us. This is a different kind of language. The body speaks with the words of sensations and movement. Tension, tingling feelings, butterfly-like feelings, numbness, and many others are the words the body uses. You could imagine creating a body satellite or a body antenna that can help you find the feelings in your body. I want you to start using your satellite or antenna and see if you can catch any body signals. I also have a "feeling finder or detector." When you use this finder, you scan or check your body from head to toe and see if you find anything."* Give the child enough time to use the feeling finder, which is a magnifying glass that the child can use to check the entire body. Menus should be provided to assist the child in connecting to the body (see Chapter 11). Strategies for children that are able to connect with some sensations are explained previously in this chapter. However, this exercise is appropriate for children that initially report no feelings or sensations in connection to the body.

Child: *Not really. I do not feel anything.*

Therapist: *Okay, no problem. Let's just start by meeting the body for the first time. Remember a time you met someone for the very first time. I invite you to just be curious about it. We are going to begin this first meeting with your body by drawing a picture or making an outline of your body.* Once it is done, go through the body outline and check with the child what may be the part or organ that has a bit more feeling or the child feels more connection to. You can ask the child to use different colors to represent the parts that have no feelings and another color for the parts that have some feelings. You could also use Play-doh® or clay to create this body part. Let the child pick the body part or organ that has some sensations or feelings. Ask the child to draw a picture of this area or part. Invite the child to converse with this part. When working with younger children, you could use a microphone as the child and you interview the body part.

Therapist: *Let's be curious about this part. Let's see what the temperature of this part may be. Let's guess. Do you think that it may be warm, cold, or hot? Is it tense and rigid, or really calm and flexible? Is it still or does it has movement inside?* When learning the ABC's of this new language, menus should be given to the child. If the child is experiencing the body or specific body parts as being apart or far away, take steps toward connection with this body part. Invite the child to visualize or actually create real strings or cords to establish some connection with this part. Once some level of connection has been established, guide the child to get closer and closer to this part until it can be fully embraced and felt as part of the body. If neutral or positive sensations arise, use BLS to enhance them. If negative responses are reported instead, playfully explore them. The fear of connecting to the body or a body part may also be a target that can be processed using EMDR therapy.

A young female client clearly stated that she never had any feelings in her body. When she started working on the above exercise, she identified her heart as the organ she felt the most connected to. She actually drew a picture of her head and her heart disconnected from her body (Figure 7.2.). She also drew her heart inside a basket that she was holding in her hand. We approached the drawing with curiosity and without judgment. When I started to interview the heart, this client drew another picture of the heart inside a box that was locked (Figure 7.3). From the outside of the box and with curiosity as if we were meeting the heart for the first time, I assisted her in guessing what the heart was saying, what the sensations, temperature, texture, shape, and color of the heart was. We played guessing games and I provided menus so she could look at different possibilities. Once again, this time was just about guessing, as if we were meeting the heart for the first time. As the sessions progressed, one day, this client reported that the heart was now outside the box. She was encouraged to imagine getting closer to the heart and to notice what happened to the heart and the other parts of her body. When the response was positive, slow and short sets of BLS were provided to enhance this positive sensory experience. Later on, a string was created to assist her in connecting to the heart and eventually she drew pictures where the heart was placed inside her body. Once the child was able to fully embrace and feel her heart, more BLS was provided. Once again, if the child responds with an "I don't know," the child is encouraged to guess what the heart or any other organ is experiencing, as it is being discovered for the very first time. These strategies can also be used as interweaves during the reprocessing phases of EMDR therapy.

It is not unusual that a child may identify a sexual organ as being the one having more connection or sensory responses. Carefully assisting the child in accepting and understanding her body without shame will be important. When the child experiences

Figure 7.2 Subjective experience of the body. Age, gender, and other details of this case have been altered to protect the identity of the client.

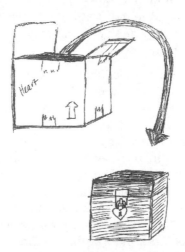

Figure 7.3 The heart inside a box.

high sexual arousal, pendulate to other parts of the body or move to a more cognitive task in order to regulate the arousal level. Use mindfulness to notice the sensations with acceptance and without judgment. You could use any of the following questions: *"As you notice your private parts having a tingling feeling, what is happening in your heart? Or, let's notice your stomach and what the stomach may be feeling as your private parts are having a tingly feeling. Is there a part of your body that feels the opposite or does not feel tingly? If the tingly feelings were translated into words, what would your private parts be saying? What do they need?"* It is always important to have the parents participate in these experiences with the understanding that the clinician will be guiding the session. The parent should be prepared and reassured that the clinician will manage what may come up and will guide the parent through any interventions where the actions of the parent are needed. This, of course, requires a good sense of efficacy and experience on the part of the clinician. If the clinician still has past traumatic or adverse experiences that have not been processed, integrated, and resolved, the child may trigger shame and discomfort when talking about the body and the private parts. Clinicians should be aware of the appropriate boundaries to practice within. Going beyond our own level of expertise or working with issues with which we do not have even a minimal level of resolution and understanding in ourselves does not constitute best clinical practice.

GAMES TO DEVELOP AND STIMULATE AFFECT REGULATION

Despite long periods of preparation, children with insecure patterns of attachment and dissociative symptoms may still have difficulty accessing the memories of trauma and adversity. As a result, these memories that lay at the core of their current impairments in various areas of functioning continue to be activated by present environmental stimuli (Shapiro, 2001). In order to promote healing, these memories at some point will need to be reprocessed and assimilated. Helping children overcome the "phobia of the memory" (van der Hart et al., 2006) is an important aspect of the preparation phase with these highly traumatized youngsters. The following games and protocols are designed to assist children in mastering the implicit fear of trauma memories. One way to understand these strategies is by using the "pool analogy" and the "in and out" strategies. In this analogy, the pool represents the memories of adverse events and trauma that these children implicitly or explicitly fear and avoid. Children with pervasive affective dysregulation do not have the "life jackets" needed to safely enter and swim inside these pools. They have actually developed a "pool phobia" that, despite long periods of preparation, still persists. During the preparation phase, the clinician has worked on helping the child develop swimming skills and has created life jackets. However, despite having all these skills and swimming gear, the child may still be fearful of diving into these memories. The clinician will have to take small steps to help the child master the fear of going inside these "pools". Using "in and out" strategies to access the "pool" while honoring what the child can tolerate is a good starting point. With this in mind, initially, the child may only tolerate to put the tip of the finger inside the pool and rapidly get back out. Later on, the clinician can support the child in building greater regulatory capacities to swim across the "pool". Several authors have proposed protocols such as constant installation of present orientation and safety (CIPOS; Knipe, 2010), which I classify as "in and out" strategies. These protocols and strategies can also be seen as pendulation (Levine, 1998/2010), oscillation (Ogden, 2006) and titration activities. Any way we call them, they are designed to help the child overcome the implicit phobia of the memory, increase affect tolerance, increase the integrative capacity of the child, and enhance the child's regulatory competencies. They can also improve the child's capacity to stay present and maintain dual awareness as the cognitive, affective, and sensorimotor aspects of the memory are being accessed and activated.

THE "MEMORY-VISITING MUSCLE"

Overcoming the phobia of the trauma memory may be one of the greatest challenges of highly traumatized and dissociative children. Oftentimes, despite extensive preparation and work on affect tolerance, these children may still refuse to reprocess traumatogenic memories. The analogy of the "memory-visiting muscle" is designed to assist children that are still fearful of even thinking about these memories. The following is a script to exemplify the use of this strategy:

Therapist: *I know it is hard to think about that bad thing that happened to you. I also know that you want the bad things that happened to stop bothering you and making you feel yucky. There is something that we could do to make it easier for you to visit the memory of what happened. Do you know what happens when we exercise or lift weights? Well... the muscles of our bodies get bigger and stronger so they can give us greater physical strength. Sometimes the "memory-visiting muscle" might need some work so it can get bigger and stronger. It might even get bigger than the yucky memories, so visiting them later on might not be as hard or difficult. We are going to start by creating a picture of what happened to you. I know it is still hard to think of or draw pictures of what happened to you, so we are going to do it slowly and we are also going to bring helpers. What helpers would you like to bring?"* Allow some time for the child to identify the helpers or even draw a picture of them. You could ask the caregiver and the child in the prior session to bring pictures from home of positive important figures in the child's life.

"I would like you to draw a picture or just imagine the helpers that would help you feel safe, good, or strong, or that help you have any feelings that you may need to start visiting the yucky memory. I want you to imagine those helpers sitting next to you." Take some time to assist the child in identifying the specific places in the office where the child wants the helpers. *"Now, tell me how you feel as you think about your helpers."*

Potential response from the child: *I feel good and safe. I want my dog Amber sitting next to me on the floor, my cousin Susie sitting by my right side, and my mom sitting on my left side.*

Therapist: *How does it feel when you imagine having your dog, Amber, your cousin, Susie, and your mom right next to you?*

Child: *I feel happy and safe.*

Therapist: *Where do you feel those feelings inside? You can use the feeling finder to find the feelings in your body?*

Child: *In my stomach.*

Therapist: *Okay, I would like you to think about your helpers and feel your helpers around you and the good feelings that you have and where those feelings are hanging out in your body.* Provide slow and short sets of BLS.

Therapist: *Okay, what do you notice now?*

Child: *I feel good and safe."* Repeat it two or three times.

Therapist: *Now, with your helpers around you, I want you to start drawing the picture of the yucky thing that happened to you. While you are drawing it, notice if the mixed up feelings and thoughts come up, and when it gets too hard and yucky, I want you to use your "I need a break" signal as many times as you need it. So let's start drawing on this piece of paper.* This can be a premade signal where you write, "I need a break," and glue a wooden stick on the back. The child may just raise the hand up to signal the need for a break. This strategy can be used with the sandtray as well. Ask the child to create the story of the bad or yucky memory and instruct the child to stop as many times as needed.

Child: *(after half of the picture is done) I want to use my "I want to take a break" signal.*

Therapist: *You really know how to use your signals. We are going to take a break. During the break I would like you to think about your helpers or to look at the picture of your helpers.* Let the child stay with the helpers for a few seconds.

"How do you feel now as you think about your helpers, Amber, Susie, and Mom?

Child: *I still feel a bit mixed-up.*

Therapist: *I am glad you are letting me know how you feel. I would like you to keep thinking about your helpers. Imagine Amber, your cousin Susie, and mom next to you and stay with them for a while.* Allow the child to fully experience the resource and then ask, *How do you feel now?*

Child: *I feel good and happy again.*

Therapist: *Okay, now, check where those good feelings are in your body and follow my fingers. What do you notice now?*

Child: *I feel really good!*

Therapist: *Now, if it is okay with you, I would like you to go back to visit the memory of that yucky thing that happened to you and see how far you can go with the drawing or the sandtray story. Remember that you are exercising the "memory-visiting muscle" and you can stop or take breaks as often as you want.*

Child: *Okay.*

Child: *I am done.*

Therapist: *Okay, good job. You were so brave to do this. You made the picture of the bad thing that happened to you!*

This strategy can also be used with specific time limits to allow the child to go back to the relational resource. For example, ask the child to stop every 10 or 20 seconds and invite the child to think about the helpers or any other resource. Every time the child goes back to the resource and reports a positive change in affect, the clinician provides a slow and short set of BLS. Keep in mind that we are not re-installing the resource; we are enhancing the child's capacity to move from a negative state to a positive affective state. With this in mind, the clinician should provide BLS each time the child goes back to the resource and reports positive affective states.

INSTALLATION OF PRESENT RESOLUTION (IPR)

The IPR was inspired by an exercise developed by Steele and Raider (2001). In this exercise, the child is asked to draw a picture of the past traumatic event followed by a picture of the child in the present. I adapted this wonderful exercise so it can be used as an EMDR protocol with children that, despite extensive preparation, continue to experience a strong fear of the disturbing memory. This protocol should only be used with children that are no longer experiencing the adverse or traumatic event. If the child is working on a memory of bullying and the child is still being bullied in the present, this protocol should not be used. The protocol is as follows:

You may say, *"We are going to create two pictures, one picture of you "Then" and another picture of you "Now." I know it is still hard to think or draw pictures of what happened to you, so we are going to bring helpers. What helpers would you like to bring? I would like you to draw a picture or just imagine the helpers that would help you feel safe, good, or strong or that would help you have any feelings that you may need to start visiting the yucky memory. I want you to imagine those helpers sitting next to you. Now, tell me how you feel as you are thinking about your helpers."* Allow enough time for the child to give you the answers or to draw the helpers. Similar to the analogy of the "memory-visiting muscle," for children with a strong fear of the memory, having a resource in place is highly beneficial. *"Now that you have the picture of your helpers, I want you to notice how you feel and then find where these feelings are hanging out in your body. Now, as you are thinking about your helper, feel those good feelings and where they are in your body."* Provide BLS and repeat the installation of this resource two or three times as long as it continues to be associated with positive states.

You may say, *"Now that you have your helpers, let's start by drawing a picture or, if you prefer, you can use the sand box. The title of the first picture is "This is me then." Think about the yucky or bad thing that happened to you and draw what was happening around you, who was there for you, how you were feeling, what you were doing, or how big you were. If while you are drawing this picture, the feelings get too big you can use your "I need a break" sign, and think about your helpers. Please know that we can take as many breaks as we need."* Once the first picture is done, say, *"Now I want you to draw a second picture titled "This is me now."* Once the child has completed the picture, assist the child in making it as thorough and specific as possible. Ask questions that can help the child recognize what is different now. Questions such as: How big are you now? How strong? What do you know now that you did not know before? In addition, inquire about the skills the child has acquired, the helpers that are present in the child's life, the strengths and resources that were not present before that are present now. In general, inquire about anything that shows any level of resolution or that shows that the adverse or traumatic event is over now. Once the two pictures are finished, start to pendulate or titrate. Ask the child to look at the "now" picture and notice the feelings and where these feelings are hanging out in the body. If the feelings are positive, provide slow and short sets of BLS. Ask the child to look at the "then" picture and notice anything that comes to the mind, the heart, or the body. Start with just a few seconds, five or ten depending on how much the child can tolerate, thinking about the disturbing event. Invite the child to go back to the "now" picture and look at it again. Sometimes giving prompts to the child is helpful in re-orienting the child to the present. You can again ask questions to the child while you both are looking at the "now" picture. Say, *"Are you safe now? Is the yucky thing still happening now? Do you have helpers now? Are you stronger? Do you know things that can help you defend yourself now?"* Wait until the child responds to each question before you ask the next. Encourage the child to look at the picture and notice the feelings and where they are in the body. If the child reports positive feelings, provide short and slow sets of BLS. Allow enough time for the child's affective states to switch and change into positive ones. Go back to the "then" picture and allow the child to look at it and notice any emotions or bodily states for a few seconds. Titrate by increasing the time as the child shows an amplified ability to tolerate the past disturbing event. Pendulate or titrate between the "then" and the "now" pictures as many times as the child can tolerate during the session. Remember to only provide BLS when the child is in a positive affective state elicited by the "now" picture. Sandtray can also be used with this protocol. Divide the sandtray in two, or use two sandtrays if you have them in your office. On one side, the child creates the "then" picture and on the other side the "now" picture. When the child is pendulating or titrating between the two, alternate covering one side and then the other. In my experience, after using this protocol with numerous children, once it has been successfully used, children can easily move into the full assessment and reprocessing of the disturbing memory. I hypothesized that this protocol may assist the child's brain in starting to locate the memory in time and space.

STATE-CHANGE INSTALLATION

Some children may not tolerate thinking or drawing pictures about the memories of adversity. As a result, the clinician may have to start with current triggers or minor disturbances. The purpose of this protocol is to enhance the child's ability to change affective states and increase regulatory capacities.

You may say, *"How about if we play and work on helping you get the "feeling muscles" stronger and bigger? Sometimes the feeling muscles might need some work, so if we can get them to be bigger and stronger, you may be able to handle feelings better.*

I know an exercise we can do to start working on making the "feeling muscles" bigger and stronger. Let's start by drawing your body on this big piece of paper that I have on the floor." Create a body outline with the child. For this you will need a big enough piece of paper where the child can lay down while you or the caregiver draw the outline of the child's body. The following is a description of how to use this protocol:

Therapist: *I want to you to think about your safe place or one of the things we put inside your "helping box" that you can use to help yourself when you are feeling mixed-up.* See prior chapter for information on how to create the "helping box."

Child: *I want to have my "good helpers" here with me.*

Therapist: *Let's think about your helpers. Tell me, what do you feel now when you think about your helpers?*

Child: *I feel happy and good.*

Therapist: *Where do you feel those feelings in your body? Or where are those feelings hanging out in your body? How is your body communicating these feelings to you? Or you can use the feeling finder and find these feelings inside your body.*

Child: *I feel those good feelings in my stomach.*

Therapist: *Let's draw a picture of your helpers on the outline of your body, right on your stomach!* The child can draw a picture or use stickers to represent each helper.

Therapist: *Now I would like you to think about something that bothers you just a bit and let me know when you have it.*

Child: *I've got it.* It may be helpful to check with the child the selected disturbing event. We want to start with minor disturbances and once the child has enough practice changing affective states, the clinician can encourage the child to bring up an event that holds a higher level of disturbance.

Therapist: *What do you feel when you think about this?*

Child: *I feel kind of sad.*

Therapist: *Where do you feel it in your body?*

Child: *In my heart.*

Therapist: *Now let's draw these sad feelings on the outline of your body, right inside your heart. See if these feelings have a shape, color, texture, or temperature and draw a picture of the feelings as you see them, feel them, and think of them.* Give the child enough time to identify and draw the different aspects of these feelings. Once the child has finished, start to pendulate from the negative state to the positive affective state elicited by the resource selected by the child.

Therapist: *I would like you now to focus on the helpers again and where you feel them in your body. Think about them sitting around you right now and see what feelings come to you.*

Child: *I am starting to feel the good feelings in my stomach again.*

Therapist: *Good job! Now just continue to imagine your helpers and all the good feelings that you are starting to feel in your stomach.* Give the child enough time to move to a positive state. Invite the child to focus on the picture of the resource previously drawn on the body outline.

Child: *I am feeling the good feelings again in my stomach.*

Therapist: *I would like you to continue to look at the picture of your helpers and focus on the good feeling in your stomach.* Provide short and slow sets of BLS.

Therapist: *What are you noticing now?*

Child: *That I am feeling safe and happy.*

Therapist: *Now we are going to go back to that thing that bothers you a bit. Let's find the drawing of the mixed-up feelings on your body outline and just notice what happens when you start thinking about it.*

Child: *I get the mixed up feelings and thoughts again in my heart.*

Therapist: *Thanks for letting me know how you feel. I know this can be hard, but remember that we are exercising the "feeling muscles" so just watch those feelings. Notice what they are doing, if they are moving or staying still. Let's just watch them with curiosity, as if this was the first time we were meeting them and getting to know them.*

Child: *They are trying to push out and they are kind of moving.*

Therapist: *Okay, let's just stay with them for a few seconds.* Give enough time for the child to notice the negative affective responses associated with the minor disturbance. You could also have a set amount of time and switch every 15 or 20 seconds. You could simply let the child stay in the negative state until the stop signal, or the "I need a break sign" is used. The amount of time the child spends thinking about the negative event could be increased slowly as the child expands affect tolerance capacities. Make sure appropriate instructions are given to the child in terms of the use of signs or if the change will happen based on time elapsed. The child may also be invited to wear two different hats of two different colors, one for the positive state and the other for the negative state. This will make this protocol more playful, fun, and the state change will be made more tangible to the child.

Therapist: *Now, we are going back to thinking about the helpers. Let's again look at the picture of your helpers on your body outline and the good feelings in your body and see what happens.*

Child: *I feel good again.*

Therapist: *Where are those good feelings in your body?*

Child: *In my stomach and in my heart, too.*

Therapist: *Okay, so let's notice those good feelings in your body and follow my fingers, or let me tap your knees.*

Continue to pendulate or titrate as you go back and forth from the negative event and the positive resources and their associated affect. You could also change the event and ask the child for an event with a higher level of disturbance.

STATE-CHANGE INSTALLATION WITH CAREGIVER

The above protocol can be used with children and their caregivers. When working with the attachment system, the inclusion of the caregiver is fundamental. Experiencing and embracing affective states while in the comforting and nurturing presence of the caregiver and the clinician can enhance this affective experience. The parent or caregiver should receive clear information prior to the session so roles are clarified and the process is predictable. When the child is experiencing positive affective states, the parent is instructed to join in and connect with the positive feelings of the child. A cord may be created to connect the parent to the child's emotion and the bodily states. Both the child and the parent are instructed to just stay in this positive state. For a child that can tolerate positive affect and physical closeness, the parent may be instructed to be close or hold the child while participating in this exercise. If the child has developed attachment strategies of avoidance, the closeness with the parent should not be forced. The child can choose a distance that feels just right from the parent. Enough information should be provided so the parent can follow directions from the clinician while feeling empowered and honored during the session. In order to assist the parent and child in joining in, while moving from different affective states, the clinician can ask them to create a string or cord. This string can make the connection more tangible and concrete for the child.

You may say, "*We are going to create a very special 'feeling string.' This string or cord will help you and your parent connect your feelings and connect with each other. You can make your string of any color or texture you want. You can also decorate the string any way you want. Let's take some time to create this special string in your mind, and when you have it let me know. Okay, let's start with mom. Please tell me about your 'feeling string.'* Give the parent enough time to describe the string and then go to the child. You could start with the child, as well, or whoever wants to start first. Once the strings have been described, use the state change installation protocol described above, starting with one of the child's resources. Once the child reports having positive emotional and bodily states, ask the parent and the child to plug in each other's strings so the parent can also feel what the child is feeling. One of the main goals of this strategy is to help the child "feel felt" and also to help the parent truly connect and resonate with the child. Once the child moves into a negative affective state, invite the parent and the child to connect their "feeling string" and have the parent connect with the child's state.

CONSTANT INSTALLATION OF PRESENT ORIENTATION AND SAFETY

This protocol was developed by Jim Knipe (2006, 2010) and later modified by Eckers (2010) to be used with children. According to Knipe, the CIPOS method is geared toward helping dissociative clients access traumatic material in a titrated, controlled, and predictable way. When using CIPOS, the client is oriented to the present safety in the clinician's office. Time is allotted to fully orient the client in the present reality of the therapist's office. This method can help dissociative children not only restore dual awareness, but also be mindful of when they are present and when they are not. It also helps the child work through the fear of the memories containing disturbing material. The following is my own adaptation to the CIPOS that I have been using successfully with highly dissociative children since 2008. The CIPOS can be used with tools such as the Dissociation Kit For Kids to strengthen the child's sense of orientation to the present. When using the CIPOS method, permission to participate should be obtained. The child should also feel safe or at least contained in the therapist's office. The following script will help you introduce the work you will be doing:

You may say, *"I have a cool exercise that we can do together today. However, at some point in this exercise we are going to think, draw, or write about the bad or yucky thing that happened to you. We are also going to work on helping you know and feel what it is like to be fully here and present in this office with me."*

It is important, especially when working with children, that the child feels safe in the office and in the therapist's presence. Helping the child understand that the traumatic or adverse event is over and it is not happening in the present is important. In order to reinforce the child's present orientation, questions about the present reality should be followed by the use of BLS. *"Can you tell me where you are right now? How many dollhouses do you see in my place? Where are you sitting right now? What are your hands touching right now? What kind of noises do you hear in this place now?"* After the child responds to each question, invite the child to notice it and use short and slow set of BLS.

Using the Dissociation Kit for Kids With the CIPOS Protocol

An important aspect of this protocol is to orient the child to present time and restore dual awareness if it has been lost. An additional strategy suggested in the CIPOS protocol is to play catch games with the client. Tossing one of the stuffed animals from the kit or a ball back and forth with the child may be an effective strategy to bring the child back into the present. Using all the dual attention tools of the Dissociation Kit For Kids and the CIPOS protocol can assist the clinician and the child by:

1. Helping the child get acquainted with dual awareness tools.
2. Allowing the clinician to test these tools and identify the most efficient and effective strategies to restore dual awareness and bring the child back to the present.

3. After each of the different tools from the Dissociation Kit For Kids have been used and practiced with the child, use the signs IN, HALF and HALF, and OUT. You can also use the "dissociation fan" or the "dissociation marionette." This is done with the purpose of assessing if the child is sufficiently grounded. For example, after tossing a stuffed animal back and forth, invite the child to use the signs and assess how present he or she is after using this exercise. Once the child is fully present, enhance the child's present awareness by using short and slow sets of BLS.

Accessing the Memories

You can invite the child to draw a picture of the event or start to create the story of the event in the sandtray. Establish a time limit for the child to work on the drawing, sandtray story, or a Play-doh® story. It could be 10 to 20 seconds. Once the time has elapsed, ask the child to stop and say, *"Very good, now let's focus your attention again on where you are right now."* Use one of the dual attention strategies from the Dissociation Kit For Kids and allow the child enough time to come back to the present. An adaptation to the CIPOS that I have incorporated is the use of the signs, dissociative fan, etc., after the child has accessed the trauma memory and used a dual attention tool. Say, *"Now, let's use the signs, fan, or puppet to see how present you are right now."* If the child is not sufficiently grounded, use another dual attention strategy until the child is grounded enough in the present. Then, ask the child to continue to draw or build the story of the memory. Repeat the process until the drawing or story has been completed. However, if at some point the child becomes highly dysregulated, continue to use dual attention tools and regulatory strategies covered in this book until dual awareness is restored and the child achieves sufficient stability and emotional equilibrium.

SUMMARY AND CONCLUSIONS

Advanced strategies are usually necessary to help children with dissociative tendencies stay grounded and present enough to endure trauma-processing procedures. Helping children understand dissociation and its survival qualities is an important aspect of the preparation phase. Helping children get acquainted with a wide range of dual attention strategies and testing their effectiveness with each child is necessary. Once the specific dissociative responses have been singled out, the clinician and the child can be prepared when these responses are activated. During the preparation phase of EMDR therapy, a common way of communicating about dissociative experiences, as well as what would be done when they surface is practiced and rehearsed. This chapter offers a wide variety of playful and developmentally appropriate strategies to ground the child and restore dual awareness. After this, the processing assimilation and integration of the memories that lay at the core of the child's suffering can be attained.

8

Phase Three: Assessment

The primary goals of the assessment phase are to:

- Access the memory network containing traumatogenic material.
- Access and activate the cognitive, affective, and somatic aspects of the memory.
- Create a baseline of the memory by using two scales: (Validity of the positive cognition (VoC) and subjective units of disturbance (SUDs).

Once a good enough level of stability has been attained and the readiness of the child to move into trauma processing has been established, the clinician, in collaboration with the child and parent, should select the target for processing. In preparation for the reprocessing of disturbing material, the following steps should be followed:

- The child should be encouraged to bring the resources previously installed. If the child created a "helping box," "safety shield," and so on, the child should bring them to the reprocessing session.
- Basic biological needs such as sleep, hunger, and physical rest, should be appropriately addressed by the caregivers. The windows of affect tolerance can expand or contract in connection to basic biological needs. A child that did not get enough sleep the night before a therapy session may be tired and get agitated easily compared to the same child when enough sleep and rest has been provided to the system. Making sure essential organic needs are met can set the stage for a productive eye movement desensitization and reprocessing (EMDR) processing session.
- All the resources that can facilitate the processing of trauma memories by keeping the child within manageable levels of arousal should be in place. If pets have participated during the preparation phase and they help the child feel safe and calm, ask the parent and the child to bring the pet to the session. Since the pet has been already familiarized with the office and the clinician, it should not cause disruptions.
- The cards, cubes, and balls containing cognitions, emotions, and sensations should be available to the child.
- If resources for containment were used during the exploration of memories and proved helpful, they could again be utilized during the assessment phase and all

the reprocessing phases. The cushion house, the shy blanket, the umbrella house, the invisible hats, etc., should be made available to the child.

▓ Prior to accessing and reprocessing a memory, the clinician should have a clear direction and plan in terms of potential resources needed, interweaves, etc. This should be arranged once it is established that the child is ready to move into the reprocessing phases of EMDR therapy. At this point, the level of involvement of the caregiver should have been established and some level of work should have been initiated with the caregiver, if possible.

▓ If the caregivers are going to be present during the reprocessing of disturbing material, the parents should understand their role clearly. The clinician should provide information in regards to what will be happening during the session so the process is predictable to the parent as well as to the child.

▓ Since the reprocessing phases of EMDR therapy follow immediately after the assessment phase, the clinician should have prepared potential interweaves in case the child's processing of the memory gets blocked. Clinicians should never go unprepared to a reprocessing session, especially with complex trauma cases.

▓ If the presence of Dissociation has been established and adequate preparation has been completed, the "Dissociation Kit for Kids" should be made available at all times to the child and the clinician. Remind the child to use the signs IN, HALF, and OUT, the "dissociation fan" or the "dissociation puppets." Make the process as predictable as possible in order to reduce any performance anxiety.

▓ Remind the child that there is no way to do EMDR right or wrong. Any way they do it is fine.

▓ Prepare your own internal state to attune and connect with the child during these profound moments of embracing the past and finding freedom from it. Take a moment to breathe and find within yourself the strength, wisdom, calmness, acceptance, and your "inner arms" or whatever you need to witness and facilitate the process of integration.

WORKING WITH CHILDREN WITH SENSITIZED SYMPATHETIC SYSTEMS

Children with complex trauma histories may already have sensitized systems that make them prone to being in fight flight mode even in the face of safety (Cozolino, 2006; Porges, 2011). When fight-flight responses have been constantly activated as a result of having memories of trauma, frequently ignited by current environmental stimuli, the "body's alarm system" remains in a constant state of activation. Consequently, during the accessing and reprocessing of traumatogenic material, these children may become easily hyperaroused, compromising the child's ability to maintain dual awareness. Children prone to moving quickly into very high levels of arousal may present with aggressiveness, severe anger outbursts, as well as children that tend to "take off" and run in the face of even minor environmental stimuli. The preparation phase for these children will provide them with suitable resources to modulate arousal appropriately. However, despite the amount of preparation, since the memories of trauma have not been yet processed, when activated during the assessment phase, these children may move out of the windows of affect tolerance. The EMDR clinician should set up reprocessing sessions carefully to optimize the child's arousal level and integrative capacity. Modulating arousal by creating greater levels of safety, containment, and connectedness can assist children in assimilating more efficiently the memories of trauma and adversity. For instance, resources that bring a greater sense of safety and calmness may be brought into the sessions before starting the assessment phase. The child may be told that he or she can bring helpers, when "visiting" the memory. A circle can be created around the child and all the helpers, real or imaginary, may be placed around the child (Shapiro, 2001; Gomez, 2008). Whether the helpers are represented with puppets, pictures, or just imagining having mom, dad, pets, angels etc., the child receives the message that he or she does not have to do this work or "visit" the memory alone. The clinician also uses the self more actively, *"I am with you all the way as we do this together. Remember you are not alone, I am with you and all your helpers."* The child may also have "advisors" ready if they are needed (see Chapter 9). As the child feels resourced, accompanied, and safe, the capacity of the child to maintain dual awareness and stay present is expanded. Once the child's physiology is modulated, a "visit" can be made to the memory of trauma or adversity.

Working With Children With Sensitized Parasympathetic Dorsal Vagal Systems

The most chronically traumatized children may present with sensitized dorsal vagal systems (Levine, 2010). The child automatically responds to even minor environmental challenges by collapsing and surrendering. As a result, when memories of trauma and hardship are accessed and activated during the assessment phase of EMDR therapy, collapse responses may arise. These are children that may tend to "live" in hypoarousal states. As a result, they may have a tendency to isolate, appear withdrawn, daydream, and dissociate. Some of these children have developed ways to adapt and to "elevate" their own arousal level. Fantasy and the creation of imaginary parallel worlds are oftentimes coping mechanisms they have used to adapt to a reality of hardship and adversity. Some others may have adapted by always "doing" instead of "being." They may constantly report feeling "bored" and needing constant entertainment. As a result, including movement and greater level of activity during the assessment phase and later on during the reprocessing sessions may help these children stay more engaged, focused, and present. Using playfulness to prepare the nervous system and motivate the child to "visit" the memories of adversity and trauma may be helpful. In addition, movement can assist them in maintaining dual awareness and staying within appropriate windows of affect tolerance. For instance, using "stations" while moving through the assessment phase can make it more playful and fun. The "station technique" consists of creating seven stations by placing seven objects, each of which represent the seven procedural steps followed during the assessment phase of EMDR therapy. Cushions or construction paper of different colors are placed on the floor. The child is told that "visiting" the memory will involve getting through seven stations. The child and the clinician start by sitting on the first cushion or near the first rectangle of construction paper. The clinician asks for the image that represents the memory. Once the child responds to the question, he or she moves to the next station where the child identifies the negative cognition. Cognition cards, balls, or cubes may be placed on the station so the child has the resources needed to identify the negative cognition. When the child moves to the third station, he or she is invited to identify the positive cognition and so forth until the assessment phase is completed. Once the child arrives to the last station and identifies where the disturbance is located in the body, desensitization phase is initiated.

TARGET SELECTION

When working with a single incident or simple PTSD, the process followed throughout the eight phases of EMDR therapy tends to be straight-forward. Basic EMDR procedures guide us to select the original event or touchstone event as the first target, followed by the worst event. However, when selecting targets for children with chronic and developmental trauma, clinicians are advised to use caution. When working with children with reduced capacity to modulate arousal, the layering or fractionation of the trauma memories may be necessary. On the other hand, keep in mind that many of these experiences of adversity and trauma were experienced at preverbal stages of development. As a result, the child may not have the cognitive recollection of these memories. However, these memories continue to be accessed and activated somatically by the current environment.

Children with reduced ability for affect regulation may need to start with targets that hold lower levels of disturbance. In addition, the clinician, in these cases, may have to bring the child to the original target more often to prevent the child from moving into other memories that hold greater emotional charge. Which means using more often EMD procedures. On the other hand, sometimes the clinician may need to start with more recent targets if the child does not connect affectively to earlier events, as oftentimes may happen with children using avoidance as a coping mechanism.

Kitchur (2005), in her Strategic Developmental Model, suggests processing first middle childhood targets (ages 4–11) before processing what she calls "first order processing" memories. These memories correspond to nonverbal and pre-verbal early experiences. Memories of middle childhood may be easily remembered by the child since they occurred when important structures in the brain needed for the development of explicit memory are already in place. The child can more easily access the different aspects of the memory, such as the cognitive, affective, and somatic elements. As a result, it may be easier for the clinician as well as the child to fully access the memory system and have a successful first experience with EMDR therapy. When working with school-age children with multiple and developmental trauma, starting with memories they can more easily verbalize and articulate may facilitate the work done in EMDR therapy. According to Kitchur (2005), "nonverbal, fragmentary early-childhood targets often involve deep somatic processing, powerful affect, and little of the cognitive or left-brain processes..." (p. 33). This, according to Kitchur, is the reason for altering the order of processing by starting with middle childhood targets followed by "first order targeting memories." When targeting very early memories, children "may be highly vulnerable and least able to verbally articulate their needs" (Kitchur, 2005, p. 33). The overall clinical landscape of the child, current level of affect tolerance, stability, etc., may need to be taken into account when deciding on the order in which memories will be reprocessed. However, the processing of deep, implicitly rooted memories, in my clinical experience, bring profound transformation to the children, adolescents, and adults who were injured early in life, usually by important attachment figures.

ACCESSING PREVERBAL TRAUMA AND ADVERSITY

Processing memories that lack the cognitive and verbal aspects due to being encoded when higher regions of the brain were underdeveloped may be challenging. The EMDR early trauma protocol (O'Shea, 2009), has provided a way of accessing and processing prenatal and perinatal trauma. It focuses on sequential time periods and the somatic sequelae of early trauma. When working with children, especially the ones with complex trauma, targeting preverbal trauma may be unavoidable. As a result, strategies that make the accessing of early memories of trauma developmentally appropriate for children are necessary. I have developed a number of strategies, some of which, are congruent with the early trauma protocol, to access preverbal experiences of trauma and adversity. The following represent potential avenues to access disturbance associated with preverbal memories and early attachment experiences.

Accessing Preverbal Memories Through Current Triggers Using Time Lines, Memory Detectors, Life Stories, Internal Satellites, and Antennas

The use of "directed float backs," "memory detectors," stories, and time lines that tap into preverbal memories can be of great assistance in finding these implicit memories (see Chapter 4 for a full description). When these memories are accessed, they may lack the cognitive component and the connection to these memories may happen through their somatic attributes. However, the emotions, bodily states, and even cognitions associated with the current eliciting stimulus may serve as an access route to the memory network. The child may be invited to create a life story; as the child explores different developmental stages, search for anything the child may know or may have heard about that time in his or her life. If the child does not report any known events connected to early stages of development, search for the emotional and somatic footprints left by these nonconscious memories. Asking for what the mind, the heart, or the body has to say about a specific time in the child's life will yield critical information. All of this data can become potential targets for processing.

Triggers are important access roads to these neural networks that remain hidden in implicit and nonconscious memory. Once the current triggers have been identified and assessed, directed float backs, time lines, and the use of the memory detector should begin with a thorough exploration of prenatal and postnatal experiences. As stated in Chapter 4, drawings of the "little me" inside mom or "belly mom" as well as drawings of different developmental stages in the child's life should be created in collaboration with the child. The current problem or trigger is accessed first and then attached to the memory detector with its associated negative cognition and emotions. An affect scan (Shapiro, 2001) can also be performed by attaching the emotions and bodily states to the memory detector instead. Even though the memory detector is an outside tool, the child is always encouraged to see it and feel it inside. The outside tool is just a representation of the real memory detector that lies in the child's heart. The child is invited to search within as the memory detector is placed on top of the drawings of each developmental stage. In addition, the child is invited to notice the current mixed-up thoughts, emotions, and/or bodily states as the search for memories is on the way. For example, a 6-year-old boy, having a strong fear of sleeping alone, identified the following negative belief: Bad things are going to happen. He expressed fear and loneliness as he thought about going to sleep in his room by himself. The parents during the initial intake stated that this child had not had any known traumatic or adverse events. He had been adopted at birth without any difficulties around the adoption process. He was invited to draw a picture of his "little me" as early in his life as possible and use the "memory detector" to find out what was happening to the little self. He started by drawing a picture of his biological mother pregnant with the "little me" inside. He stated that his "little me" was feeling safe inside his biological mom's belly. However, when he placed the memory detector by the drawing of his younger self, right after he was born, he said he was scared. He stated that his "little me" did not feel safe and thought that bad things were going to happen back then. I asked him what was making his "little me" scared and he stated that he was scared, sad, and very lonely because his mommy had left and he was alone in the hospital. The adoptive mother stated that he had not been alone at all at the hospital. However, this child's subjective perception and most likely how this memory was encoded in his brain had this deep sense of loneliness and despair. As you can see, the current trigger served as the accessing route to find the preverbal memory that was being constantly activated every night as this child had to go to sleep alone in his room.

An 8-year-old girl, Beth, diagnosed with mood disorder, presented with extreme anger outbursts and extreme episodes of sadness and crying. She reported feeling that no one loved her because she was a very bad kid. She had serious difficulties socializing at school, and despite being a very good student, she always isolated from her peers. After appropriate preparation was done, the exploration of past memories was initiated. The major trigger for this child was the mother's emotional state and the mother showing any love or nurturance toward any of her three sisters. When the triggers were explored, they all shared the same negative belief: My mom does not love me. It translated into I am a bad, unlovable kid. The mother presented with history of serious emotional problems as well as dissociation. She did not have much recollection of her daughter's second year through the fourth. She could not even find pictures of Beth from ages two to four. I encouraged her to gather information from friends and relatives to find out what had happened during those fundamental times in her daughter's life. Her friends and relatives reported that right around when her daughter turned two she went into a really deep depression, and without treatment she slept and smoked all day. Her neighbor reported that she had helped her care for her child at times. When Beth turned four, the mother was able to start psychiatric treatment and was put on psychotropic medication. The mother reported a lifetime struggle with extreme emotion dysregulation and a past full of trauma and hardship. However, the mother's depression and emotional problems when Beth was only two was never brought up or discussed with Beth or during the initial therapy intake. This child was invited to write the book of her life titled, *The Hero in Me*. She started her book when she was in her mother's womb. With the triggers in mind, and the mixed-up thoughts and feelings she had identified in prior sessions, she was encouraged to search through her book and find when these thoughts and feelings had been born. Beth was encouraged to tune in her "inside compass or satellite" while searching through her story. She stated that she did not have such feelings or thoughts when she was in her mom's belly, or when she was just born. I invited her to look closely to the inside compass in her heart and gut and see when the yucky stuff had started. By inviting her to connect with her body when these memories were explored, I was searching for the input from the right brain. She pointed to age two as the time when these feelings and thoughts had been born. She did not have any images of what had happened, just a feeling in her heart. I was extremely touched by this child's ability to find the exact time when her mother completely disconnected from her and her heart. Other memories were also accessed about her mother yelling or rejecting her, which in turn became targets for reprocessing. The mother created a story of what had happened when Beth was two years of age. The story was told to Beth as an interweave during the reprocessing of this memory. This case will be further discussed in the next chapter.

TARGETING ATTACHMENT BEHAVIORS

Current attachment and caregiving behaviors can give us a window into the attachment system. Identifying early wounding attachment experiences that remain so deeply ingrained in implicit memory could be an arduous task. Avoidance, preoccupation, and disorganization around attachment-related experiences are usually not consciously available to the child or the parent(s). The exploring and the accessing of these memories of attachment may start with the present eliciting stimuli that activates the attachment system.

Working With Children With Avoidant Strategies

Current caregiving and attachment behaviors have the potential for activating the attachment system, and with it past dysfunctional attachment experiences. For children with avoidant attachment patterns toward their parents, detachment and dismissal of attachment needs have been the primary mechanism of adaptation. In order to protect themselves from the pain of not having parents that are able and willing to meet their needs for love and connection, these children have used avoidance and detachment for survival. For these children, eye contact, physical contact, and shared positive interactive experiences with caregivers and others can potentially activate negative affect and emotional pain. A simple eye-to-eye contact with the parent can make these children uncomfortable as it taps into the painful implicit memories of attachment. Remember that these are the children that had or have parents that encouraged early independence and self-sufficiency; parents that, in the face of these children experiencing physical and emotional pain, told them to get a grip and toughen up. When we work with these children we are working with an attachment system that may be shut down or deactivated (Main, 1995; Siegel, 2010). The Adult Attachment Interview (AAI) developed in 1984 by Carol George, Nancy Kaplan, and Mary Main, has given us a window into the mind of adults with insecure states of mind. Some of the AAI findings can be extrapolated to how the minds of school age and older children may function as a result of their early attachment experiences. Sometimes children with avoidant patterns may have great difficulty remembering any attachment related and/or negative events from the past. Even when doing directed float backs and affect scans, they may report lack of memories. This tends to be distinctive of adults with dismissing states of mind with regards to attachment and may also be seen in avoidant children. In addition, to the lack of memories, idealization of the caregivers may be present. They tend to report having perfect and great early and current experiences, but fail to provide any supporting facts or specific memories. These children usually inform in therapy that everything is fine despite how symptomatic they are based on reports from parents and teachers. In the absence of memories of past attachment experiences that may be laying at the core of current symptoms, attachment behaviors can be targeted. Needless to say, the processing of attachment behaviors may be counterproductive if the parent continues to reinforce avoidance and dismissal of connection. The work with the caregiver should precede the targeting of attachment behaviors and memories for best treatment outcome.

When working with children with avoidant patterns of attachment, a hierarchy of caregiving and attachment behaviors can be developed. Starting from the ones that are more tolerable and followed by the ones that activate the highest levels of disturbance may be appropriate. The following are examples of attachment behaviors that could be targeted:

- Eye contact with a caregiver. Be aware that one caregiver may trigger more disturbance than the other.
- A distant hug.
- A very close hug.

- A compliment.
- An expression of love with or without eye contact.
- Sitting on the parent's lap.
- Feeding the child, even for an older child.
- Nurturing activities such as face painting, nail painting, and in general, receiving loving care.
- Playful activities such as catching bubbles with the caregiver.

Once a hierarchy has been created, follow assessment, desensitization, installation, and body scan procedures with each attachment behavior. However, if the parent is still rejecting and neglecting of the child's need for connection, targeting attachment behaviors is not recommended. Moreover, be aware that if the parent has not received some level of treatment (see Chapter 5 for strategies for working with parents) these targets can also be activating for the parent. Keep in mind that, most likely, the avoidant strategies of this child were developed in response to the parent's caregiving behaviors. Sometimes the targeting of attachment behaviors may begin without the parent being present in the session. In this case, you could use pictures of the parent or you may ask the child to imagine looking at the parent's eyes or sitting on his or her lap. Later on, the parent may be invited to provide a more tangible experience. If the targeting of attachment behaviors is not considered appropriate for the child, targeting recent events may be a usual starting point in children with avoidant attachment patterns. As a result of the lack of memories or the inability to connect affectively with past experiences, starting with recent and even future events may be necessary. Sometimes, children that have used avoidance as the main strategy to deal with the lack of connection from their caregivers may report remembering some past memories of adversity. However, oftentimes they may not be able to connect affectively with these memories. According to Porges (2011), primary emotions have a right hemisphere bias. Children with avoidant patterns of attachment are learning to heavily rely on left hemisphere processes, as a way of dealing with painful emotions connected to attachment experiences (Siegel, 2010). Their left hemispheres may tend to dominate, as a result, they may tend to speak in a very emotionally detached manner. Even when potential unresolved and painful memories are accessed, oftentimes these children will again report great difficulty relating to the emotional and somatic aspects of these memories. They may state that these events do not bother them any more and there is no point in working on them. Great deal of preparation should be done with this population in helping them awaken right hemisphere processes. A number of strategies are listed in prior chapters that are directed at accomplishing this goal.

Working With Children With Ambivalent Strategies

On the other hand, children with anxious-ambivalent patterns of attachment may actually recall many past memories, but when they remember them the level of activation may be so high that they are scared of talking and remembering these memories. These children present with overactivated attachment systems (Main, 1995; Siegel, 1999). They tend to be clingy and feel like the attention received from the caregiver is never enough. Role reversing, emotional entanglement, and diffused boundaries are usually present in the relationship with their current or past caregivers. For these children, separation from the caregiver may be a source of great anxiety. Witnessing the parent give attention, gifts, or compliments to a sibling is a source of disturbance. These children, as opposed to the children with avoidant patterns of attachment, may have an overactive right hemisphere as it is observed in adults with preoccupied states of mind (Siegel, 2010). These children may be flooded with affect; as a result, extensive preparation to help them modulate affect more efficiently will be necessary. Helping the left hemisphere soothe the right hemisphere and promote horizontal integration and balance will be an important goal during early phases of EMDR therapy. Furthermore, working with the caregiver will be critical in helping these children achieve balance and integration. Some targets and triggers that are of extreme importance for these children may remain buried in nonconscious implicit memory. As a result, neither the child nor the parent will report this information during the initial therapy intake. Consequently, EMDR clinicians are left thinking that adversity may not be present in the child's life since targets cannot be found. For children with anxious features stemming from attachment experiences with the caregiver, the parent's emotional states and facial expressions may be powerful activating stimuli. Remember that these children have been overwhelmed by the parents' affect and, without clear individuation and boundaries with the parent, the child's internal states are constantly affected by the parent's emotional states. The parent's inconsistencies and overwhelming affect were the wounding agents that may lie at the core of the child's current anxiety and symptoms. Potential targets for these children are the parent's emotional states, voice, facial expressions of disapproval, frustration, etc. Asking the child about the mixed-up thoughts, emotions, and somatic responses when the parent is upset, sad, or angry may yield relevant targets for processing. Asking for pictures of the caregiver or drawing pictures of the different facial expressions of the caregiver may greatly enhance the experience. Needless to say, this is only done after the parent has arrived at a clear understanding of his or her own states of mind and how they have affected the child. In addition, the caregiver should also be receiving EMDR therapy. The parent's pictures can serve as a springboard to explore other attachment experiences in the past. You may use a time line, memory detector, or a story in combination with the exploration of the memory network through the current eliciting stimuli (parent's emotional states and nonverbal expressions). Invite the child to draw pictures of the parent's feeling faces. Ask the child to notice what happens as he or she looks at the picture of the parent's face. If the child reports negative reactions or feelings when looking at the pictures, invite the child to explore the experience. Ask the child to identify mixed-up thoughts, feelings, and bodily states associated with the picture of the parent's face. Invite the child to identify moments or events where the parent exhibited the emotions being explored. If the child is able to identify a specific event, then the picture of the event along with the parent's facial expression could be used as the target. If greater distance is needed, a facial expression of "a person" that is mad, frustrated, or sad, etc., may be the target.

Children With Disorganized Strategies

A third category is children with disorganized attachment. These children most likely have been exposed to frightened or frightening caregiving behaviors. In addition, their interactions with current or past caregivers have been marked by asynchrony, dysregulation, and lack of sensitivity and most likely have been left to experience prolonged states of high or low arousal (Schore, 2009). As with children with avoidant and ambivalent attachment patterns, targets may be found within the parent-child interactions. Oftentimes, current triggers with this population may be targeted first before tapping deeply into the attachment system. Processing early frightening attachment experiences may be too overwhelming initially for the child even after extensive preparation work. Needless to say, the parents of children with disorganized patterns of attachment should also receive full EMDR therapy. Moreover, these children may be more prone to exhibiting dissociative responses and, as a result, extensive preparation around dissociation will be necessary along with comprehensive work with the family system. In addition, the layering and titration of the reprocessing of disturbing memories most likely will be required.

THE "HEART JAR" AS A TARGET

The heart jar exercise described thoroughly in Chapter 5 may be an access route to the memory systems containing injurious attachment experiences and, in some cases, it may be a target itself. A hierarchy may be created with the different attachment behaviors that are activated during the heart jar exercise: Eye contact, physical contact, receiving compliments, and giving compliments. They each may be targeted separately and the order will depend on the affect tolerance of the child. When the child has a good enough ability to tolerate affective states, the attachment behavior eliciting the highest level of disturbance may be targeted. However, children with limited capacities to modulate affect should start with the attachment behavior that is the least activating.

TARGETING DEVELOPMENTAL STAGES

When early traumatic events are not remembered explicitly by the child, different developmental stages and times in the child's life may be targeted (Gomez, 2009b, 2010a; Kitchur, 2005; O'Shea, 2009). The child may be encouraged with the assistance of the clinician to create a time line. As stated previously, the first time line may be dedicated to finding "acts of triumph" and for the child to receive "medals." Mastery experiences and resources may be mapped and enhanced with BLS before exploring the negative events with highly dysregulated children. Using pictures (Kitchur, 2005; Gomez, 2008) may facilitate the process of accessing positive and negative experiences. Each developmental stage, especially after the age of 3 or 4, may contain "mixed-up" thoughts, feelings, and bodily states. Even though the event occurred when the brain's capacity to move information into explicit memory was not developed yet, we are assessing how the child responds now when he or she is thinking about a certain developmental stage. We are looking at how the child has come to organize this experience, cognitively, somatically and emotionally in the here and now. Even though when the memory was initially encoded, the cognitive aspects were not present, some children may have come to develop a "meta-perception" of this experience. For some others, the experience may still remain somatically and implicitly encoded. According to Siegel (2012), each time a memory is retrieved, it is transformed. New experiences that activate similar patterns of neural firing may have added, enhanced or changed the information originally encoded in a specific memory system. With this in mind, we should start by assessing the aspects of the memory that the child is able to access, and creating a baseline with this information. *"As you look at the picture when you were four, let's see if you have a 'mixed-up thought' about yourself that goes with that time in your life."* If the child is unable to find a cognition, access the affect by asking the child for the feelings associated with that time in his or her life, get the SUDs and the location in the body. Once again, we are encouraging the child to listen to the different languages we speak: The language of the mind, which speak with thoughts and words; the language of the heart, which speaks through feelings; and the language of the body, which speaks through sensations and movement. The child is then encouraged to just look at the real picture or the picture that he or she created of a specific developmental stage or time period, the feelings associated with it and where they are experienced in the body and engage in BLS. We invite the child to closely listen to what the mind, the heart, and the body are saying and notice it. See Chapter 11 for the use of somatic interventions within EMDR therapy with children. As reviewed previously in this chapter, the child may start with the time when he or she was "inside mom's belly." The child is first invited to explore anything he or she knows about this time in his or her life. Whatever is disclosed that may be negative becomes a target. However, if the child does not have any explicit recollections or memories, just thinking about a time or age in the child's life may bring negative thoughts, affects, and bodily states that can be targeted with standard procedural steps. Once again, the developmental stage or age may be the target. The child is invited to bring or draw a picture of that age. However, if the child is unable to identify cognitions, during the assessment phase, the emotions, SUDs, and location in the body may be accessed. The lack of a negative belief may be an occurrence when targeting preverbal memories, as these memories were encoded when important brain structures needed for explicit encoding were not fully developed. During the reprocessing of developmental stages, more specific memories may surface that can be reprocessed later on.

WORKING WITHIN WINDOWS OF AFFECT TOLERANCE

Working with children with good affect tolerance may not require the active intervention of the clinician as the memories of adversity are accessed. However, children with complex trauma and low affect tolerance usually require greater levels of participation from the clinician. The EMDR clinician may have to work on modulating and decreasing the intensity of arousal, as well as restricting the neuronal networks activated during the assessment and reprocessing phases. The following are strategies that can serve the goal of restricting and titrating the amount of disturbing material accessed during the assessment phase:

Diagramming and Outlining the Memory: Finding the Lost Treasure

One of the assessment phase procedural steps is the identification of the image that represents the worst part of the memory. An advanced adaptation for complex trauma cases may be to start by accessing the image that represents the least disturbing part of the memory. This is a playful strategy that allows children to access and process the entire memory while staying in playful states. This by itself has the potential for reducing the level of arousal experienced by the child as the memory is activated. The child may be invited to think about the memory in three different colors: Green, yellow, and red. Outlining the memory with these three colors that represent different levels of intensity and charge will yield the parts of the memory that are more tolerable. The memory can be outlined using drawings or narratives. The child may be invited to draw the sequence of events using green, yellow, and red paper. The child may also write the story using small cards of the three different colors. Each part of the memory will have a color that represents the level of disturbance, from light green to medium-yellow to high-red. Start with the green area of the memory and ask for the image that represents the green area. A full assessment is executed by identifying the negative cognition, positive cognition, VoC, emotions, SUDs, and location in the body. The goal of the first part of this game is to get to the lost treasure: The positive cognition. During the desensitization phase, the clinician may have to bring the child back to the image more often to prevent the child from going into red areas that are highly charged by disturbance. The child may identify one or several green areas, as the level of disturbance associated with the first green area reaches a zero level of disturbance, the access to the next green area is granted. If more than one green area has been identified, place them in chronological order. Once all the green areas have reached a zero SUD, the yellow areas are unlocked while preventing access to red areas. The clinician may gently invite the child to visit the yellow areas, *"Now, that you have unlocked the yellow areas, how yucky, from zero to ten, does it feel now, as you notice the first yellow parts of this memory?"* Every time the child reports access to a red-high disturbance area, the child is once again invited to go back to the yellow area. Once disturbances associated with yellow areas reach a SUDs of zero, the clinician and the child may move to the red areas. Once all the areas have reached SUDs of zero, the installation phase and body scan should be completed. This strategy can turn into a fun game where the SUDs of 0 become the key to unlock the next area. A maze can be sketched once the different areas of the memory have been outlined. The parts identified as "green" are sketched with doors to the yellow areas and the parts identified as "yellow" are sketched with doors to the red areas. A fun name could be given to this strategy such as, "in search of the lost treasure" or "the story of (name of the child) and the lost treasure." The treasure is the positive cognition. The positive cognition then is placed at the end of the game, and once it is found (once all the red areas have reached a SUDs of zero) the installation phase and body scan are performed.

Layering the Memory

Similar to the recent event protocol, the memory can be layered into smaller scenes. Initially, the memory is layered starting from the time right before the traumatic incident happened until the moment that marked the end of the event. Breaking the memory into small scenes may make the amount of disturbing material more manageable for the child. Introduce playfulness by asking the child to be a movie director and create different movie scenes starting from right before the adverse or traumatic event occurred. Some children may enjoy wearing an actual "director's hat." This hat should only be worn when working on a specific memory.

Scene #1	Scene #2	Scene #3	Scene #4

Create a narrative of the memory, or ask the child to draw separate scenes on different sheets of paper. The child may also choose to create a puppet show for each scene. Once the entire narrative of the total memory has been created, as it is done in the recent event protocol (Shapiro, 2001), start with the image of the first sign the child received that something "yucky" was about to happen. Once the scene is delineated, do full assessment, desensitization, and installation for that part of the memory. Continue in chronological order with each scene until they each achieve a SUDs of zero and a VoC of seven. Once all the scenes have been addressed with full assessment, desensitization, and installation, identify the SUDs of the entire memory. If the SUDs are higher than zero, continue to invite the child to think about the complete memory until the SUDs reach a zero level of disturbance. Then, follow with a full installation of the positive cognition with the entire memory following basic EMDR installation procedures. Next, invite the child to do a body scan of the entire memory. Ask the child to think about the complete memory while using the "feeling finder" or "detector" or to just scan the body from head to toe. Body scan procedures should be followed. One of the differences with the recent event protocol is that the worst part of the memory is not accessed first. Instead, the peripheral scenes right before the event become the initial target. The reprocessing of all the other scenes in chronological order should be done thereafter. These peripheral scenes tend to be less activating and, as a result, easy to reprocess first for children with greater difficulties in affect regulation. Despite all the steps that need to be followed by the clinician to reprocess a highly activating memory, when it is well done, the process should flow for the child. This is like a dance choreography, that despite all the pieces and technicalities the professional dancer had to practice and incorporate into the entire dance routine, the public will see it and feel it as a whole masterpiece. If the clinician does not have any of the EMDR procedures and protocols well integrated, the child or the client of any age may have a choppy and fragmented processing experience.

THE EMDR KIT FOR KIDS

This kit has been well known by EMDR clinicians as it is showed in one of the videos used during the basic EMDR training in the US. The new kit consists of a box with six drawers on one side and two drawers on the other side. The original kit only had three drawers on one side and one on the other side (see Figure 8.1). I developed this kit with the goal in mind of making EMDR therapy procedures developmentally appropriate for children as well as appealing, concrete, tangible, and, as a result, safe. The following are some of the benefits the "EMDR Kit for Kids" offers to children undergoing EMDR treatment.

- It provides a playful way of introducing EMDR therapy.
- It provides visual cues to guide children during the assessment phase and reprocessing phases of EMDR therapy.
- It provides tools for children to play during the preparation phase, while developing emotional, cognitive, and sensory literacy.
- It contains, in a very tangible way, the same sequence of the assessment phase, which facilitates the identification of the negative cognition (NC), positive cognition (PC), VoC feelings, SUDs and location in the body when targeting a memory.
- It makes EMDR more appealing, familiar, predictable, and safe for the child.

Figure 8.1 The original EMDR kit for kids with four drawers.

The six drawers contain each of the procedural steps of the assessment phase of EMDR therapy and are organized as follows:

1. The first drawer contains all the illustrated negative cognition cards.
2. The second drawer contains all the illustrated positive cognition cards.
3. The third drawer contains a small foam puzzle numbered from one to seven that can be assembled to form the "thought scale." It also has small figures of children of different racial backgrounds. You could use animals instead that can "walk" on the "thought scale."
4. The fourth drawer contains illustrated cards with a wide variety of feeling faces.
5. The fifth drawer contains foam numbers from zero to ten to form the "bothering scale." It also includes, a few figures of animals or children of different ethnic and racial backgrounds that can "walk" on the "bothering scale."
6. The sixth drawer contains "the feeling finder" or "detector," which is represented by a magnifying glass.
7. The two drawers on the right side of the box contain the puppets introduced to the child as the "EMDR helpers," as well as the cubes with cognitions, emotions, and sensations. The first drawer is labeled as "EMDR helpers" and the second as "EMDR games."

Having all the procedural steps available to the child in such a tangible way makes the accessing of the memory network easier and less overwhelming for the child.

THE EMDR TEAM

The EMDR team is based on the same ideas of the EMDR kit for kids. In order to build the EMDR team, Russian dolls are needed (Figure 8.2). These dolls come in different sizes and are stored inside each other. You will need six dolls, so each procedural step of the assessment phase can be placed inside each doll. Names are given to each doll, for example: Emma will contain small cards with negative cognitions appropriate for children. Marques will have all the cards with the positive cognitions, and Dora will have numbers from 0 to

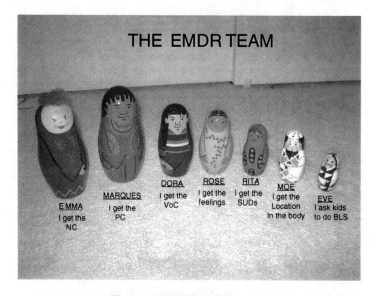

Figure 8.2 The EMDR team.

7 and instructions for using the "thought scale." Rose will have cards with feeling faces; Rita will have the numbers from 0 to 10 and instructions for using "the bothering scale." Last, Moe will have instructions for using "the feeling finder" and finding the location in the body. During the assessment phase, the child is invited to look inside each doll and find out the task or question each doll holds. When accessing the memory during the assessment phase, the child is invited to open up each doll and find the message and questions inside each. As the child opens up the first doll, the clinician encourages the child to find the mixed-up thought that is associated with the memory that is being accessed. Once the thought is found, the child is invited to open the next doll, and the next, until the baseline of the memory is completed and with it the assessment phase. The EMDR team can also be used with the "stations" exercise covered earlier in this chapter (see also Chapter 9). Each team member is placed at one of the 7 stations. These stations are represented by cushions or other objects. The child is then invited to visit each station and its own team member until the assessment phase is complete. In my clinical experience, once the first memory has been reprocessed successfully and the child is familiarized with EMDR methodology and procedures, the child tends to take agency and ownership of the process. Many children carry the lead in moving through the assessment phase steps by using the kit for kids or the EMDR team. They will know what comes next and may open the drawers or the dolls with minimal direction from the clinician. As a result, the child will experience a greater sense of control and ownership of his or her own healing process. Nevertheless, the child is at all times supported and accompanied through the process. Having agency, control, and ownership does not mean being lonely in the process. On the contrary, as the memory is explored, accessed, and moved to adaptive resolution, healing happens while held and supported in the gentle power of connection with the caregiver and the clinician.

The EMDR kit for kids and the EMDR team make the assessment phase fun, playful, predictable, and tangible for the child. They highly facilitate the process of following the assessment phase procedural steps. These games can introduce a playful element to what otherwise may be a difficult and abstract process for children.

USING EMDR THERAPY AND SANDTRAY THERAPY

One of the best adjunct approaches that can be used within a comprehensive EMDR treatment is sandtray therapy. According to Homeyer and Sweeney (2011), "Sandtray therapy gives expression to nonverbalized emotional issues. Since play is the language of childhood, as well as a language for a client of any age who is unable or unwilling to verbalize, the sandtray provides a safe medium for expression. If play is the language, then the miniatures are the words." (p. 8). Due to the symbolic nature of sandtray work, it is one of the forms of treatment that offers various levels of distance and a gentle access route to the "implicit" self and the right hemisphere. Accessing memories that remain buried in nonconscious implicit memory could be challenging, as they may not be available during intake or regular interviews with the parents and the child. Deep-rooted attachment experiences such as neglect, role reversing, and emotional unavailability, among others may rarely be openly expressed by the caregivers or the child. In addition, the use of symbols and figures utilized in sandtray work allow the distance children oftentimes need to explore experiences that may be otherwise overwhelming (see Figure 8.3). It also allows for the easy accessing of early and preverbal memories of trauma and adversity. Highly traumatized and dysregulated children may start at a great distance from the memory by creating a story or a world in a nondirective way. A child may also create a story representing a difficulty, annoyance,

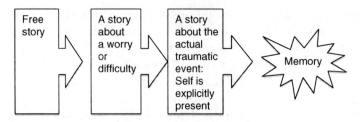

Figure 8.3 Levels of distance from the traumatic or adverse event using sandtray
therapy within a comprehensive EMDR treatment.

or something they worry about in the present, or a child may actually create in the
sandtray the story of what happened during the traumatic or adverse event.

The stories created by the child in the sandtray may be great targets, especially
when the child, despite extensive preparation, still finds the accessing of trauma memories overwhelming. On the other hand, children who had adapted by using avoidant
strategies may be able through the sandtray to slowly embrace the painful experiences
that remain implicitly encoded and that they have worked so hard to detach from.
Especially in children with avoidant strategies, the initial stories they present in the
sandtray may tend to be superficial and very much influenced by the leftbrain. According to Badenoch (2008), "a person suffering with an avoidant attachment may create a
tray that is almost entirely a product of left-brain processes." (p. 225). Many therapists
get discouraged, as they see this as the child NOT doing any therapeutic work. Many
times, once EMDR work is initiated, the mechanisms of adaptation used by the child
will come to the surface as they are also ingrained in the memory networks. On the
other hand, children with ambivalent strategies come with highly dysregulated affective systems. Sandtray therapy work can help them access memories of hardship in a
titrated way without causing the child to feel flooded with affect.

It is important to highlight that it is fundamental to have an appropriate selection
of sandtray figures. "A random collection of sandtray miniatures is not appropriate;
an intentional and deliberate selection is. A client may be confused by a disorganized
collection, emotionally flooded by an unlimited collection, or confined by a limited
collection." (Homeyer & Sweeney, 2011, p. 3). The following represent different levels
of distance that sandtray therapy work may offer to children in EMDR therapy.

1. **Free story:** When the child, regardless of having extensive resources, is still objecting
   to the reprocessing of trauma memories, free stories can still capture the inner conflicts of the child proving the greatest level of distance. In this case, the child is invited
   to pick the sandtray figures that they feel a "call" for without too much thinking. "The
   sand player is assembling a largely right-brained narrative, often based in implicit,
   previously nonconcious themes." (Badenoch, 2008, p. 223). Once the figures are
   picked, the child is invited to create a story or a "world." Time is allotted for the child
   to look at the story and have a "felt sense of completion." Does the story feel complete
   to the child or he or she needs to add or omit something? Once the child has created
   the story, he or she is invited to tell the story. According to Badenoch (2008), talking
   about the story created in the sandtray can help promote connection between right
   and left brain by bringing words to the experience and a story that developed nonverbally. The EMDR clinician may start by inviting the child to tell the story and later on
   asking about general feelings and the affective experience imprinted in the sandtray
   world. The clinician may also ask questions about who the main character is and if

the child is part of the story. The assessment phase with its procedural steps will be done with the main character of the story or the child if he or she is part of the story. However, to create a greater level of distance if the child has chosen a "monkey" to represent himself or herself, then all the questions are asked to the "monkey." For instance, *"I wonder what is the part of the story that stands out or the yuckiest part of the story for the monkey?"* The child may also be invited to be the voice or the translator for the main character. The negative and positive beliefs as well as the other aspects of the assessment phase are directed to the main character. Noa, a 9-year-old girl in foster care, was exhibiting symptoms of depression, having anger outbursts and sexualized behaviors. She grew up with both parents and witnessed severe domestic violence as her father brutally abused her mother. Noa created a story of a Piggy living in a farm with other farm animals. There was a "really bad farmer" that treated all the other animals "really bad." Noa states that the main character, the piggy, was angry and wanted to help the other animals but was fearful of the farmer. Noa denied being part of the story but through the "piggy" she accessed important aspects of the memory networks containing disturbing material. The next chapters will address the work with sandtray during desensitization and other reprocessing phases.

2. **A story about a current worry or difficulty:** The child may object to addressing actual traumatic events and, despite extensive preparation, he or she may still not be ready to fully embrace the memory system containing the adverse event. However, the child may be open to address a current worry or difficulty. This may be a current trigger or eliciting environmental stimuli that still holds connection to the neural network. The child is invited to create a story or a "sandtray picture" of his or her family. This approach may be very valuable when the injuring agents are in the family system and family dynamics. The child is asked to pick miniatures that represent each member of the family and create a story or a world with all the family members. In this story, "the self" is part of the story; however, it is represented by a figure. In order to create distance, once the story has been completed, the child's left-brain is invited to support the emergence of a coherent narrative (Badenoch, 2011) and integration of memory systems. First, invite the child to observe the complete sandtray so "the entire scene can be visually perceived as a single unit" (Homeyer & Sweeney, 2011, p. 40). Then, the child is invited to describe the story. Once again, the main character is identified and the procedural steps of the assessment phase of EMDR therapy are done with the main character. Another approach that may be used is to ask the child to be an observer of the story and ask the child to look at the story from his or her perspective to identify the part of the story or world that stands out for him or her as the "yuckiest part." *"As you look at this story or world, what mixed up thoughts do you have about yourself now?"* or, *"What mixed-up thoughts does the 'horsey' or 'the boy' in the story have about himself now, as he looks at this part of the story? What is the good thought 'the horsey' or 'the boy' would like to have about himself as he looks at this part of the story?"* All the other procedural steps of the assessment phase may be done with the character representing the child in the story.

3. **A story about the actual traumatic event: Self is explicitly present:** If the child is ready to fully access the memory and have "the self" be an active participant, the child may be invited to actually create in the sandtray the story of the traumatic or adverse event. At this level the child may choose to create distance by using animals instead of human figures. The EMDR clinician may ask the main character again all the customary questions during the assessment phase. The child has already identified the main character as a figure representing him or her. Highly traumatized children may work for a while during reprocessing sessions with "free stories" and then move to "stories

about worries in the present" and later on they can finally fully embrace the memory either in the sandtray or using other means such as drawings. It is important to notice that the same memory systems are being accessed in the free story as well as the story of the actual traumatic event. However, by starting with a free story, the child is able to enter the memory net from the "back door" in a titrated manner. As the memory is slowly integrated, the level of disturbance is reduced, allowing the child to each time move into new memory channels and greater levels of assimilation. The accessing and reprocessing of the memory is done progressively and in layers so the transition from implicit memory to the emergence of explicit autobiographical memory is done without causing further dysregulation to the child's system.

ASSESSMENT PHASE SCRIPT

The following is an example of how the assessment phase may be scripted for children. Language modifications may be needed depending on the target selected.

"Today we are going to start helping your brain digest and chew up some of the yucky things that happened to you. We are going to be working on helping your brain put together all the pieces and organize the files that have that difficult thing that happened to you. While we are doing EMDR, I will ask you to pay attention to what your mind, your heart, or your body is telling you. I will be asking you things like, what happened? What do you notice? I would like you to let me know of any thoughts you may have, any feelings, anything that you may see in your mind or anything that you may feel in your body. There is no right or wrong way to do EMDR, any way you do it is fine; just let your brain do the work. Remember that if you start to have mixed-up feelings or thoughts, or if you start to have uncomfortable feelings in your body, it's the brain's signal saying, 'Hey it's me chewing up the mixed-up stuff. I am just putting all the pieces together and organizing these files.' If it gets way too hard, remember that you can use your stop signal. Let's practice your stop signal. Good job!"

When working with dissociative children, you may want to remind them to use the "dissociation kit for kids." You may say, *"I will also have the Dissociation Kit for Kids', which we have played with before. We will be using the signs in, out, and half and half if we need them, or the dissociation puppet or fan. These things will help you stay present here and now and not go away as we work on organizing this memory. If you start to go away, you do not hear my voice as much, or you start to feel me and see me really far, just let me know by using the signs or just use your stop signal."* Repeat some of the dissociative experiences the child reported during the initial phases of EMDR therapy and ask him or her to let you know if and when these experiences come up.

Select the helper the child would like to have provide BLS (Elizabeth, Mario, David, or Robbie).

"Which EMDR helper would you like to have today?" If the child does not want eye movement, identify the type of BLS preferred by the child. Select the memory that will be reprocessed from the targeting sequence previously developed with the child and the caregiver.

Say to the child, *"You have told me about some of the yucky things that happened to you. Now we are going to pick the one thing your brain will be chewing up, digesting, and organizing today."* If the child created a "memory box" or a "memory wand," have them available to select the target.

You may say, *"How about if we start with that yucky thing that happened when you were* (state age or time reference)" If the child agrees, move forward with the assessment phase. If the child is hesitant to work on this memory, identify and explore where the hesitancy comes from. The child may need specific resources to "visit" this memory.

Explore if there is another memory the child is more willing to address and explore what makes "visiting" this memory easier for the child.

1. **Image:**

    First option: *"What is the image, part or picture that stands out about the yucky thing that happened to you? Let's draw a picture of this image."*

    Second option: *"What is the image or picture of the easiest part of this yucky thing that happened to you? Let's draw a picture of the easiest part of this memory."*

    Third option: *"What is the image or picture of the worst part of this yucky thing that happened to you? Let's draw a picture of the part that is the hardest for you."*

2. **Negative Cognition (NC):**

    "When you think about (repeat the image that represents the memory or show the drawing), *what mixed-up or negative thought do you have about yourself now?"* Or, *"What is the mixed-up or negative thought about yourself that goes with* (repeat the image that represents the memory or show the drawing)? *You can look at the mixed-up or negative thoughts cards, ball, or cubes and find the mixed-up or negative thought that you have."*

3. **Positive Cognition (PC):**

    "When you think about (repeat the image that represents the memory or show the drawing), *what is the good or positive thought that you would like to have about yourself now?"* You can look at the cards, ball, or cubes and find the good or positive thought that you would like to have."*

4. **VoC (The "Thought Scale"—Validity of the Positive Cognition):** Use the "Thought Scale" and put the foam numbers from 1 to 7 in front of the child (see diagram below). Give the child the helper or a small doll that can walk on the Thought Scale. Place the card with the PC by the number 7 and say:

    ☺
    | 1 | 2 | 3 | 4 | 5 | 6 | 7 | PC |

    "Now we are going to use this cool thing called the Thought Scale. The Thought Scale helps kids check how true the good thought feels to them. Let me show you how it works. The Thought Scale has numbers that go from 1 to 7. The number 1 means that the good thought does not FEEL true and the number 7 means that it FEELS really true. Now, let's practice using the Thought Scale with the good thought that you picked. When you think about (repeat the image that represents the memory or show the drawing), *how true do those words* (repeat the PC) *feel to you now? Remember that 1 feels completely false and 7 feels completely true."* Allow the child to 'walk' the doll or helper on the Thought Scale until he or she can provide the VoC.

5. **Emotions:**

    You may say: *"When you think about* (repeat the image that represents the memory or show the drawing), *and the words* (repeat the NC) *what feelings do you have now?"*

6. **SUDs—The "Bothering Scale"—Subjective Units of Disturbance:**

    Using the Bothering Scale, put the foam numbers from 0 to 10 in front of the child (see diagram below). Give the child the helper or a small doll that can walk on the Bothering Scale.

    ☺
    | 0 | 1 | 2 | 3 | 4 | 5 | 6 | 7 | 8 | 9 | 10 |

"Now we are going to use this cool thing called the Bothering Scale. The Bothering Scale helps kids check how much things bother them or make them feel bad. Let me show you how it works. The Bothering Scale has numbers that go from 0 to 10. The number 0 means that it does not bother you or that it feels neutral, and the number 10 means that it bothers you a lot. Now, let's practice using the Bothering Scale with the yucky thing that happened to you. When you think about (repeat the image that represents the memory or show the drawing) *and the mixed-up thought* (repeat the NC), *how much does it bother you now or how bad does it feel now? Remember that 0 means it is neutral and 10 means it bothers you a lot."* Allow the child to 'walk' the doll or helper on the Bothering Scale until he or she can provide the level of disturbance.

7. **Location in Body Sensation:**

   Have the "feeling finder" or "feeling detector" available. Remember that the child has already been acquainted with these procedures during the preparation phase, so finding the location in the body may be easy at this point.

   "Now you can use the 'feeling finder' and find where you feel it in your body." Or, *"Where do you feel it inside?"*

   "I would like you to think about (repeat the image that represents the memory or show the drawing), *the mixed-up or negative thought (repeat the NC), and the feelings and where you feel it in your body and follow the helper* (repeat the helper's name or use the BLS selected by the child)." Begin desensitization.

SUMMARY AND CONCLUSIONS

The assessment phase of EMDR therapy represents a crucial moment for the child and the clinician. At this point, sufficient preparation with the child and the parents has been attained and reprocessing of traumatogenic material is appropriate. However, complex trauma cases most likely will require a more active participation of the clinician to maintain the child within appropriate levels of arousal and affect tolerance. Since more is not better for individuals with restricted regulatory capacities, limiting the amount of disturbing information and neuronal networks children access at any given point may be necessary. Several strategies to limit the networks activated during reprocessing are described in this chapter. Some of these strategies are: Selecting targets initially that hold low disturbance, selecting recent events instead of the touchstone event, and using fractionating and layering strategies. Having the child practice and experience EMDR therapy first, with events that hold a manageable level of disturbance, may be appropriate for this population. However, I would like to highlight the importance of eventually targeting all the early events, as early as possible for best treatment outcome. Once the child has practiced and was successful with less activating events, move to the early and more disturbing memories. Nevertheless, some complexly traumatized children show great levels of resiliency. As a result, they may be able to dive into trauma processing faster than we would expect. A clear and thorough initial clinical landscape can guide clinical practice and the appropriate pace of treatment for each individual child. Playfulness and fun strategies should be incorporated into the assessment phase. The EMDR kit for kids and the EMDR team can make the procedural steps of the assessment phase easy to follow. They also make the process of accessing networks containing information of trauma and adversity more appealing, tangible, concrete, and playful for children.

9

Phase Four: Desensitization

This is a complex and important phase of eye movement desensitization and repro- cessing (EMDR) therapy. Even though during the preparation phase some level of integration of the disturbing material has already taken place, more rapid processing happens during the desensitization phase and other reprocessing phases of EMDR therapy. When working with children that can tolerate affect and can remain contained while accessing and processing disturbing material, the desensitization phase may be a rather straight-forward process. In addition, it may require minimal intervention from the clinician. However, when working with children with pervasive dysregula- tion of the affective system, the desensitization phase may be in fact more complex and convoluted. These children will indeed require higher levels of attunement, emotional resonance, and mindfulness on the part of the clinician. Advanced strategies to main- tain children within manageable levels of arousal and activation will be needed as the trauma memories are accessed and moved to an adaptive resolution. Children with complex trauma, insecure patterns of attachment, and children that dissociate may move into states of hyper- or hypoarousal relatively quickly. If the clinician does not remain attuned and attentive enough to the rather settled physiological changes in the child's organism, the clinician could be eliciting dysregulation and the re-experiencing of the traumatic event instead of the integration of memory. It is important to highlight that the goal of the desensitization phase and in general all the reprocessing phases is not to elicit and produce catharsis, instead it is the assimilation, binding, and integration of traumatogenic material. If the child has moved out of windows of affect tolerance, the child's integrative capacity is compromised. As a result, EMDR clinicians should be well versed in the use of strategies to manage hyper- and hypoarousal states. When working with children with compromised social engagement systems, clinicians may need to actually reduce the amount of disturbing material and affect accessed at any given point during reprocessing. During the desensitization phase, maintaining para- sympathetic ventral vagal activation is pivotal. This chapter will cover child-friendly strategies and interweaves that support and stimulate the social engagement system, maintain dual awareness and kindle children's integrative capacities.

This chapter will be dedicated to presenting advanced strategies and interweaves that can facilitate the assimilation of memories of trauma and adversity as well as to promote vertical (right and left brain information processing) and horizontal (top down and bottom-up processing) integration. However, basic procedures will not be reviewed, as they need to be adequately known and used by the EMDR clinician prior to working with complex trauma cases.

THE INTERWEAVE

Shapiro (2001) developed a strategy to jump-start blocked processing that she called "The Cognitive Interweave." Considering the different information processing levels accessed during processing, and to avoid confusion by naming interweaves as cognitive, emotional, or somatic, I will refer to the cognitive interweave as just the interweave. According to Shapiro (2001), interweaves are used when the client is "looping" and processing remains blocked. Spontaneous processing is preferred and encouraged by having the clinician "stay out of the way." Allowing children to embrace their own reality without much interference from the clinician is ideal. It appears that during the reprocessing of traumatogenic material, synthesis, and linkage of memory networks occur. According to the AIP model (Shapiro, 1995, 2001), dysfunctional material is held in neuro networks in state-specific form. These neural systems remain isolated from other memories of adaptive experiences. During EMDR reprocessing, these networks link up so assimilation and binding among the memories containing disturbing information and the ones containing positive and adaptive material can take place. "By using the cognitive interweave the clinician attempts to change the client's perspective, somatic reactions, and personal reference...to the adaptive perspective" (Shapiro, 2001, p. 252).

As these memories are integrated, they can finally be located in time and space, the negative affect they hold can be discharged, defense responses can be completed, emotions can be reclaimed, and pent up somatic energy can be released. When working with children with early and complex trauma, the scarcity of memories containing positive and adaptive experiences make the reprocessing phases of EMDR therapy more elaborate and convoluted. The EMDR clinician needs to deal with the possibility of these children moving quickly into states of hyper- and hypoarousal. They may also present with dissociative symptoms, unmet attachment needs, lack of adaptive information, deprivation of appropriate developmental experiences, compromised and reduced integrative capacity, and compromised social engagement systems, among others. Considering the serious deficits these children present, EMDR clinicians need a wide variety of strategies that can effectively and successfully assist children in embracing the memories of adversity. The use of strategies during the desensitization phase without the appropriate ability to attune and resonate with the child's affective states may not be as effective. A great deal of flexibility and internal regulation on the part of the clinician will highly enhance the EMDR reprocessing experience for the child. In my clinical experience, working with highly dysregulated children may require a more active participation on the part of the clinician in comparison to the level of input required when treating children with simple PTSD, a single trauma event, and with overall appropriate attachment experiences. In order to more efficiently facilitate in these children the assimilation of maladaptive material, clinicians will need to have a clear path and direction when entering these fragmented and disturbing memories. Anticipating the potential "stalling" points based on the child's history may highly improve the outcome of EMDR reprocessing sessions. The clinician should spend appropriate time selecting the potential interweaves that may be needed and used with each child. How and when these interweaves will be provided and who will provide them depends

on the clinical landscape of each child and his or her family. When selecting potential interweaves, the clinician should determine if the parent will be present during
reprocessing sessions or not. Does the parent need to repair? Is the parent at a place
where repair can take place? Has the parent been prepared for the reprocessing session in advance? Will the child be accessing a memory where attachment needs were
not met and helping the child meet attachment needs may be needed? Did the child
experience trauma where defense responses were truncated and now they may need
to be completed? Does the child have the tendency to move into high arousal states
and, as a result, interweaves that modulate arousal may be needed? Or, on the contrary, does the child tend to move into low arousal states? Does the child present
with a lack of information that may need to be provided during the reprocessing
session? Anticipating the latent areas where information processing may stall with
appropriate strategies that can move this information into adaptive resolution will
highly enhance the reprocessing experience for the child. Needless to say, the clinician only uses these strategies when necessary, which is when spontaneous information processing stalls. Sometimes the anticipated "turbulence" does not occur and
the interweave does not need to be used. However, if it does, and the clinician is
unprepared, the child may be left to re-experience prolonged dysregulated states
that mirror the very same experience that brought them to therapy. The purpose of
accessing the trauma memory is not to relive it but to integrate it.

PROMOTING HORIZONTAL INTEGRATION: WHEN
WE CAN SEE THE PARTS AND THE WHOLE

The term "horizontal integration" was brought up by Siegel (1999/2010) to refer to the
opening of the wisdom of our two brains: Right and left. However, McGilchrist (2009),
in his masterpiece book, *The Master and his Emissary*, brings the ultimate compelling
evidence and calls for the need of interhemispheric integration.

Coming to a greater understanding of how our "two brains" function will greatly
enhance our capacity to bring the wisdom of each at different times throughout the
processing of memories during EMDR therapy. According to Siegel (2010), "the right
side develops early and is the realm of imagery, holistic thinking, nonverbal language
and autobiographical memory" (p. 72). According to McGilchrist (2009), the right
hemisphere possesses a wider field of attention and integration over time and space,
which enables it to distinguish wider and more complex patterns. In other words, it
is able to see the whole and the big picture in contrast with the left, which sees things
broken into parts.

The right side of the brain is more closely connected to the limbic and subcortical
systems and the memories of emotional language, while the left specializes in superficial social emotions. The right frontal lobe also regulates the hypothalamic-pituitary
axis and is in charge of our subjective experience of the systems that regulate the body.
According to McGilchrist (2009), with the exception of anger, which is strongly linked
to left frontal activation, the right brain is essential for emotional expression of every
kind through the face and body posture. Moreover, the left side of the brain processes
cognitive, verbal, and predictable cause and effect patterns and is responsible for logic,
language, lists, and linear thinking (Badenoch, 2008; Siege, 2011).

As brilliantly stated by McGilchrist (2009), each brain has its own talents and
voices; both of which are essential, but *"alone they are destructive"* (p. 93). It is important to highlight how attachment experiences are fundamental organizers of brain

development (Schore, 2010). Early experiences of hardship, adversity, and trauma within the caregiving system may interfere with the ability of the brain to integrate right and left activity and energy flow. Individuals may present with extreme emotional dysregulation due to having excessive right hemisphere activation without the appropriate intervention of the left (Siegel, 2010). The opposite may happen with individuals for whom the left hemisphere has become extremely dominant.

When working with children with histories of trauma that present with excessive participation of the left hemisphere as it is seen with children with avoidant patterns of attachment, stimulating emotional and somatic awareness is done gradually. Meeting them where they can perform well, in the left processing mode, and gently inviting the right hemisphere to participate may bring integration and a greater capacity for affect tolerance. However, inviting the voice of the right side of the brain more often, as the child can tolerate it, may be necessary. Interweaves that gently stimulate children's emotional and body awareness should be utilized without dishonoring their cognitive processing capacities. On the other hand, children with ambivalent attachment patterns may present with great difficulties regulating affective states and great anxiety, concern and fixation with attachment needs, and attachment figures. These children may need to enter the right hemisphere with the assistance of the labeling and logic abilities of the left hemisphere. At other times, they may benefit from just visiting the memories of the "implicit self" (Schore, 2010) and the right side of the brain without the interference of the left. In our western society, the strong participation of the left hemisphere has been proposed (McGilchrist, 2009), leaving us in a world of great technological advances, but impoverished relational lives. As a result, "right brain activists" may now advocate for mostly embracing in therapy the voice of the right-brain. However, honoring the two wonderful ways of knowing the world will bring us to a place of wholeness and integration, not the other way. When assisting children during the reprocessing sessions of EMDR therapy, wisely allowing, encouraging, and stimulating the two modes of information processing will best honor the goal of assimilation, binding, and integration of memories. Considering how the right and left hemispheres have different voices and their own ways of processing information, both hemispheres should be invited to participate at different times and in very unique ways during EMDR therapy. Since the right contains all the memories of the "implicit self," for many children, it may need to be nourished and accessed first; however, the left may be invited to complement and soothe the right brain. The opposite may be true for children that have learned to "live" in their left hemispheres. Moving too fast into the right and accessing emotions, when in order to survive they had to detach from them, could be scary and dysregulating. Bringing balance and harmony between the two, not creating further separation, may be the key.

PROMOTING VERTICAL INTEGRATION

According to Siegel (2010), who gave life to the term "vertical integration," "our nervous system is distributed, ascending from the body proper through the brainstem and limbic areas and finally arriving at the cortex. From head to toe and back again, vertical integration links these differentiated areas into a functional whole."

Different directions of information processing have been proposed: Top-down and bottom-up processing (Ogden et al., 2006). Clients come into therapy with different tendencies for information processing: Cognitive, emotional, and somatic.

For some, connecting with the body and movement may be challenging, while keeping information processing mostly at a cognitive level may appear comfortable. It is important to notice the information processing that is foremost available to the client as well as the ones that represent a challenge and gently embracing them, can deepen the outcome of EMDR therapy. Having interweaves available that stimulate and access the cognitive, emotional, and somatosensory aspects of the memory can highly enhance the assimilation and binding of memory systems. One of the unique aspects of EMDR therapy is how it honors the client's system and choice of information processing route and direction. Once the memory and its different aspects are accessed, individuals go where they want or need to go at their own timing and pace. Some individuals may go spontaneously to the body and its somatic or sensorimotor reactions. Some clients may access emotions and new images. Other clients may have new insights and may bring new cognitions or thoughts. When needed, the attuned-enough therapist is able to intervene in a gentle way to keep information processing going. However, the timing and information processing mode chosen by the client is foremost honored. In some cases, when dysregulation of the affective system occurs during EMDR reprocessing, the EMDR therapist may gently guide the client to move into a mode of information processing that may be more tolerable. The EMDR therapist also stimulates the client's ability to access different channels of association and stimulates information processing modes that the client may not access spontaneously, as they are less familiar for the client. *"As you have this new thought, what do you notice happening in your body?"* The opposite may also be used with a client getting lost and stuck with high physiological arousal, *"As you notice the pressure in your chest, is there a thought or a belief that goes with that sensation?"* EMDR therapy accesses bottom-up and top-down information processing flow; however, the starting point, timing, and mode is guided and orchestrated by the client's system.

In the face of high arousal, newly trained EMDR clinicians may tend to stop or give the signal to the child that taking a break may be necessary. In addition, they may immediately try to bring in a resource or even the safe place for the fear of the child moving out of windows of tolerance. To use an analogy, we could see the reprocessing of a memory as a flying journey, and what happens when the child is moving into hyper- or hypoarousal as turbulence encountered during the flight. The experienced pilot will assess the situation depending on the size, strength of the plane, the intensity of the turbulence, and how much passengers can tolerate turbulence, and may decide at that point to move to a different altitude or stay and embrace the turbulence. The experienced pilot will not land the plane just because there is high turbulence; instead, the pilot finds an altitude where turbulence is reduced and more tolerable. An inexperienced pilot may become fearful and go for an emergency landing, which is what many newly trained EMDR clinicians do in the presence of "turbulence" by moving into resourcing and stopping reprocessing. The different altitudes are represented by the different levels of information processing: Cognitive, affective, and somatic. For instance, moving to the "body altitude" may reduce the intensity of the "turbulence," bringing arousal again to an optimal level without having to necessarily go for an emergency landing and stop processing.

Many of the interweaves proposed in this chapter may access more than one direction and level of information processing flow. It is important to highlight the use of play, which is the native language of children. The use of play, metaphors, and a good sense of humor during reprocessing phases of EMDR therapy can be very powerful integrative agents. Knowing and understanding from the child's history, the modes of information processing he or she has learned to utilize more often, as well as the child's tendencies into hyper- or hypoarousal will assist clinicians to select potential interweaves as well as to set up the session to maintain optimal levels of arousal that will translate into an increased ability for mindfulness and dual awareness. As discussed in Chapter 8, some children may present with highly sensitized sympathetic systems, making them prone to experiencing high arousal states. These children may exhibit more emotions and reactions during the reprocessing of memories. On the other hand, children with sensitized parasympathetic dorsal vagal systems may be prone to experiencing low arousal states during the reprocessing of memories and report feeling sleepy, tired, and very often bored. EMDR clinicians need to set up the session with resources that either increase or reduce arousal. For instance, for a child that tends to experience hypoarousal states, the EMDR reprocessing session may contain movement and greater engagement of the body and the stimulation of present awareness. Using music for instance, may keep some children more engaged and present. Considering that now there is technology that allows for a CD player to be connected to a device that plays music bilaterally, the use of music during EMDR reprocessing sessions is facilitated. It is worth noting that any stimulus depending on the child could also create further dysregulation. Even music can be potentially overwhelming for some children. Please be mindful of individual differences. Moreover, making the session "extra" playful, such as using the "cushion stations" described in Chapter 8, will prepare the child's system and set up the nervous system at an optimal level of arousal so the reprocessing and assimilation of disturbing memories is optimized. In addition, the presence of the clinician, eye contact, tone, pitch, and inflection of the clinician's voice can also bring arousal to an optimal level where the child's integrative capacity is maximized. Helping the child feel safe and contained will also expand his or her ability to stay present and avoid moving into immobilization or collapsing states.

On the other hand, when working with children with the tendency to move into high arousal states, extra work will be needed to create a sense of safety. For instance, the parent, pet, etc., may be invited to the session if they foster greater confidence and sense of safety. These strategies will amplify EMDR therapy outcome and will reduce the probability of children not wanting to do EMDR. Interweaves that modulate arousal will also need to be in place in case they are needed. Considering that children with complex trauma histories have reduced tolerance for experiencing negative and even positive affect, the active attuned intervention of the clinician to maintain information processing may be necessary. Needless to say, the EMDR clinician only intervenes when it is required, either because information processing stalled or because the capacity for dual awareness is lost.

PLATEAUS OF INFORMATION PROCESSING: RESPONSIBILITY, SAFETY, AND CONTROL/POWER

According to Shapiro (2001), clients spontaneously move through the three plateaus: Responsibility, safety, and control/power, to a more adaptive perspective during reprocessing. A thorough exploration and the specifics of assisting complexly traumatized children move through each of these plateaus follows.

Responsibility

Most children injured and traumatized in the adult-child relationship carry within the responsibility of the event. Assigning appropriate responsibility and placing account- ability where it belongs, in the hands of the perpetrator or injuring agent, is an impor- tant aspect of healing and the integration of such memories. According to Shapiro (2001), "By allowing responsibility for the abuse to rest squarely on the shoulders of the perpetrator...the client is able to move from primary identification with the trauma to an externalized vantage point of appropriate judgment" (p. 260). When dealing with overt past abuse and the perpetrator is no longer part of the child's life, assigning responsibility and attaining a present sense of safety may be easily attainable. In addi- tion, if the perpetrator is not a primary attachment figure, this will further expedite the process. However, greater difficulties may be encountered when the injuring agent is an important attachment figure and, the child continues to live and depend upon this caregiver that engages in overt forms of abuse, role reversing, and boundary violations (see Chapter 5 for strategies on how to work with caregivers). Care should be exercised when using interweaves that place the responsibility on the primary attachment figure, since the child's survival is still depending on this figure. However, interweaves that provide corrective information and promote organization in the child's mind should be utilized gently and carefully when information processing gets blocked. For instance, either the clinician directly or indirectly, by using the "EMDR advisors," can say, "*Even good moms and good dads can have some "hurts" in their hearts that only they can heal. Kids can't do that for their moms and dads. When moms and dads hold on to these hurts they can say or do things that can hurt others, especially their own kids. Sometimes these hurts don't let them feel or show love for their kids and kids may think that there is something wrong with them or that they are unlovable, when in reality it is the mom's or dad's own hurts that get in the way. Remember that it is not the kid's job or responsibility to take care of these hurts. It is only the parent's. Also remember that it is not the kid's fault if parents act in ways that are hurtful. This does not mean that the parents are bad; it means that they carry hurts in their hearts. However, kids have the right to protect themselves from the hurts of their parents.*" After the corrective information has been provided, the Socratic method can be used as follows:

Therapist: *When dad drinks and gets mad, is that your fault or it may be that dad car- ries hurts in his heart?*

Child: *No it is not my fault, he may have hurts.*

Therapist: *Is it your job to fix it?*

Child: *No.*

Therapist: *Just notice that or think of that.*

If the child has developed a way of adapting by rescuing the parent, talking about the parent having hurts may trigger the child's needs to protect, rescue, and fix the situation for the parent. If another interweave is needed to deal with the child's role- reversing tendencies, the clinician may use the "jackets analogy" as an interweave: "*We humans sometimes have to live in different places in our lives. For instance, if we had to live and survive in the North Pole, we have to learn to survive by wearing heavy jackets. The same thing happens when we have to live with moms and dads that have hurts, and we work so hard to try to fix their hurts. We may feel responsible for making parents feel good again....but you know.... that is a 'mission impossible' because only they can fix it. Sometimes kids have learned to wear the "mission impossible jacket" as they try hard to be the parent instead of being the kid. Remember, it is never the kid's job to fix the parent's problems and kids can't fix them either."*

> Therapist: *So....when you* (describe the role reversing behavior), *are you wearing the "mission impossible jacket?"*
>
> Child: *I guess, yes, I am wearing this jacket a lot.*
>
> Therapist: *Go with that or notice that.*

Sometimes children develop trauma bonds with the perpetrator and internalize aspects of the perpetrator as a survival mechanism. The "jacket analogy" once again can be used as an interweave as follows: *"Sometimes kids learn to use another jacket that can help them survive. I call it the "bear jacket." While living in the North Pole, if we had been attacked or hurt by a big scary bear, we may try to be like the bear so we get to feel powerful like the bear and we think that this way we will not be hurt again by the bear. We create a jacket with the same fur, we may want to be friends with the bear, please the bear, convince ourselves that the bear didn't do anything hurtful, defend the bear, and act like the bear. Even when the bear is gone, we still continue to act like it. All this with the goal of not feeling so small and scared again like we did when the bear attack happened. Of course this jacket does not protect us because big wild bears are not safe to be around, even when we please them, defend them, or act like them. If we act like the bear with others, then others don't get to feel and be safe around us."*

> Therapist: *"What your uncle did I know was hurtful for you so I wonder if to survive you have been wearing the "uncle jacket."*

The child may be encouraged to even draw a picture of the "uncle jacket," containing all the internalizations and over-identification of the child with the perpetrator. Then the child may be encouraged to look at the jacket while engaging in BLS. The purpose of the "jacket analogy" is to help children understand that they used it to survive the "cold," but now that the sun is out (perpetrator is gone or not part of the child's life), the jacket keeps them from feeling the warmth of the sun.

Safety

Children in the specific area of safety are in a very different place compared to adults. Children are still dependent on their caregivers to provide safety and security. However, children can learn safety tips and things they can do to help themselves and help their parents keep them safe. When information processing stalls in this area, helping children learn what they can do to stay safe not only can help them feel safe, but also empowered. *"Even though it's mom's and dad's job to keep you safe, what can you do to help them keep you safe (such as tell,* ask for help, say "no," etc.)?"

On the other hand, children may be safe in the present but continue to experience the present as if the past was still happening (Shapiro, 1995/2001), resulting in the activation of the fear system and defense system in the absence of real danger. Helping the child feel oriented in time and space will help locate the memory where it belongs; in the past. The Installation of Present Resolution (IPR) exercise, described in Chapter 7, may also be used as an interweave during the reprocessing phases of EMDR therapy. In this interweave, the child is asked to draw a picture of the past traumatic event followed by a picture of the child in the present. This interweave is inspired by the exercise developed by Steele & Raider (2001), "this is me then and this is me now," and addresses issues of safety, responsibility and power. When using this interweave the child is invited to either think or draw a "this is me then" and "this is me now" picture. The child is then invited to look at the two pictures while engaging in BLS. The clinician may follow up with questions such as:

Therapist: *As you look or think about "you then" and "you now," can you tell or see if you are safe now?*

Child: *Yes, I am safe now.*

Therapist: *Notice that.*

An example using the Socratic method while the child is looking at or thinking about the two pictures (then and now) would be:

Therapist: *Are you safe now?*

Child: *Yes, I am safe now.*

Therapist: *Is the yucky thing still happening now?*

Child: *No.*

Therapist: *Do you have helpers that keep you safe now?*

Child: *Yes, I have helpers now.*

Therapist: *Are you stronger, bigger, etc.?*

Child: *Yes, I am bigger now and stronger.*

Therapist: *Do you know things that can help you defend yourself and keep yourself safe now?*

Child: *Yes.*

Therapist: *Notice that or go with that or think of that.*

Control/Power

This third and final informational plateau "evokes the client's sense of confidence in being able to make effective choices in the future which should incorporate an internal locus of control" (Shapiro, 2001, p. 261). Children, however, are still very much dependent on their caregivers and other adults in their lives. When using EMDR therapy with adults, the clinician is assisting the client in moving from an external to an internal locus of control. However, children are in a different developmental stage and hold different attachment needs in comparison to adults. Despite children's reliance on adult care, they can find and develop a sense of empowerment within. Having some sense of control over their environment and not feeling at the complete mercy of life circumstances is important. On the other hand, children still need a healthy reliance on adults. In addition, some children may have learned to adapt by using control as a mechanism of adaptation and learning to rely on their support system may be a corrective and a healing experience. Relinquishing some level of control to embrace, trust, and rely on safe adult care in their lives may be what is needed. Children's processing may get stuck when feelings of powerlessness take over and they completely lack a sense of internal power. Helping them regain a sense of healthy personal power and choices may be fundamental. Learning to identify safe people in their lives and rely on their inner and outer "helpers" could be provided through interweaves. Ego state and Internal Family Systems (IFS) strategies (see Chapter 13) can assist children in finding a healthy reliance on the "bright shiny me" and the "internal rainbow," as well as the "outside safe helpers." If you are not using an ego state approach, invite the child to think about the "inside helpers" that are representations of the child's internal resources and strengths as well as the external resources. These may be relational in nature or soothing and regulating activities that act as "external helpers."

CHILD-FRIENDLY INTERWEAVES

EMDR clinicians should be versatile and flexible as they assist children in accessing different routes, levels and directions of information processing. Using the capacities of the left hemisphere to verbalize and use words, as well as the voice of the right hemisphere to retrieve and process the nonverbal and affective aspects of the memory, can enrich the experience for the child. The use of metaphors, symbols, stories, music and body focused interventions can enhance and expedite the accessing, assimilation and binding of neural networks containing maladaptive material. The following interweaves are designed to honor the different voices of the mind and the different levels and modes of information processing.

The Throw-Up Interweave

This interweave can be used with children who, despite all the preparation, still lack appropriate understanding of boundaries and, consequently tend to make everything very personal. These children, as a result of poor mirroring and lack of appropriate boundary modeling, are constantly defined by the views, actions, and words of others. You may decide to give this information during the preparation phase and just remind the child of what he or she learned during processing, or provide it entirely as an intervention to restore blocked processing. This interweave is also appropriate for children who have been the victims of bullying or that have bullied other children themselves (Figure 9.1). You may say, *"Do you know what happens when people eat too much to the point of feeling sick to their stomach? They throw up. They throw up because they do not feel good inside. Have you ever seen throw up? Have you seen all the stuff inside the throw up?"* Most children have seen throw up. In addition, since the question is so gross, it calls the attention of the child as well as a smile. *"So the stuff you see inside the throw up, is that yours or does it belong to the person who threw up because that is what they ate?"* Children always say, no, that is not mine. *"Okay, would you try to take the throw up and eat it?"* At this point children are saying something like, oh no, that is gross, of course I would not eat it. *"Okay, because if you eat it, it could make you sick or at least stink. Well the same thing happens to people when they do not feel good in their minds and their hearts; they throw up, but this time they throw up with words and actions. So, when kids say or do mean things, those are 'throw up words or actions.' They do this because they do not feel good inside about themselves. That does not mean that they are bad, they just do not feel good."* Now go to the memory where the child "took throw up" and say, *"So, when Rosie said you were a bad kid, was that a throw-up word? Is that throw up yours or hers? Are you going to take it and eat it?"* After the child responds, say, *"Just think or notice that,"* and start BLS. This interweave also

Figure 9.1 The throw-up interweave.

helps children that bully understand that they do not do this because they are "bad" but because they have "big feelings inside" and they do not feel good.

The EMDR Advisors

In order to make interweaves more playful for younger children, I created the EMDR advisors. They could be very helpful for children where parents are not present and unable to provide corrective information. These advisors are puppets that represent a mother, father, grandmother, grandfather, a brother, and a sister. I also included a puppet that represents an animal or person that used to make "bad choices," so it knows about people that make these choices. Each advisor is knowledgeable in different subjects. For instance, Ed, the "dad," knows about dad's issues. He can talk about how grown-ups and dads can take care of themselves and it is not the children's responsibility to take care of their dads. He also knows that when dads have emotions such as anger, dads are responsible for the emotions and how they express them. Advisors use the Socratic method to assist children in taking data in and connecting it to other existing information encoded in memory. For instance, if the child is working on a memory associated with the divorce of his or her parents, and is getting stuck on issues of responsibility, either dad, "Ed," or mom, "Maria," can provide the information to the child. They may say something like, *"kids are not responsible for the choices that grown-ups make. Moms and dads do not get divorced because of what kids do or don't do. Kids don't make parents separate and they can't make them get back together."* The advisor follows up with a question before initiating BLS, *"So are you responsible for the choices mom and dad made?"* Another case scenario is the child that is processing a memory of both parents fighting, and it stalls as the child continues to believe that he or she is responsible for the emotions and behaviors of both parents. The advisor, in this case mom, "Maria," may say, *"Mommies and daddies and grown ups are responsible for taking care of their feelings and what they do with them. Kids are just learning to take care of their feelings, so they can't be responsible for mom's and dad's feelings. When mom and dad have mad feelings and do "mad things" with each other, who needs to take care of those mad feelings?"* If additional information is needed, the advisor can provide it. This is done interactively as the advisor asks questions to the child to assist him or her in the synthesis and linkage of memory systems.

George, "the wolf that made bad choices," can assist when the child is dealing with memories of being hurt by other human beings. For instance, for a child that has been bullied and information processing stalled as a result of the child defining him- or herself by the actions of the other, George can be invited. He may say, *"You know, when I said mean things to others, it was because I was feeling bad about myself. When I told others they were bad or stupid, it was because I was the one feeling bad and stupid. When this kid at school called you names, was it because it was true what he said or because he was the one not feeling good?"* In cases of abuse, for example, of course George will not say he did these things, but he can say that he has known people that have hurt kids. He can provide information about how the child was not responsible, did not deserve it, and it only reflects on the person who did it. Needless to say, language and stories that are appropriate for children should be used. Advisors can also tell stories about someone they "knew" that resembles what the child may be experiencing to give the child information and hints necessary for appropriate assimilation of the target memory.

Using Illustrations

Illustrations are wonderful tools that can assist children when information processing halts. Illustrations and visual aids also engage the right hemisphere, assisting children in looking at the bigger picture. The following are some of these interweaves:

■ **Families come in different shapes and colors:** This interweave is designed to help children who have experienced changes in their family systems as a result of divorce; death; moving to another country or state; or a parent having to leave for a prolonged period of time, such as parents in the military. Many of these children, when reprocessing these memories, may get stuck as they feel that they do not have a family anymore since the original family arrangement has been lost. This interweave assists children in looking at the bigger picture of what a family is.

In this illustration, families of different racial groups and sexual orientation are presented. You can download a number of art clips from the internet that show a variety of families. For instance, a family may be the mother and the child, or two grandparents and a child, or a dad and three children, or two moms and two children. Once the art clips are organized on a sheet of paper, you can laminate it. You may have to cut and paste single illustrations to form different families, and have various options that can honor the cultural heritage of each child's family system. It is important to assess the values of the family and parents to determine what illustrations may be appropriate for the child. When using this laminated illustration, go over all the options and say, *"Everything in this wonderful universe comes in different colors, shapes, and sizes: Flowers, animals, rainbows, trees, and plants. Families are the same; they come in different sizes, colors, and shapes. A family could be a mom, a dad, and a child. A family could also be a mom and two kids or a dad and one kid. A family could be a grandmother and four kids or a grandfather and one kid. A family could be a mom and a dad that live apart and kids that spend time with each parent at different times. A family could be a mom and three kids and a dad that is far away working."* The child may also be invited to circle his or her family once it is found on the laminated illustrations.

Once you have gone through all the small family pictures, ask the child, *"So your family has changed, as so many families do, but do you still have a family?"* Once the child responds, follow up with BLS.

■ **Families change:** This is another wonderful interweave that can help children understand the rhythm of life and how everything that exists is meant to go through changes. If you feel comfortable sharing your family and the different stages of transformation it has endured, you can show the diagram of your own family. You could also use a standard illustration of a family you know and the metamorphosis it has gone through. This interweave invites children to see change as a part of life. It also helps them feel that they are not alone in the metamorphosis of life. Once the child has witnessed how families change, follow up with a question that assists the child in linking this information to the target memory and do BLS.

■ **We all have "hurts:"** This interweave is intended to help children not feel alone in their experiences of pain. This interweave is used after enough validation for the pain and enough work has been done to meet unmet needs and the child is still caught up in the victim posture. Children are invited to look at difficult situations that are experienced by human beings. This interweave is not intended to give the message of "stop complaining" or "get a grip"; we all have problems! Instead, it is meant to honor the pain of the child while helping him or her feel accompanied and normalized. Children may feel different, weird, abnormal, and stigmatized for the hurts and pain they experienced. When using this interweave, have laminated illustrations of a variety of adverse situations available to the child. These child-friendly cartoons can be downloaded from the Internet. You may say, *You know, it is hard but all of us people, animals and every living thing in this world goes through difficult experiences. Some people have experienced illnesses, divorce, accidents, fires, separations from the people they love, etc. All of us have to go through hurts and boo-boos in life. However, pain has the power to make us stronger and wiser."* After going through all the illustrations, follow up with a question such as, *"Are you the only one that has hurts and difficulties or do we all go through them in different ways?"* Usually the child will respond, *"No, I guess I am not the only one."* Then, the child is invited to just "notice that" while BLS is initiated. In all the years I have used this interweave, I have not had even one child say "Yes, I am the only one." However, if this is the case, invite the child to keep noticing while engaged in BLS. Another interweave may be necessary or a further exploration of what keeps the child in this place.

■ **I am not the only one:** This interweave has a similar intent as the prior interweave, but this time, superheroes and people the child may look up to are utilized to convey the same message. If the child feels accompanied, and the pain is normalized by having heroes or people the child admires having hurts and difficult experiences (similar to those experienced by the child) these experiences may not be seen as shameful. Fortunately enough, most of the superheroes have incredible histories that show a great ability to survive and overcome hardship and suffering. Finding a superhero that has gone through something similar to that of the child is the starting point. For instance, Spiderman witnessed the murder of his uncle, and Superman was adopted from another planet, among others. Many of these superheroes developed their powers as a result of enduring adversity. Aquaman developed the power to communicate and get help from all the sea animals as a result of being raised by dolphins after he was abandoned in the water as a baby. History is full of people that, despite trauma and suffering, were able to survive and even help others. Humanity and the animal kingdom have marvelous stories of survival that will make wonderful and powerful interweaves that bring hope as we get to see the incredible capacity we human beings have to overcome adversity.

STIMULATING MINDFULNESS DURING REPROCESSING

■ **The "watching self:"** Mindful awareness in EMDR is pivotal during the reprocessing phases. The capacity for maintaining dual awareness requires the presence of the observing self. In order to help children use directed mindfulness, playful analogies and strategies may be used. I developed the use of the "watching self" or the "watching me" to explain mindfulness to children. In fact, I use a really big pair of glasses without lenses to symbolize this aspect of us that can study and observe things. To make it more tangible for children, the child may be asked to put the big glasses on when needing focused, directed mindfulness during the desensitization phase and other reprocessing phases. It is also important to emphasize the power of "watching" and "observing." Like superheroes, we human beings also possess "special powers," one being the power of observation and mindfulness. When the child's information processing stalls and basic procedures such as manipulating mechanics do not work, mindfulness may be used as an interweave. Invite the child to watch and notice where this is occurring in the body and just observe. The clinician may say, *"Where are these feelings hanging out in your body?"* If the child says, *"I feel it in my stomach,"* then say, *"We are going to invite the 'watching you' to come closer and really watch/notice/observe what is happening in your stomach. You can put the 'watching you' glasses on as you invite the 'watching you' to come and observe."*

■ **The zoom in and out camera or telescope:** In order to help children use mindfulness and focus attention, the "zoom in" and "zoom out" features of the "inside camera" or the "inside telescope" may concretize and make more playful the concept of mindful observation. Mel, a 6-year-old girl, brought to therapy because she was experiencing great anxiety at night and was having frequent nightmares. Mel had witnessed her oldest sister being raped by her step-father at the age of four. While Mel was reprocessing the memory of one of her dreams where monsters were attacking her sister and eating her alive, the monsters started to grow in number and strength after each set of BLS. Despite changing the speed and direction of the BLS, the monsters were taking over and Mel's fear grew. Mel was encouraged to bring her watching self and notice what was happening in the body as she was watching the monsters and feeling the fear. Mel stated that her body was feeling "yucky" mostly in her heart and stomach. Mel was encourage to get her telescope and watch her stomach and heart. After a set of BLS, Mel reported that the scared feelings were coming closer and closer to the heart. Mel was invited to use the "zoom in" feature and closely look at the scared feelings, what they looked like, what shape they had, what color they were, and if they were cold or warm. Mel stated, after the set of BLS, that the feelings were very cold, heavy, and blue and looked like triangles. Mel continued to explore these feelings with the "zoom in" feature. She even had a conversation with the feelings, asking them what they needed to feel better. Later on, the "zoom out" feature was used as Mel was invited to search for other parts or areas in the body where she felt the opposite or where these feelings were not present. Mel found a place in her of strength. At this point, the "zoom in" feature was used again to help Mel in getting in touch with her strength.

The zoom in and zoom out features are also helpful when looking at the memory of an event, the people involved, or even past events and their relationship to present symptoms. Sometimes an aspect of the memory of a traumatic episode may appear overwhelming when looking at it closely, but when we "zoom out" and gain a bigger, greater perspective, the same event, person, or feeling may not be as overwhelming or as big and powerful. A "monster" may appear huge and powerful; however, when we "zoom out" the monster may look actually small. Children may also be able to find resources that are out of the child's perceptual field. However, when a bigger view and expansion of the perceptual field takes place, "helpers" and resources may be found that can empower, give a new meaning, and/or assist the child. By the same token, the "zoom in" feature may help an overwhelmed child reduce the amount of material being accessed at any given point during reprocessing. The child may be invited to focus on just a small portion of the memory.

USING IMAGES AND STORIES INSPIRED FROM NATURE: ANIMAL AND PLANT TOTEMS

The greatest inspiration and stories come from nature. Animals and plants and everything nature surround us with contain incredible teachings full of wisdom. Because these stories contain images, analogies, and metaphors that can deeply touch the right hemisphere, they can be extremely powerful. The symbolism and meaning that each animal or nature totem brings can assist children in learning about themselves. According to Andrews (2011), there are archetypal powers that reside behind all manifestations in nature. *"These archetypes have their own qualities and characteristics which are reflected through the behaviors and activities of animals and other expressions of nature"* (Andrews, 2011, p 2). The process of assisting children in identifying their own animal and nature totems during the preparation phase, was covered earlier in this book. Once the animal or plant has been identified, it can then accompany the child through his or her entire journey toward integration and wholeness. Animal and nature totems are great companions as the child embraces the memories of trauma and hardship. Since the animals and plants selected during the preparation phase already hold the qualities either possessed by the child or longed by the child, they can be amazing advisors and supporters of the child's reprocessing sessions. During the session, the animal or plant is invited to be present and a special place such as a cushion may be placed for the toy or figure representing the animal. When the moment comes to invite the animal to participate because reprocessing has stalled, questions or advice are asked to the animal. Questions such as: What would the butterfly tell you about this? What would the Tabanuco tree do in this situation? How would your special animal see what you are seeing? Which special talents would the Palm tree tell you that you have? How can your special animal help you in this situation? In addition, the child may sometimes embody the animal or the plant and see the situation through their eyes and notice what naturally comes for them. Masks representing the animal may be used to make this a more tangible and playful experience for the child. The use of nature and animals has the great benefit of keeping the child attention-focused, the social engagement and play-systems involved, in addition to engaging the right hemisphere. This will result in a greater ability on the child's part to stay present and maintain dual awareness. The following are just a few examples of potential animal and nature totems that can be used with children.

- **Oak trees:** Oak trees are one of the symbols of longevity since these trees can live for many years and reach up to 60 feet or more in height. Oak trees grow in spurts followed by a quiet period where the Oak tree goes deep into its roots before another new growth period. This tree takes the time to go deep within itself to get in touch with its own roots before coming back to grow in the outside world. When children and their parents are so busy reaching only the outside world without taking the time to look within, the Oak tree becomes the master that shows us the importance to take the time to go deep within. This may be what makes them reach such height, strength, and longevity. When inviting children to look within during EMDR reprocessing sessions, the Oak tree may be the guide and the example. This metaphor in a gentle and powerful way may assist the child in entering the exploration of his or her body and access the right hemisphere. In my clinical experience, with the metaphors and images nature provides, children can deeply understand and openly embrace their "roots."

- **Understanding the need for connection with others – The story of the Tabanuco trees:** Many children that come with attachment wounds and injuries have given up their need for connection with others. They find it difficult to grasp the idea that through these deep connections with others that are safe and trustworthy we blossom and survive. Some of these children have shut down their need and desire to connect even when in the presence of safe environments and new promising relationships. Tabanuco trees live in the rainforest where life may be quite challenging. These trees offer a beautiful story of connection and survival that can be shared with children during their reprocessing journeys. Tabanuco trees survive hurricanes and powerful storms that cause landslides and structural instability by connecting with each other. The Tabanuco trees, instead of competing, have learned to cooperate and connect with each other through root grafting. Tabanuco trees join in with neighbor trees by connecting through their roots. These relationships and coalitions anchor them, increasing their chances of survival during powerful storms. In addition, these root links improve terrain condition, allowing nutrients to be retained. It has been discovered that through root grafting Tabanuco trees share nutrients among each other. Not only is the story of the Tabanuco trees a story of survival, but a story of bonding, connection and togetherness. This story may be shared during the preparation phase of EMDR therapy with children and families, but it can be used as an interweave during reprocessing. This interweave was used with Cary, an 8-year-old adopted at the age of five. After going through several foster homes and several disrupted adoptions, Cary did not let anybody get close to her. Despite having new adoptive parents that were embracing her with open hearts, Cary did not allow any level of closeness. When reprocessing a memory of being rejected by a potential adoptive family, Cary said she would never get close to people. When reprocessing started to stall, I told Cary the story and showed her pictures of the amazing Tabanuco trees. Cary was invited to think about this story while engaging in BLS. Cary then stated that she wanted to do what the Tabanuco trees did, but she was also scared the other "trees" might not want her. The story of the Tabanuco trees opened the door for Cary to connect with her inner need for bonding and to express the fear of potential rejection.

- **Palm trees and flexibility:** Palm trees are an example of survival resulting from flexibility. Palm trees help us understand that strength comes from being flexible and not rigid. It is well known that trees with elastic trunks survive better that those with brittle trunks. Palm trees can bend, helping them withstand even the strongest storms and hurricanes. When rigidity is present, or the inability to "bend" and adapt to the "winds" of life, palms can be great teachers for children.

- **Butterflies and transformation:** Butterflies have an incredible journey full of wisdom and courage. Butterflies endure one of the greatest transformations and metamorphosis in a lifetime. The genesis of the caterpillar is initiated by what has been called "imaginal disks." Once inside the cocoon, these imaginal cells begin to change the physical structure and destiny of the caterpillar. This transformation consumes a great amount of energy, making the caterpillar lose nearly half of its weight. When the incredible metamorphosis is complete, the new butterfly will have another battle to overcome, the breaking of the cocoon. By breaking the cocoon, the butterfly actually strengthens its wings. However, if helped, the butterfly will never fly. Thanks to the great symbolism of the journey of the butterfly, different aspects of its metamorphosis may be presented to the child during the reprocessing of traumatic material. In fact, the preparation phase may be initiated by inviting the child to embrace the butterfly "within." The imaginal disks represent the child's explicit and latent resources that are activated to help the child in the genesis and birth of his or her new wings. During EMDR reprocessing sessions, there are moments of "melting down" and moments of enduring darkness as we embrace the memories of "yucky" events. However, right when we are "visiting" the memory and we may be feeling the "dark" feelings, our "imaginal disks" begin to create our wings that will help us find our true self, our inside rainbow, and our freedom. The butterfly teaches us that in order to strengthen our wings, some struggle as we break the cocoon may be necessary. During reprocessing, remind the child of how not only the wings are growing but they are getting stronger. In addition, help the child get in touch with the amazing strength we possess within. If such a small and apparently fragile insect such as the butterfly is capable of such heroic changes, imagine what we human beings can do. The story of the butterfly can actually accompany children in their journey throughout the eight phases of EMDR therapy.

- **The chameleon:** Chameleons are wonderful animals with color-changing abilities that allow them to blend in and camouflage. Their faculty to change color seems to also be associated with social signaling. Children with role reversing and pleasing tendencies have great difficulty seeing and acknowledging such survival, mechanisms, most likely due to these coping strategies remaining buried so deeply in implicit memory. However, chameleons, through their stories of color-changing and survival, give us a visual, metaphorical right hemisphere experience of what is to adapt by conforming and becoming what and who our surroundings demand. Chameleons offer us the opportunity to honor the camouflaging abilities in us while understanding the profound purpose of becoming the color that our vicinities may require of us. Children of parents with diffused boundaries, intrusive and overpowering styles, as well as parents experienced by the child as incompetent, fragile, and unable to care for the child may elicit children that please and conform to meet the needs of the parent and other important attachment figures. In addition, children without appropriate mirroring experiences or children receiving multiple and incongruent representations of the self and other may never develop an appropriate sense of who they are. As a result, they may learn to "color-change," conforming to the colors that surround them, never finding who they really are and what their real colors are. Paige, a 7-year-old girl, was brought to therapy because her body was getting paralyzed and unable to move. After multiple medical tests and finding no organic deficits, Paige was referred to receive psychological services. Paige lived with both parents and paternal grandparents. It was discovered that the father and paternal grandfather were very strict and had high standards for Paige. Paige's mother was very submissive and had great difficulty standing up for herself. Paige was always demanded to make the "right choices" when her cousin and friends visited her. In order to conform to the rules of "altruism" imposed by the grandfather and father, Paige had to share all her toys and allow everybody to come and go into her room without restrictions. She learned to not have a voice and conform just like her mother did. In addition, her school was extremely demanding and she was expected to be the "perfect child" and meet the needs of her caregivers, that included not only her parents, but mostly her grandparents. A year prior to entering therapy, Paige was accidentally locked in the bathroom for about thirty minutes. After this incident, the anxiety and feelings of entrapment increased significantly. Paige began to fear close spaces and could not be in the bathroom or any small room by herself. Paige suffered from anxiety in silence but her body started to express what her voice could not. Paige started to have nightmares and great difficulty sleeping at night. Paige everyday tried to be in every way what her caregivers wanted her to be, with no space to honor what she was experiencing inside. Extensive family work was done with the caregivers parallel to the reprocessing of Paige's memories linked to her anxiety. Besides the memory of being locked in the bathroom, Paige identified memories of her mother not standing up for her when her cousins were bullying her in her own home and forcing her to give her toys and most precious belongings. When the time came during the reprocessing of the memory with her cousins, the chameleon told its story. A puppet representing the chameleon spoke of its "color-changing "strategies and struggles as it could never find its true colors, and when in some rare times it did, it still was unable to honor its own. Paige was encouraged to find the chameleon in her and establish a relationship with it. Later on, Paige honored the work it had done for her but talked about how she could find her won colors and show them to the world. Since the parents had also been involved in therapy, they had an opportunity to repair and honor Paige's right to her space and her own colors. Paige's parents also interacted with the chameleon and apologized to Paige for not allowing her to honor and express her own colors. Each of these interweaves were followed by BLS and standard EMDR procedures for the use of interweaves. The chameleon brought a powerful story that allowed Paige in a gentle way to get in touch with, honor, and integrate these mechanisms of adaptation and move them to adaptive resolution.

■ **The Oyster mushroom:** These mushrooms, with their magical powers, are amazing nature survivors. They possess the power to kill bacteria and some of the most toxic substances and turn them into nutritious and healthy matter. Oyster mushrooms have the capacity to break down bonds of toxic chemicals. If such a small plant is capable of such heroic and extraordinary feats, imagine what us human beings can do. Not only do the Oyster mushrooms have the capacity to take toxicity, but they transform it into what now is being investigated as healing agents. Metaphorically, when we are in the face of adversity, we take in lies, "yucky stuff," and "toxicity," but like the Oyster mushroom, we have the capacity to turn this toxicity into a healing agent for ourselves and others. Following the example of the Oyster mushroom, we invite children to transform the "yucky things" we took in from the negative events in our lives and transform them during EMDR therapy. When children report not wanting to do EMDR again, after exploring the underlying reasons, the story of the Oyster mushroom may be shared with the child. This may be an interweave that will remind the child of their "Oyster mushroom" powers they possess inside to transform the "yucky" into the "bright."

Animal stories can accompany children starting as early as the preparation phase. They can help them find target memories, resources, honor their survival capacities, and ultimately find healing and completeness within themselves. Children could find the companion animal during the preparation phase assisted by the EMDR clinician. Which animal or plant resembles and represents best the journey of the child? After listening to stories of different animals, which animal or plant appeals more to the child? These questions may help the clinician assist the child in finding their "animal or plant totem." Different animals and plants may accompany the child through the EMDR journey. Once it is found, it can greatly facilitate the openness of the child to fully embrace EMDR therapy.

Unlimited stories inspired by nature are available and may require a separate book. Wisdom surrounds us every day and every moment, and oftentimes it comes from the least expected creatures on this planet.

PUTTING IT ALL TOGETHER: CREATING THE CHILD'S "TOOLS AND ADVISORS"

This is another wonderful way of utilizing all the child's resources and creative interweaves. The session is actually set up with potential resources and advisors needed by the child. For instance, a semi circle may be created around the child with advisors and helpers, whom the child has chosen and worked with since the preparation phase. The child's "personal advisors and tools" are placed around the child. The clinician may suggest advisors based on potential strengths, deficits, and needs of each individual child. The butterfly may be part of the advisors as well as Spiderman. The Oyster mushroom may be present along with tools such as the glasses representing the "watching self" and the "inside telescope." These advisors and tools may not be necessary, needed, or used, but if the opportunity comes, they are accessible to the child and the clinician. They also provide a greater sense of safety, containment, and support for the child, even if they are never asked to participate with advice or a suggestion.

When working with children that need constant movement or children with sensitized parasympathetic dorsal vagal systems, extra playfulness and movement may help them achieve optimal levels of arousal and, as a result, maintain dual awareness easily. They also may be more engaged and motivated to participate. Instead of having the advisors and tools in a semi circle, "EMDR stations" may be created. Each station is demarcated by using cushions of different colors, or in the absence of cushions, colored paper with the name of the station may be used. For instance, if the butterfly is part of the advisors, it will have its own station, "the butterfly station." The telescope will have its own station as well as the "watching self," superheroes, chameleons, and Tabanuco trees, etc. When the child's information processing halts and the clinician is ready to intervene and use an interweave, the child is directed to the specific station. The child may need advice from the Tabanuco tree, use the glasses of the "watching self," or use the "inside telescope." Children experiencing chronic states of hypoarousal and constantly reporting that they feel "bored" and "tired" will benefit form the playfulness and movement this strategy offers.

Sage, a 7-year-old boy, was brought to therapy because of having symptoms of depression, social isolation, and difficulty relating with peers at home. His father, who was in the military, brought him to therapy. He had divorced Sage's mother after finding out about the severe neglect Sage suffered with his mother. Sage's father was deployed and the mother was in complete charge of the care of this child. According to the father, the mother would leave Sage in his crib the entire day, and would only feed him and change his diaper once a day. Child protective services were called and custody was granted to his father after he returned to the country. Sage, from the beginning, reported feeling bored and referred to EMDR as "boring." His tone of voice was soft and he seemed tired and unmotivated. Noticing how Sage was for the most part "living" in low arousal states, I took special care in finding what Sage liked and what brought more excitement into his life. Sage liked movies, video games, and stories. His favorite superhero was Spiderman and he responded well to the story of the butterfly. Before each of the reprocessing sessions, we worked on "preparing" the nervous system by having physical activities such as jumping rope or playing with the "freeze" and "unfreeze" remote control while we were moving and jumping around the office. After five to ten minutes, we were ready to move into EMDR reprocessing. These activities seemed to elevate the child's arousal level. We also included the "cushion stations" and Sage was very excited to pick his own advisors and tools for the "visit" to the "yucky" memories. We had the first station for Spiderman, the second one for the butterfly, the third one for the "watching self," the fourth one for the "inside telescope," and the last one for his helpers and all the people, angels, etc., that gave him strength and a sense of safety.

As we started to reprocess a memory of kids at school bullying him, Sage reported feeling like he wanted to help himself, but he could not. Sage started to move into a deep sense of powerlessness. As an interweave, I suggested to go to one of the stations for advice. Sage went to the butterfly station and asked the butterfly for ideas on what to do about helping himself. When I asked Sage what the butterfly had said, he stated: "The butterfly said to hang on and be strong and that my wings are coming out." I said, "Notice the advice of the butterfly" and initiated BLS. Later on, I also asked Sage to go to his helper station and find who could help him, and he brought the picture of his father and God who could help him. I asked Sage to just notice his father and God helping him while he engaged in BLS. The visual stimulation, movement, and playfulness of these interweaves kept Sage's social engagement system stimulated, allowing Sage to be present while using his tools, resources, advisors, and helpers. As the reprocessing sessions were progressing, Sage was more engaged and motivated. Sometimes we changed the stations and had "guest advisors" in addition to the "regular advisors." In one of the sessions, when we reprocessed the memory of his parent's divorce, we had Apolo Ohno in one of our stations. Apolo is a speed skater and an Olympic gold medalist that Sage reported looking up to. Apolo's parents divorced when he was an infant, and his father raised him. With this information,

I researched Apolo's life and was pleased to find out that Sage had several things in common with Apolo: They both experienced the divorce of their parents, they both liked sports, they both lived with their fathers, and they both were bi-racial. While reprocessing the memory of his parents' divorce, Sage was stuck in seeing himself as defective for not having his two parents. I invited Sage to move to the Apolo station. As we moved to this station, I told Sage the story of Apolo. I asked Sage what Apolo would say about his statement of him being less than other kids for not having both of his parents. We spent some time at this station, as several interweaves were done utilizing Apolo's story.

Stations may vary and change as the sessions progress. As you get to know the child and what interests him or her, new "guest advisors" may be invited. This will also keep the child motivated as new stations are added and new guests are invited.

TOOLS INSPIRED BY THE WORLD OF "SUPERHEROES" AND "FAIRYTALES"

Amazing tools and treasures coming from different stories and even video games can be used during the reprocessing phases of EMDR therapy. The story and passages of *Harry Potter* could be inspiring, in addition to bringing playfulness to the integration of memories of adversity in children. The Time Turner, Xenophilius Lovegood's Necklace, Harry Potter's wand, and many other wands that appear as helpful instruments and objects can also be used by the child as he or she embraces the memories of trauma and hardship. These instruments may assist the child in facing fear, powerlessness, and hurtful circumstances embedded in the memories of trauma. In addition, they maintain the child engaged and in playful states. Video games like "Super Mario" contain helpers and powers that assist Mario and his friends in facing negative circumstances. It is important to explore what is motivating to the child and investigate the characters and games, that he or she may be attracted to. If the child is very much into *Star Wars, Harry Potter, The Lord of the Rings*, Mario and many others, these interests become resources to engage and empower the child during the different phases of EMDR therapy. On the other hand, we keep the child grounded without getting lost in fantasy. We remind the child of the wonderful power of imagination and pretending, and how through them we can help ourselves overcome adversity. However, we keep the child present and grounded in the here and now.

Inner-Self Helpers

The concept of inner helpers was brought up to me by an adult client diagnosed with dissociative identity disorder (DID). Our work, has provided me with an entrance to the wisdom of clients diagnosed with DID. "Inside helpers" can be of incredible assistance as the child embraces the search, retrieval and integration of memories of trauma. The child may be asked to create or invite helpers that can provide support, guidance, and strength when visiting difficult memories. The child may have several helpers, from the ones that assist the child in finding the memories of adversity to the ones that help with advice, empowerment, etc. For instance, a client identified "internal butterflies" as the helpers that assisted her find "hidden events" and gave them a voice. There were some "secret events" that this client reported were locked away and the keys were held by "the butterflies."

There was also a "fairy godmother" that provided support and a sense of safety as these "secrets" were revealed. The symbolism and playfulness added by the "inner helpers" allowed this child to access memories of sexual abuse with the help of the "wise butterflies" and later on reprocess the memories of abuse with the help of the "fairy godmother." With younger children it will be important to clarify that these are "pretend" helpers and they do not necessarily exist in real form inside our bodies. Some children may believe they actually have a fairy living inside. However, when clearly explained, they can be amazing resources that accompany children in their journeys toward healing and can facilitate the exploration, accessing, and processing of memories.

USING OBJECTS AND DEVICES TO PROMOTE PLAYFULNESS AND CONTAINMENT

The use of walkie-talkies, phone toys, and microphones, among others, can maximize the child's sense of containment and integrative capacity through the stimulation of the play circuitry. For instance, when the child is experiencing disturbance and is able to locate it in the heart, the clinician can bring a microphone and ask permission to interview the heart. "*Mr. Heart, I hear that you are feeling some yucky stuff. Please notice if this yucky stuff has a shape.*" Once the heart responds, the clinician invites the heart to notice the disturbance and the shape that has been identified while engaging in BLS. "*What temperature does it have? Is it cold, warm, or really hot?*" When directing the questions to the heart, the microphone is directed toward the heart, the stomach, or the part or place where the disturbance is experienced in the body. Walkie-talkies may be used in the same manner. If the child is inside the "cushion house," from a distance, the clinician may ask the child to put the heart on the phone or have the heart talk through the child by using the walkie-talkie.

Sandtray figures can assist children express an emotion, sensation, or any information they are having difficulty verbalizing. For instance, a 6-year-old experiencing a lot of fear during the reprocessing of the memory of his father molesting him had great difficulty using words. However, his face and body language showed the incredible fear he was experiencing. He looked at me, but had no words. Initially, I encouraged him to bring the watching self and notice. However, the fear seemed to continue to escalate. Despite changing the direction and speed of the BLS, this child was clearly stuck in high states of fear. I reassured him that it was okay not to have words, since this was just one kind of the many languages we human beings were capable of using. I asked him to look at my sandtray figures and find the one that represented what he was experiencing inside. He chose a small snake and I asked him to just watch the snake and notice how he was much bigger than the snake. Children may experience their negative feelings as being bigger and more powerful than themselves. He followed the snake as he performed eye movements. When I asked him what he was noticing, he said that the snake was mean, but it felt good to know that he was bigger than the snake. I invited him to continue to notice if there was any message the snake had for him. After the set, the child stated that the snake was just showing him his scared feelings. Being able to externalize a feeling, conflict, or a body sensation through a figure or symbol provides the child with the distance needed to explore the feeling. It also allowed this child, with the participation of his left hemisphere, to give a voice and a label to the feeling.

The Shy Blanket and the Invisible Hats

A very creative and powerful interweave can be done through the use of objects that promote containment and, as a result, regulate arousal. Many children, especially the highly traumatized and dysregulated, often express the need to hide. After observing numerous children in my office calm down and relax once they were able to hide, I started to use objects that could help children hide as a way of regulating arousal. The "shy blanket" is a wonderful instrument that children can use to hide and disappear. This blanket should have the following important qualities: 1) The child should be able to see through, but not be seen; 2) it needs a fair amount of weight so the child can experience the felt sense of containment; 3) it should be big enough to cover the child's entire body. As explained in prior chapters, before reprocessing, the child should be acquainted with the use of the blanket. When reprocessing stalls, the clinician can ask the child if the use of the "shy blanket" could help. Once the child goes under the blanket, the child is invited to notice what happens as he or she can see others but cannot be seen. As the child is noticing this experience of containment, the clinician continues to provide BLS. The child can be invited to continue to visit the yucky memory while feeling contained and safe under the blanket. A 7-year-old reprocessing the memory of one of her nightmares where big monsters attacked her, expressed the desire to have the shy blanket around her for protection. Once under the blanket, she stated that she was going to fight the monsters and I invited her to go with that. I watched a lot of movement under the blanket while performing tactile BLS. When I asked the customary questions, take a breath, let it go, what happened, she came out from under the blanket and said, "I am still fighting them, I am almost done." I asked her if she needed help, but she stated that she was doing pretty well herself. After four full sets of BLS, she came out from under the blanket and said that she was done and did not need the blanket anymore. At this point, the SUD level decreased significantly, as the monsters were defeated and the child was able to come out triumphant.

The shy blanket can be extremely helpful when working with children that cannot tolerate eye contact due to their attachment injuries and traumas. Since one of the qualities of the shy blanket is the opportunity that it offers to the child to see others, but not be seen, children can engage in a form of eye contact that is more tolerable. When targeting attachment behaviors such as eye contact, the shy blanket offers the child the opportunity to look at his or her parent without being seen. Francisco was a boy brought to therapy due to the frequent nightmares and aggressiveness with his siblings. Francisco did not present with any history of abuse, but instead his parents reported that the mother suffered severe depression the first three years of his life. The father had great difficulty connecting emotionally with Francisco and used work as a way to remain peripheral and not connected to this child. Francisco was becoming increasingly fearful of being alone and was telling his parents that there were monsters in his room. When I attempted to reprocess his nightmares, the monsters grew and became stronger. Francisco did not respond well to any interweaves and asked to stop EMDR. The mother presented with unresolved trauma connected to sexual abuse, physical abuse and emotional abuse at the hands of her parents. Due to Francisco's experiences with both parents, incongruent and multiple models of the self were developed. As a result, Francisco was unable to develop a sense of permanence and the internalization of parents that were capable of meeting his needs for connection and safety. Without this sense of permanence, Francisco could not internalize a "felt sense of safety" and security. I noticed how Francisco could not tolerate having eye contact with both of his parents. It was really difficult and dysregulating to look at his mother's eyes. A hierarchy of attachment behaviors was created (see Chapter 8). Francisco could not tolerate physical contact, mostly with his mother, and expressions of affection made him feel "highly embarrassed." The first target was the eye contact. The negative belief was "it's not safe to show my feelings" when I look at mom. Francisco reported feeling embarrassed and the SUD was at a ten. When reprocessing began, Francisco stated that he felt yucky and soon after started to say, "I don't know, I don't get anything." With the help of the shy blanket, he was able to look at his mother while engaging in tactile BLS. Francisco reported that with the shy blanket the SUD was at a zero, but without it was at a ten. After one reprocessing session, Francisco was able to engage in eye contact with his mother, while the mother was also verbalizing loving words. Francisco went from feeling disturbed, to feeling neutral, to feeling "love" as he engaged in eye contact with his mother. It is important to highlight, in this case, that the mother participated in extensive EMDR treatment herself and the targeting of attachment behaviors was initiated after the mother had enough awareness of how her own unresolved trauma and depression had impacted Francisco. Sessions with the father were also done using attachment behaviors as the primary targets. Nightmares started to go away after the first two sessions, where eye contact and physical affection with the mother were targeted. The monsters in his room started to disappear as Francisco and his parents found greater levels of connection, and as the memory networks containing information of injuring attachment experiences with his parents were accessed and reprocessed through the attachment behavior.

Invisible hats as well as eyeglasses may also be used, when eye contact is difficult for children. They can be used similarly to the shy blanket.

INTERWEAVES USING STORYTELLING

Stories that heal may be used during reprocessing phases when processing gets blocked. Some of these stories come from nature or passages of movies and books. Harry Potter, the Lord of the Rings, among many others may bring light into the issue where the child is getting stuck. On the other hand, real stories that may be unknown or partially known by the child may be told during reprocessing sessions in the form of interweaves when the time is right and information processing is getting blocked. Jennifer, an 8-year-old girl, was brought to therapy due to extreme separation anxiety from her mother. She also had difficulty falling asleep at night and insisted on sleeping with her mother. The mother reported that Jennifer's anxiety had begun early in her life, even before her molestation in the hands of a family friend. After reprocessing the memory of the sexual abuse, Jennifer showed improvement in symptoms related to aggressiveness and oppositional behaviors; however, the separation anxiety symptoms only had a slight decrease. Further exploration of the early attachment experiences yielded information about Jennifer's mother experiencing high anxiety and fear that something could happen to her. Jennifer's father had left right after he found out about the pregnancy. Raising Jennifer alone and having to leave her with babysitters or family members so she could work, had Jennifer's mother in a state of high fear and anxiety for the safety and well-being of her daughter. The mother reported that she had been able to overcome this fear, but now her daughter was constantly afraid that something could happen to her. The earliest memory of Jennifer, where she had to be left with a babysitter, was targeted. Spontaneous processing was foremost honored, but when information processing was blocked because of the high fear of losing her mother, I invited the mother to tell Jennifer the story of her fear. It is worth highlighting that preparation sessions were done with the mother to assist her in creating and writing her story in a concise and child-friendly manner. Jennifer's mother held her in her arms while she told the story. BLS was provided as the story was being told. This was a very powerful interweave that assisted Jennifer in integrating information, that even though was affectively and somatically encoded in Jennifer's brain, the cognitive understanding of the root of her fear was not integrated. In many cases though, the cognitive aspect of the memory may always remain unknown and integration of the affective and somatic material is still possible and attainable. However, if the story is available and is developmentally appropriate for the child to know it, the parent can be encouraged to prepare it, so it can be used as an interweave. In my clinical experience, using story telling in the form of interweaves does not need to be extensive and long, but they do need to contain the core and essence connected to the child's current symptom. This may be different from other approaches, where the centerpiece is the story told by the caregiver (see Lovett, 1999) that requires a more extensive, thorough script and narrative of the memory.

STIMULATING THE USE OF NONVERBAL COMMUNICATION THROUGH THE USE OF INTERWEAVES

When accessing memories of early attachment trauma, we are accessing the language of the lower brain and the right hemisphere. The use of nonverbal strategies can greatly facilitate the process for children working on memories of events occurring pre-verbally. Drawings and musical instruments may be used. The following represents some examples.

Using Drawings and Art

Drawings have long been used in therapy with children and in the use of EMDR therapy. Art and drawings can provide distance from the disturbing material, so it is more tolerable to the child. The following represents some of the ways drawings may be used during the desensitization phase of EMDR therapy with children:

1. When the child's reprocessing halts, the child is invited to notice inside the body, the heart and the mind what is happening and draw a figure that represents it. This could be an amorphous figure of a color that best represents the feeling, sensation or thought coming up for the child. This interweave works well when the child reports no clear images and is feeling "something" that he or she is unable to put into words. It also helps children that report feeling "nothing" or that respond after a set of BLS, "I don't know what is happening." It is important to highlight the need of the clinician to attune to the child's physiological changes, since any of these responses may be indicative of a child moving into dissociative states. The child is invited to bring "the watching me" to mindfully observe what is happening and without words put it on paper. First the child picks the color or colors and then the child is encouraged to draw what his or her "watching self" is observing that is unfolding inside. The "inside camera" described in Chapter 11 may also be used. The child is then invited to "zoom in" and "zoom out" as the child, or the "watching me," is observing and drawing it on the paper. The clinician uses the

drawing to engage the child in eye movement. The child is asked to just notice the drawing. After the set of BLS, the child is given another piece of paper to draw what his or her "watching me" is noticing and once again the child is invited to follow the drawing. No words are needed unless the child wants to add an emotion, sensation, thought and express them through words. José, a child adopted at the age of four from an orphanage in Central America, while working on the memory of his biological mother abandoning him, stated that "nothing" was happening. I asked him if nothing meant he was going away, or nothing meant he was feeling yucky, but did not know how to tell me. He stated nothing meant, *"I feel bad, but I don't know how to tell you."* I invited José to bring his "watching me/self" to "watch" what was happening inside, pick a color and put what he was feeling/seeing inside on a piece of paper. The child was asked to let this inner-subjective experience to come out in any form it wanted to come out and in any color it wanted to be seen. José drew a fairly large round, green shape with lots of spikes. José was invited to follow his drawing with his eyes. After the second set of BLS, José was asked again to draw a picture of how this inner experience was now perceived. José drew a smaller figure with similar spikes. After drawing the figure, José was again asked to follow it with his eyes while he was focusing on this inner experience. As BLS continued, the shape representing José's internal state was getting smaller and smaller until it reached the shape of a little dot. At this point he stated that he was feeling better and the "inside yucky stuff" was gone.

2. The clinician may use a board for the child to draw pictures after every set. The child does not need to use verbal language. In addition, the clinician may use a laser pen to provide the BLS. Once the child has finished drawing on the board the picture of what he or she is noticing after the set, the clinician invites the child to follow the laser pen's dot, which is reflected on the board. After each set, the child or the clinician erases the previous drawing, so a new illustration can be created. Paper may also be used so every drawing may be preserved. In this case, the laser pen is reflected on the paper that contains the drawing created by the child.

3. Children tend to greatly enjoy painting and the felt sense painting, and especially what finger painting offers. Painting keeps the child in playful states and, as a result, more engaged. When working with children with sensitized sympathetic, and parasympathetic systems that have the tendency to either move into hyper- or hypoarousal, they may benefit from the use of art and nonverbal strategies during the reprocessing phases of EMDR therapy. In fact, these sensory-based, right-brain strategies may facilitate the activation of the social engagement system, keeping children within optimal arousal levels.

Using Music and Musical Instruments

Music is also a wonderful way of speaking the language of the right hemisphere. Children that have already developed a relationship with a musical instrument and music in general can use this as a resource and a vehicle of connection between the inside and the outside world. The child may be invited to connect the musical instrument to his or her "inside" world and allow the instrument to become the voice of the inside world, as described in Chapter 11. The child can also find melodies already known by the child that best represents internal states. In between sets, the child is invited to play the "inside" songs and "inside" music. After the child has expressed what he or she is noticing through the musical instrument, the child is invited to engage in BLS while listening to this inner sound. Musical instruments help children maintain dual awareness and focused attention and, as a result, facilitate reprocessing. Musical instruments may be incorporated starting at the preparation phase. Children that already have a close relationship with music and a specific instrument may have them as companions of their healing journeys. They may use them as a resource and as the voice of their inner worlds. They can use the musical instrument at any point during the reprocessing phases. They may use them most of the time or just for a few sets. Initially, nonverbal communication may be easier for the child as it offers a voice to the right hemisphere and the "implicit self" (Schore, 2010). However, as the level of disturbance decreases, verbal communication and cognitive left-brain processing mode may come naturally for the child.

Working With the Attachment System: Reparative Interweaves

Several interweaves designed to repair and heal the attachment system have been presented in Chapters 12 and 13, which involve the use of Theraplay and Internal Family Systems (IFS) strategies. In this chapter we will cover the use of interweaves provided by the parent, under the guidance of the EMDR clinician, as well as the use of ego state tactics. When parents have been the wounding agent, repair may be imperative for healing to take place. However, true repair cannot happen unless the parent has been able to restore the capacity for mentalization, reflective functioning and insight. This means that the parent would need an appropriate level of assimilation and integration of his or her memories of trauma and adversity. Otherwise, if the parent repairs during reprocessing sessions, but continues to engage in the same behaviors at home that were wounding to the child, it may cause greater damage. When reparative interweaves are done sincerely, truthfully and heart felt, they can be extremely powerful. Once again, the EMDR clinician will need to look at the overall clinical landscape; readiness of the parent to give and readiness of the child to receive, before deciding on the types of interweaves that may be needed. Does the presence of the parent promote a sense of safety and openness in the child? Or, on the contrary, does it inhibit the ability of the child to open up and process disturbing material? Ideally, if the injuries were inflicted within the caregiving system, the parent's ability and openness to repair will, in my clinical experience, speed up the process of integration and, ultimately, healing for the child. The following procedures and interweaves assume the appropriate participation of the parent in therapy. This includes individual work at any of the levels proposed in Chapter 5, as well as the willingness to understand the mind of the child and act accordingly. Parents of adopted children that did not directly cause such injuries will also benefit from at a minimum receiving psychoeducation and some work on self-regulation. However, I have had parents that either received extensive EMDR work prior to bringing their children for therapy, or they possess the ability to know their children at a deeper level and respond contingently to their needs. These are parents with secure states of mind that only require basic psychoeducation, if any. Non-offending parents of biological or adoptive children with histories of neglect, abuse, abandonment and, in general, children with unmet attachment needs will benefit from having the parent present to repair and meet attachment needs. Children of divorced parents and insecurely attached children may greatly benefit from having the parent present to provide reparative interweaves. Needless to say, if the child does not want to have the parent present, it should not be forced upon the child. The child and the clinician alone can accomplish a great deal of work, while the parent is also doing individual therapeutic work. However, the child's refusal to have the parent present can be explored and used therapeutically to tap into potential targets for reprocessing. Once it has been agreed to have the parent present during the child's reprocessing sessions, a preparation session should be scheduled with the parent. As stated in Chapter 5, the process should be predictable for the child and the parent. Roles should be clarified and understood by the caregiver. In addition, since the child has either agreed to have the parent participate or actually requested the presence of the parent, the process will be more predictable for the child.

When the opportunity comes, because reprocessing stalled, the clinician intervenes by asking the parent to participate. These sessions are usually very moving and powerful and clinicians need to prepare internally to attune, resonate and synchronize with both the child and the caregiver in a compassionate and honoring way. The tone of voice, internal state, body posture, and physical closeness should be taken into consideration. For children with some tolerance for shared positive experiences and affection, the sessions are set up in a way that promotes closeness. We may sit on the floor using comfortable cushions that allow us to sit fairly close to one another. However, children with avoidant strategies, or children with "phobia" of touch and closeness may need, in the beginning, a level of closeness they can tolerate such as the therapist sitting on a chair, while the child and the parent sit on the couch. The child is given the chance to choose where he or she wants everybody to sit and how close we all should be from each other. As the sessions progress, so is the physical closeness children can tolerate. Oftentimes, we start sitting on chairs and couches, and after several sessions, the child is ready to choose the floor cushions as well as greater levels of closeness, until the child and the parent can arrive to a level of closeness that feels appropriate for them. This, of course, is not dictated by the clinician's standards, but by what deeply nourishes and feeds the child.

Once the moment is appropriate because the child is "looping" at a place where repairing is necessary, the clinician guides the reparative process. I have called these "reparative interweaves." For instance, a child that was not nurtured as a result of neglect, may need to hear the parent truly apologize and validate the child's experience. In addition, the child's "younger self" may need to have unmet needs met by the parent now. A child of divorced parents that gets stuck in "it's my fault that my parents are not together" may need to have the parent assign appropriate responsibility by owning it and expressing accountability in the presence of the child. A child victim of sexual abuse may need to hear from the nonoffending parent an apology for not keeping him or her safe or not noticing what was happening, even though as a parent it was his or her job to protect the child. A child that had to comply with very high standards from the parent, resulting in high stress and anxiety on the child's part, may benefit from hearing the parent truly apologize and own his or her need for perfection. The same child may need to hear that he or she is good, lovable, etc., even when a mistake has been made or when the best grades were not achieved.

When the EMDR clinician considers it appropriate to include a "reparative interweave," the parent is invited to *"connect the voice to your heart and let the child know from your voice and your heart that . . . ."* The parent may be encouraged to elaborate more in terms of the specific situation of the child. A parent may say that when mom and dad yelled at each other it was because grown-ups sometimes have problems with "big feelings" that kids are not responsible for. The parent may also say, *"I am so sorry that I did not protect you, even though it was my job to do that. Mom had problems and could not do what mom needed to do for you, but mom is working on being a mom that can keep you safe and take care of you now."* BLS may be provided as follows:

1. While the parent is providing the interweave.
2. After the parent has finished repairing and the child is invited to notice what is coming up for him or her. In some cases where eye movement is being used, waiting until the parent completes the reparative interweave may be necessary unless tapping or the butterfly hug is being used. The profound moment of repair needs the full engagement of the child and the parent, and this involves eye contact, if tolerable to the child. In these cases where eye movement is used, the clinician waits and asks the child to notice what is happening in the moment after the complete interweave has been provided.
3. After the parent provides a reparative interweave, the clinician asks a question to help the child link up the information provided by the parent to the memory being processed. The clinician in this case may say something like, *"Are kids responsible for the choices parents make? So, are you responsible for the problems your parents had?"* Once the child responds, the clinician says, *"Notice that or go with that."* The third approach involves more of a Socratic method in conjunction with the reparative interweave. The clinician may use questions to elicit the information needed from the parent. For instance, *"Mom, is there anything that Laurie could do that may make you stop loving her?"* The mother responds, no, there is nothing she can do to make me stop loving her. *"Even if she makes a mistake?"* Mother responds, even if Laurie makes a mistake I will still love her. *"What if Laurie gets a bad grade? What about when she is angry? Or sad? Or frustrated?"* The child may also be invited to ask the parent the "what if questions."

Brandon, a 6-year-old boy who was working on a memory of him acting sexually on another child his age, carried extreme shame. His biological father had molested him at the age of 3 and his mother had abandoned him shortly after the abuse. During the reprocessing of the memory of touching the private parts of another child, Brandon stated that his adoptive parents did not love him because he had been bad with the other boy. The adoptive mother found him and the other boy in his room and she yelled at Brandon and told him he was a really bad boy. When the reparative interweave was used, the therapist asked the mother questions that conveyed unconditional love to Brandon. His action was a bad choice, but even then he was lovable and good. After the clinician asked a series of questions as the ones described above, Brandon asked his adoptive mother the following: *"What if I break a house, would you still love me?"* The mother responded; even if you broke a house I will still love you. *"What if I go to jail, would you still love me?"* The mother responded, you are not going to jail, but even if as a grown-up you did, which I do not believe you would, I will still love you and I will be waiting for you when you get out. This was a very powerful interweave for Brandon, as he was able to receive unconditional love and acceptance, even when he made a bad choice. This is the true nature of interweaves that convey unconditional love. Loving the perfect child may be easy, but loving a child when he or she is at his or her worst behavior is the true heart and essence of unconditional love.

REPARATIVE INTERWEAVES WITH THE YOUNGER SELF

Reparative interweaves can be very powerful when used in conjunction with inner child work. Many different approaches have long used inner child work. Inner child work has been introduced in the EMDR therapeutic work by many clinicians and authors (Paulsen & Lanius, 2009; Wesselmann, 2007, 2010), each of them using different avenues and styles to access, engage and heal the younger part of the self. When working with the younger self, honoring this part's mechanisms of adaptation is fundamental. The inner child from the AIP perspective represents the early attachment experiences encoded in memory that contain representations of the self and other. These memories are gently explored, accessed and reprocessed through the "inner child." Many mental health practitioners from different schools of thought may assume that most of us when meeting the younger self, want to hug, nurture and connect with the "inner child" right away. In my experience, many people with attachment injuries may have great difficulties engaging with their inner, younger parts. Based on my clinical observations, the relationship we have with our "inner child" mirrors our states of mind with regards to early attachment experiences and the mechanisms we have learned to use to adapt when not having our attachment needs met. Children using avoidant strategies may not like to get close to their "little selves." Connecting with this vulnerable younger part may feel uncomfortable and "awkward." Children with disorganized strategies and attachment patterns may have contradicting responses from loving to violent interactions with the "little self." Sometimes they express impulses of hitting and telling the younger self to go away. They may engage in bizarre behaviors that seem to replicate how their parental figures interacted with them. Children with ambivalent patterns of attachment may oscillate between a lot of togetherness and a desire to nurture the part that represents the "little me," while at times expressing anger toward this vulnerable part. In many years of using "inner child" work with parents as interweaves during the reprocessing phases, I have discovered a parallel between how they relate to their own "inner child", the state of mind with regards to their own early attachment experiences and how they relate to their children. Once again, parents with dismissing, preoccupied and unresolved states of mind tend to react differently when meeting their younger selves. From complete distance and refusal to get close to the younger self, to a high desire to hold and nurture the inner child accompanied by intense expressions of emotions, to feeling angered and frustrated in the presence of the younger self. With this in mind, it is important not to assume that right away all of our clients want to nurture, hug and embrace their younger selves. In fact, many of them can get highly activated when a clinician moves too fast too soon in the process of connecting to the inner child. The following is a sequence that may be followed to guide children, adolescents and adults when meeting the inner child:

1. Start by explaining to the child that you are going to meet the "little me" "younger me," "tiny me," "the baby me" or the "littler me." Keep in mind the age of the child at the time of the event that is being targeted. The younger self is invited to come into the present or to receive the visit in the past from the child and whomever the child chooses to bring. The child is given the choice, however, that at some point the "present self" may need to visit the "past self" to help, nurture, honor or finish unfinished business in the past. There are several ways to access the younger self that have been addressed in different chapters in this book. 1) The first option is by using imagery and inviting the child to visualize giving a visit to his or her "little me" or "the baby me." 2) The second option is by using dolls or baby animals that represent the younger self. Even though the visit may happen in the past

or the present, the child, parent and the clinician interact, connect and nurture the doll that represents him or her. 3) The third option is by using sandtray therapy, and in the story created by the child, extend an invitation to the younger self to choose a baby, animal or figure that will represent him or her. Chapter 12 describes strategies where Theraplay and IFS are combined to work with the younger self. Chapter 13 also addresses the use of IFS strategies with the "little self." Since the second and third options are covered in other chapters, we will concentrate on the first option.

2. If the child chose to go to the past, the child is invited to give a "visit" to the "baby me, little me or younger me." The child is invited to imagine where the "little self" is. "*Notice where he/she is, is he/she inside or outside? What is he/she doing? What is he/she wearing? See if you can see his/her face. Is there anybody else with him/her? Is this a good time to visit him/her?*" If yes, go on; if not, invite the child to explore it with the younger self. What makes this not a good time? When may be a good time? Is there anything needed by the younger self in order to have the visit? Once the younger self has granted permission for the visit, ask the child to notice any impulses either to move closer or to distance from the younger self. "*When you see your 'baby you' or 'baby Maria,' check inside and see what your body, your heart and your mind are wanting to do. Do you find yourself wanting to get close, really close or on the other side, to get far or really far from him/her?*" The child may say that he or she wants to get really close. The clinician will respond with "notice that, or think about that or go with that" and initiate BLS. When BLS stops and customary EMDR procedures are used, such as take a breath, the child may report feeling sad for the "little me" and the clinician's response will be, "*Just watch that sadness with your 'watching self.'*" If the child gets "stuck" in this sadness, a new interweave is used to help the child resolve this early and old sadness. "*As you see and feel the sadness of the 'baby you,' let him/her tell you or show you what he/she needs or longs for that can help him/her with this sadness.*" BLS is initiated again. If the "inside baby" reports wanting or needing care, ask the "inside baby" to let the child know how he/she wants to be cared for. Menus can be offered, such as: "*Maybe the 'baby you' would like to be rocked, or fed, or played with. Maybe he/she needs someone to talk to him/her, or he/she may want someone to guess what he/she wants.*" Once the child reports what the younger self needs or wants, the next question is, "*Is there anybody in particular that "the little me" would like to have to help with this? Does he/she want you or mom or me to do that for him/her?*" Once the child lets you know how the younger self wants the need to be met, the clinician ensures that the younger self receives what he or she is needing or longing for. If the younger self wants the parent to meet the attachment needs, the parent is prompted to do what the younger self is requesting. If the child has chosen a doll to represent the younger self, the doll receives the care needed. If the child is visualizing the younger self inside and in the past, the "baby self" is invited to choose where in the body of the child wants to create a home. The younger self may be placed in the heart, the mind or the eyes. Either way, the younger self is invited to be present in the body of the child and receive the care he or she is longing for. The parent is encouraged to feed, rock, play or sing to the child. It is important to have blankets, food (such as cookies, water, juice, pudding) baby bottles, baby toys and baby books so the needs can be met at the developmental stage of the younger self. BLS may be provided while the younger self is being nurtured. Once the first request from

the younger self is fulfilled, the clinician stops BLS, asks the child to breathe, let go and notice what is coming up or what is happening. If the child reports positive or negative responses, BLS continues until this need is completely and fully experienced. The clinician then asks again and again if there is anything the younger self needs, longs for, wants to know, wants help with, wants to say or do and so on.

3. The younger self may be invited to come to the present to get a "tour." This inter-weave can be very effective in helping locate the memory in time and space. For instance, a child that spent the first four years of life in an orphanage and now has a loving adoptive family, may be presenting with fear of being alone and not having parents now. Inviting the "little self" to come to the present and have a tour, so he or she can see and experience all the positive changes attained by the child in the present can be very powerful. Invite the child to have the younger self see through his or her eyes: the new parents, the new place where they live, the new friends, and how the younger self as well as the child are safe now and have a permanent family. You can also invite the child or the parent to show the figure or doll that represents the "little self" all the positive current life circumstances that surround the child.

As covered in Chapter 8, an appropriate target for children may be a specific developmental stage where, based on history, it is well known that the child experienced trauma and adversity. These types of targets, especially, will need reparative interweaves using "inner child" strategies. When targeting a memory of an event that occurred early in the life of the child, the "littler self" may be accessed and assisted, as well. For instance, a child that could not run or escape may now have the opportunity to imagine visiting the younger self and helping him or her escape. If the child wants the parent or the therapist to accompany him or her in this visit, then they all will go to support the younger self. Reparative interweaves not only assist the child in meeting unmet attachment needs, but in addition, they help the child complete defense responses, speak unspoken words and perform victorious acts that could not be executed at the time of the event.

CULTURAL ISSUES

It is of critical importance to be aware and respectful of the cultural heritage of the child and his or her family system. For many cultures and ethnic groups, physical contact and connection as well as eye contact may at times be even considered a sign of disrespect. Getting information and becoming educated by the parents and the child on important cultural issues is pivotal during the initial phases of EMDR therapy so the reprocessing phases include interweaves that honor the child and the family system's values. How much the EMDR therapist participates in the child's healing journey may be also guided by the cultural views of the family. For instance, in some cases, it may not be appropriate to even give the child the option of having the therapist assist in nurturing the "younger self" and only the child or the parent should be invited. Generally speaking, the clinician should facilitate the process and be an agent that promotes connection between the parent and the child. Maintaining appropriate boundaries while maintaining an attuned and caring presence will promote and facilitate change. In addition, religious beliefs and values should be explored, as they can be extremely powerful resources for the child and the family. For instance, when reprocessing issues related to grief and loss, getting educated on the beliefs of the family with regards to death and dying may help in creating potential interweaves that can help the child remain connected to the loved one that passed away. If the family believes in the existence of human spirit, an interweave where the child connects his or her heart through a "heart string" may be used. Several children's books have stories of "heart strings or cords" and these stories may be read with the child during the preparation phase. During the reprocessing phases of EMDR therapy, if the child gets stuck in feelings of sadness because of feeling disconnected from the loved one, you can invite the child to create a "heart string" of any color and let it fly and travel until it finds the heart in the spirit of the loved one. It may travel to heaven or any beautiful place in the universe. Oftentimes, I invite the child to look at books with pictures of galaxies and the beautiful universe we live in to show children how we are part of something greater than ourselves. However, the values of the family should be explored and foremost honored. Only then, adequate and healing interweaves that can assist the child in integrating memories of loss can be prepared and effectively utilized. In addition, God, angels, and Buddha, among others may be invited to assist the child during the session as helpers and advisors.

Each culture may possess symbols and stories that can assist the child and the family in arriving to a better understanding of trauma, trauma symptoms and resources already held by the cultural self and the cultural context of the child. For instance, Native American culture possesses wonderful symbols and resources pertaining to nature and the journey of human kind. I had a wonderful experience working with the Saginaw Indian tribe in MI in 2011, where I learned about important and profound teachings of Native Americans. The "sacred tree" and the "medicine wheel" can be honored and embraced during EMDR therapy. The medicine wheel is an ancient symbol of the universe. Through the eight phases of EMDR therapy, a journey around the medicine wheel can be incorporated. Each point of the medicine wheel represents the cycles of nature, such as the seasons and the four directions; children can identify the resources and positive experiences of the east and "spring," a season of abundance. Children may also identify the experiences of the exciting summer and the decaying fall; times in our lives where we felt that "our leaves" were falling apart. The cold experiences of the winter can also be explored, accessed and processed as the child is invited to visit the "winter" in his or her life and identify the different "winter experiences." With the help of each direction: The east, south, west and north children can travel around the medicine wheel searching for resources, mastery experiences, helpers and memories of adversity and hardship. Different animals and symbols come to the assistance of the traveler in the Native American culture. The mountain, for instance, is one of the symbols of the North and winter, which remind us that the higher we are, the steeper it may get. We could get the eagle and the mouse which are the teachers and masters of the east. Each direction and season come with their own teachers and helpers who can assist the child in traveling through life and through the different phases of EMDR therapy.

In Central America, more specifically in Guatemala, the "trouble dolls" may assist children in identifying targets for EMDR processing. In Guatemala, children can talk to each doll and tell them his or her problems. Bringing the dolls and inviting the child to tell each a worry, concern or "yucky" thing from the past may be appropriate for target identification.

In summary, getting curious about the cultural self and the traditions that bring cultural context to the therapeutic process is fundamental. Cultural practices and traditions may also make the therapeutic process more familiar, safe and enjoyable for children. Needless to say, any stimulus and strategy that may be well intended could potentially be activating to the child. Even benign cultural practices may hold negative associations to the child and as a result be counterproductive. It is always a good clinical practice to get acquainted with what the child and his or her family finds enjoyable and life-giving from their culture. However, if they are triggering and negative, they can be placed as potential targets for processing.

USING SANDTRAY THERAPY STRATEGIES

Once the child has created the "story" or "world" and the baseline of the memory has been established as it is done during the assessment phase (see Chapter 8), the child is instructed to think about the story, however all the questions are directed to the main character of the story. It may be the child as he or she recognizes himself or herself in the story, but it may be just "the horsey" or "the boy" or whatever name is given by the child to the main character. While the child is engaging in BLS, the child may just be looking at the story or world in the sandtray or he or she may be moving the characters around. After each set, the child is instructed to take a breath and if the child is able to understand the concept of "let go," then the child can be invited to let go. In my clinical experience, this concept may be confusing for children and we may be giving too many directives: take a breath, let it go, what do you notice? Oftentimes, I just invite the child to breathe and then I ask what is happening or what he or she is noticing. The child may be invited to just show in the sandtray what is happening and what is coming up for him or her without words. Words may also be invited, but are not required. However, at some point, the more active participation of the left hemisphere may be important in labeling the experience and creating a narrative of what is happening, as the child is working on assimilating and integrating the memory. It is worth highlighting that the collection of sandtray miniatures should contain figures needed for the appropriate use of interweaves. For instance, figures representing different developmental stages, genders and racial groups should be part of the collection. In addition, animals, plants, trees, nature metaphors and totems, helpers or advisors introduced to the child during the preparation phase, or that may be needed during the reprocessing phases of EMDR therapy should be part of the collection. Moreover, items to nurture, feed and play with the "younger self" should also be available to the child. When information processing stalls, interweaves can be used in such beautiful ways, as the sandtray therapy work provides the symbols, figures and the opportunity for the "implicit self" to express itself. Most of the interweaves covered in this chapter can be adapted to be used with sandtray therapy work. If the character of the story is feeling powerless and needs assistance, it may be asked what the character needs. Let the "horsey" show you or tell you what it needs. If the "horsey" needs helpers, ask the "horsey" who could help him and bring the figures chosen by the "horsey" to help, assist and empower the "horsey." If there are actions that could not be performed during the traumatic or adverse event, or there were unspoken words, the main character may be encouraged to execute the actions or say what could not be said before.

If the child wants to bring advisors or nature totems as he or she visits the memory, a special place or corner of the sandtray can be used to place all the advisors and helpers. When information processing stalls, the child or the main character may be invited to go to the "advisors or helpers' corner" and ask for advice or help. Along the same lines, the child and the EMDR clinician can work with "the younger self" while using sandtray therapy strategies. The strategies described early in this chapter to work with the "little me" may also be utilized when using sandtray approaches in combination with EMDR therapy.

STANDARD PROCEDURAL STEPS FOR THE DESENSITIZATION PHASE WITH CHILDREN (ADAPTED FROM SHAPIRO, 2010)

During the desensitization phase, reprocessing continues with repeated cycles of BLS and questioning until the SUD = 0. Remember that the sets are long (approximately 24) and fast (highest speed the child can tolerate).

1. At the end of each set of BLS say, ***"Take a breath*** (breathe with the child), *let it go, what happened or what do you notice."* Say, *"Go with that, notice that or think about that,"* with whatever the child reports followed by another cycle of BLS and questioning. If the child needs clarification say, *"When I say think about that, notice that or go with that, what I would like you to do is to just notice any feelings that are coming up, any thoughts, anything that you see in your mind or anything that you feel in your body."*
2. Continue alternating sets of BLS with the child's reports until they become positive or neutral.
3. Going Back to Target: You will go back to target for the following reasons:

    When the child's reports become neutral or positive for several sets of BLS say,

    "I want you to think about that memory your brain has been working on. When you think about this memory, what happens now?" If the child needs clarification say, ***"As we visit this memory, what thoughts, feelings do you notice or what do you see in your mind or feel in your body now?"*** Say, *"Go with that, notice that or think about that,"* with whatever the child reports and do another set of BLS. If the child forgets the memory being reprocessed, give the memory a general title and say, ***"The memory of mom and dad, or the memory of the car."*** DO NOT repeat again the memory in detail or what the child reported as the worst part, considering that the child may be in a different portion or aspect of the memory.

    If after the set of BLS, the child reports new material, continue reprocessing with repeated cycles of BLS and questioning until no new material is coming up, or the material is positive. It may be necessary to return to target several times during reprocessing before all channels are clear and taking a SUD becomes necessary (Shapiro, 2001,2005).

- **If the child's processing gets stuck**: If after **two** sets of BLS the child reports no changes while indicating identical or similar negative emotions, thoughts or bodily states, it may be that the negative reactions continue to escalate with no insight, movement or resolution. It may be that the child continues to say "I get nothing" or the child goes into several things or issues that are very distant or completely unrelated to the memory being processed. At this point, change mechanics (speed, type or direction of the BLS) and if processing is not reinitiated, **go back to target** and see if processing starts or is initiated again. If going back to target does not jump start processing, use any of the interweaves covered in this chapter.

4. Checking the SUD:
   When going back to target, if the child reports:

■ Something new or anything negative or disturbing say, *"Go with that or notice that."*

■ Nothing new, check the SUD's level. Using the "Bothering Scale" put the foam numbers from 0 to 10 in front of the child. Give the child the helper or a small doll that can walk on the "Bothering Scale."

   Say, *"Now we are going to use the "Bothering Scale" again. When you think about the memory your brain has been visiting, working on or sorting out, how bad does it feel now from 0 to 10? Remember that 0 means it is neutral and 10 means it bothers you a lot."* Allow the child to 'walk' the doll or helper on the 'Bothering Scale' until he or she can provide the level of disturbance.

SUMMARY AND CONCLUSIONS

The desensitization phase and, in general, all the reprocessing phases of EMDR therapy promote the assimilation and integration of memory systems. Children who have experienced complex trauma may present with severe deficits in affect regulation and tolerance. As a result of the lack of appropriate attachment and developmental experiences, these children present with scarcity of memory systems that contain adaptive information about the self and other. Due to the presence of dissociation and dissociative disorders in children with early trauma and abuse, the attuned presence of the clinician is pivotal in order to support different forms of information processing as well as various levels of integration: vertical and horizontal. The EMDR clinician needs to be well versed in the use of standard EMDR procedures when using interweaves as well as to have a comprehensive pool of interweaves that can assist the child when information processing stalls. Spontaneous information processing is foremost encouraged and honored; however, children with highly dysregulated systems may tend to move into hyper- or hypoarousal states and as a result move out of the windows of affect tolerance. The attuned EMDR clinician will then be able to assist the child to stay within optimal arousal states where dual awareness and mindfulness are possible. Working with complexly traumatized and dissociative children may require a more active participation of the clinician in comparison to the level of input required when treating children with simple PTSD, a single trauma event and with overall appropriate attachment experiences. This chapter offered a wide range of interweaves that are child friendly and developmentally appropriate. Even though a number of interweaves were presented, we want to mostly honor the child's wisdom by intervening only when information processing has stalled, or when assistance is needed to facilitate the linkage among memory networks in the child's brain.

10

Installation, Body Scan, Closure,
Reevaluation, and the Future Template

PHASE FIVE: INSTALLATION

Once the child has reported a SUDs level of zero, the installation of the positive cognition is underway. An important goal of the installation phase is the enhancement of positive and adaptive networks and the complete assimilation of the new positive "felt" belief. Amplifying and heightening the strength of the positive cognition as well as augmenting the accessing to adaptive and positive memory networks are also important goals of the installation phase. During the installation phase, the child can experience a felt positive belief about himself or herself in association with the memory being reprocessed.

Children with history of early and chronic trauma have difficulty tolerating positive affect. Enhancing and amplifying their ability to tolerate and experience positive emotions and to hold positive views of the self are pivotal aspects of eye movement desensitization and reprocessing (EMDR) therapy.

According to Shapiro (2001), it is fundamental that the client identifies a positive cognition that is most meaningful for the child. The installation of the positive cognition for children may contain playful elements to make it developmentally appropriate and more appealing for children. In turn, this will keep the child more engaged and focused and, as a result, an active participant of the process. Singing the positive cognition is a great playful alternative. The child may pick a song in which lyrics are changed to include the positive cognition. For instance, the positive cognition (PC) "I am safe" may be sung using the music of Barney's "I love you" song. The child may choose to sing it alone, or invite the parent and the clinician to sing the song together. Children have picked various rhythms and songs to sing their positive cognitions. Some of them have also chosen to dance and sing the PC during installation. The mind, the heart, and the body of the child are intimately involved in embracing a new positive perspective and metaperception about the self in reference to the target memory.

Children with complex traumas may experience "turbulence" during the installation phase. Reprocessing may get blocked and the attuned intervention of the clinician may be necessary to provide appropriate interweaves. The first line of intervention is minimally invasive and requires just the change in speed, direction, and form of BLS. However, interweaves that can assist children in restoring dual awareness, modulate arousal, and stimulate different levels of information processing may be necessary at this time. In addition, other memories that induce high levels of arousal may be accessed at any point. However, the new associative channels that are still accompanied by some level of disturbance usually clear by engaging in BLS and inviting the child to just notice them.

Sometimes children may report quickly a validity of the positive cognition (VoC) of 7, which may mean that in reality the PC feels completely true, but mechanisms of adaptation used by the child may continue to surface during the installation phase. Pleasing, avoidance, and role reversing may be at the bottom of a VoC of 7. In order to avoid this, the EMDR clinician should address these mechanisms of adaptation early on during the initial phases of EMDR therapy. Honoring these resources used by the child for survival may set an atmosphere of acceptance. Puppets of different animals that represent these strategies may be used. For instance, the chameleon is a good representative of role reversing and pleasing strategies. If they show up during the installation or other reprocessing phases, the animal or metaphor representing the mechanism of survival may be brought up. The child may be invited to notice it and engage in BLS.

Noticing the nonverbal right-brain communication during all the phases of EMDR therapy is relevant. During the installation phase, I look at the congruency and coherence among the verbal and nonverbal cues given by the child. The child may be expressing that the PC "I am strong" is completely true. However, the child presents with a droopy, sad face and a collapsed body posture. Checking with the child as we bring up what we observe in a gentle and caring way may assist the child in noticing how the mind and his or her voice communicate one thing but the body may be saying something different. Even though this is not a standard EMDR therapy procedure, it helps bring to awareness information that may not be explicitly available to the child. In my clinical experience, when the PC is truly integrated and expressed through the right and the left hemisphere, congruency between the verbal and nonverbal communication starts to become evident. However, information held somatically may still be disturbing and, as a result, the bodily states during the installation phase may not be as congruent with the positive cognition.

Sometimes, children who have "lived" for a prolonged period of time experiencing negative affective states or very high and low levels of arousal may be hesitant to completely "leave" them. The cognitive, affective, and bodily states have become familiar and in a distorted way "safe" for these children. Many of these children fear the unknown, even if it has the potential to be positive. Mark, an 11-year-old client struggling with anxiety and panic attacks, chose the PC "I am safe now," but the VoC never reached a 7. Mark stated that in order for him to be truly safe, he needed his fear even a "little bit" so he could be vigilant and protect himself in the face of danger. At this point, Mark was invited to notice the fear of not being fearful. "Somatic" interweaves were used to help Mark notice the bodily states associated with the fear of not being afraid (see Chapter 11). Later on, interweaves more cognitive in nature were used to assist Mark in understanding that he did not need to completely give up on his fear as it was a great messenger when he needed it. Mark also understood that he always carried with him his wonderful "alarm system" that was designed to alert him of any danger in his environment.

During the installation phase, it is helpful to have the cards, cubes, balls, etc., used during the preparation phase for the child to pick a new PC if needed. In addition, the "thought scale" should be available to the child when getting the VoC. The following is the script adapted for children from the EMDR Institute training manual that can be used during the installation phase with children:

1. Checking the initial positive cognition: You may say, *"When you think about the memory you have been working on* (if the child does not remember the initial memory, say a quick title for the memory, such as the kids at school, mom and dad, the car memory, etc.), *does the good thought that you picked* (repeat the PC) *still fit or is there now a better good thought?"*

2. Check the VoC: At this point you may use the "Thought Scale" and put the foam numbers in front of the child. Give the child the helper or a small doll that can walk on the numbers. Place the card with the PC by the number 7.

   You may say, *"Now we are going to use the Thought Scale again. Remember that the number 1 means that the good thought does not FEEL true and the number 7 means that it FEELS really true. When you think about the memory you have been working on, how true do the words* (repeat the selected positive cognition) *FEEL to you now?"* Allow the child to "walk" the doll or helper on the Thought Scale, until he or she can provide the VoC.

3. Linking the PC and the target: You may say, *"Now, I would like you to think about the memory we have been working on, and at the same time, repeat in your mind the words* (repeat the selected positive cognition, such as, I am good, I like myself the way I am).*"* At this point, the PC may be installed, while the child thinks about it, sings it, or dances with the PC, while thinking about the target memory.

Do sets of BLS using the same speed and approximate duration as in the desensitization phase to fully install the PC (VoC = 7).

Check the VoC after each set of BLS until the PC is fully installed (VoC=7).

If VoC does not go up to 7, check for feeder memories or blocking beliefs.

Say, *"What is keeping you from going to a 7?"*

If the child tends to please, remind the child that there is no way to do EMDR incorrectly, and that whatever number they come up with is fine. *"However, we want to make sure the brain has chewed up all the yucky stuff, so we want to know what keeps you from believing that the good thought is true."* Extra reassurance may be needed for children that tend to please and feel compelled to meet the needs of others, especially authority figures.

PHASE SIX: BODY SCAN

An important goal of the body scan is to access any residual disturbance held somatically (Shapiro, 2001). Interoceptive awareness is invited to access, process, and integrate somatic and sensory information that is still disturbing in association with the target memory. Many playful approaches may assist children in connecting with the body (see Chapter 11). Tools such as the "feeling finder/detector" or "internal camera or telescope" with the zoom in and out features can assist children in working with the body in EMDR therapy. If disturbance is accessed, interweaves may be needed to assist children in moving disturbing information to adaptive resolution. Below is a script that may be used with children during the body scan phase.

"I would like you to close your eyes and keep in mind that memory (say a quick title for the memory, do not say any details, such as the kids at school, mom and dad, the car memory, etc.) *and the words* (repeat the selected positive cognition) *and check your body from head to toe and tell me if you have any feelings or sensations anywhere in your body."*

During the body scan phase of EMDR therapy, new associations may emerge, which should be completely reprocessed (Shapiro, 1995/2001). Once the reprocessing of the chosen target is complete and the body scan is cleared of all negatively associated sensations, the body scan phase is finalized.

PHASE SEVEN: CLOSURE

Assisting children in achieving emotional and psychological equilibrium after each reprocessing session as well as ensuring their overall stability are fundamental goals of the closure phase of EMDR therapy. Warranting balance and homeostasis in the child's system after each session of EMDR therapy as well as when treatment is concluded are also important objectives of the closure phase. Resources and strategies extensively covered in Chapters 3 and 4 can be used at the end of treatment sessions to assist the child in restoring psychological equilibrium. Any session where disturbing experiences were explored, accessed, or processed should be concluded with the use of regulatory strategies. The clinician may ask the child to bring up the safe place or a resource previously installed, or to place any disturbing material inside a container. The child is instructed to place all the "mixed-up feelings and thoughts" or any "yucky things" that may still be in the mind, the heart, or the body. The child is invited to notice any thoughts, feelings, or body sensations that need to be contained.

Activities that involve play, laughter, connection, and nurturance may work really well at the end of EMDR sessions. Theraplay (Booth & Jernberg, 2010) offers a wide variety of activities that promote emotional equilibrium through the use of play, touch, nurturance, and laughter (see Chapter 12). In addition, the parents or caregivers are given information about how to best care for the child as he or she is undergoing EMDR therapy. Parents learn how to accompany their children through their healing journeys. Caregivers by now are already acquainted with all the resources and regulatory strategies that are part of the child's coping repertoire. Parents can assist the child by either supporting him or her when using such resources or by prompting the child to actually use these resources when needed. In addition, caregivers have been prepared to be efficient, "emotional thermostats" for their child. During the closure phase of EMDR therapy, the clinician reminds the child and the caregiver of the importance of using these strategies as the memories of trauma and hardship are being accessed. This will increase the likelihood that the child will remain stable and will maintain emotional balance as the dysfunctional material is being processed (Shapiro, 2001). The following are the specific procedures for closing EMDR therapy sessions with children:

Allow 10 to 15 minutes before the session ends for the use of closure strategies. If the session was especially difficult for the child, allow enough time to bring the child to a hemostatic state. If the parents were present and the child responds well to interactive regulatory strategies, using the connection with the parent to bring the child back to balance may be a route taken to end the session. It is important to remember that the purpose of using closure activities is to ensure the overall stability of the child during EMDR therapy; as a result, closure activities should be selected based on the needs of each child at any given session. Even though safe place is usually used as a closure activity, when working with complex trauma cases, attunement on the clinician's part is critical. The same child may benefit from using different closure activities depending on the session they have finished. Work directed toward ensuring that the child is alert and completely present in cases of highly dissociative children is fundamental. If the child is still in low arousal states, using closure activities that activate the social engagement system and involve movement may be the ideal avenue into restoring equilibrium. If the session ends and high arousal is observed in the child's system, regulatory activities that increase a sense of safety and modulate arousal may be the best choice.

1. Instructions for closing complete sessions:

(SUDs = 0, VoC = 7, Clear Body Scan)

"You have done really good work today, great! How are you feeling?" Debriefing, if needed, can help the child in preparing to end the session. It is important to always check with the child if he or she wants to use any of the resources previously installed, even when ending a complete session.

2. Instructions for closing all sessions:

"Since today your brain started to work on chewing up mixed-up stuff, you might have dreams or thoughts or feelings, or you might remember things, or you might not. Please draw pictures or write down in your special notebook anything that comes up for you this week. We will talk about that next time. I want you to remember to use (mention the resources developed with the child) *whenever you feel down or you have mixed-up feelings and thoughts."*

Encourage the caregivers to prompt the child to use the safe place or other resources when the child is experiencing turmoil.

3. Instructions for closing incomplete sessions:

Let the child know it is time to stop and use the safe place or any other state change strategy or resources. Instruct the child to use these resources between sessions as well.

"Now, I am going to say that special word (repeat the cue word) *and I want you to think about your safe place. Think about all the colors in this place and everything that you see around. Think about all the sounds of this place, the smells, and everything that makes you feel good."* Allow the child to stay in his or her safe-happy place as much time as the child needs. Say, *"How do you feel now?"* When working with highly dissociative children, check how present they are. You may use the signs or other strategies described in Chapter 7 to assess the child's present orientation. If the child reports not feeling completely present, use strategies described in Chapter 7 to restore dual awareness and enhance present orientation. Some children may never report feeling completely present. Since a baseline has already been established during the preparation phase, the clinician will have an idea of the child's usual state of present awareness. Dual awareness strategies will be used to bring the child to an optimal level of awareness that the child is capable of at this point in treatment.

Once the child has been stabilized, give encouragement. Say, *"Good job! You have done really good work today. How are you feeling?"*

Closure at the end of treatment will also ensure the child's stability after treatment is terminated. Some children will be able to work through the entire targeting sequence and the three prongs. However, many children due to various reasons may not be able to complete a comprehensive treatment. Relocation, financial issues, and parent's difficulties, among others, may cause early termination. As stated in other chapters of this book, some parents come into therapy with their children to clean up a table, a room, or the entire house. Some of them may be satisfied with a treatment outcome that has only cleaned up one room. As a result, some parents, despite all the education and information provided during early phases of EMDR therapy, will terminate treatment even when it is not considered clinically completed. The child may have arrived to a more positive place, even if not all the targets have been reprocessed. Closure should involve appropriate information about how the memory networks that were not targeted may be activated in the future, requiring the child to return to therapy. Allowing the parents to make an informed decision in terms of the potential risks of terminating treatment earlier should be discussed. A plan that includes the continued use of the state change and regulatory strategies developed in EMDR therapy should be developed. Some parents and children, once treatment is terminated, stop using all the resources they developed during EMDR therapy. Encouraging the use of such strategies, if needed, should be part of the plan and recommendations made by the EMDR clinician before ending treatment. Moreover, different developmental stages, especially adolescence, have the potential of activating memory networks that may have remained "dormant" and deactivated during treatment. Parents of complexly traumatized children should know that they might need more EMDR therapy as they go on into new phases of development. For instance, a new loss, crisis, or experience that has the potential of activating these neural nets can bring up symptoms or exacerbate existing ones that were not seen before.

PHASE EIGHT: REEVALUATION

The reevaluation phase of EMDR therapy ensures that adequate integration and assimilation of maladaptive material has been made. Moreover, it warrants that all the relevant targets and associated material have been reprocessed and that all the elements of the treatment plan have been followed to completion.

The level of functioning of the client is assessed and explored as well as the target memory being processed after each EMDR reprocessing session. New insight may have arisen as well as new potential targets. Each session in EMDR is integrated into a comprehensive treatment plan (Shapiro, 2001) that ensures that the client can meet treatment goals and objectives.

Reevaluation is done after each session as well as at the end of treatment. The EMDR three-pronged protocol targets past experiences, current eliciting events that may have created negative imprints in the brain, as well as future events to ensure adaptive responses in the future when facing formerly activating stimuli.

The reevaluation phase is embedded throughout each session of EMDR therapy so the EMDR clinician can assess if adequate assimilation of all the memory networks has been achieved (Shapiro, 1995/2001). The EMDR clinician during the reevaluation phase is making sure that the targets have been fully reprocessed and integrated. This allows for an improved functioning in the present and an increased capacity to make positive choices for the future. When the memory is accessed again during reevaluation, if disturbance is still elicited by the remembrance of the memory, reprocessing will continue. When the memory is completely processed, a new target will be identified. When working with complex trauma cases, reevaluating the child's level of stability and treatment gains is critical. Due to the frequent chaos and instability that is present in the lives of these children, the reprocessing of targets may not be linear and straightforward. Oftentimes, the reprocessing of memories of adversity may be combined with sessions of resourcing and stabilization not only of the child, but the family system. Some children may be in situations where constant changes are made to their current living environments. Moving to a new foster home, having adoptions disrupted, having a new court order that changes from family reunification to the severance of parental rights and so on, can create great levels of instability which affects the organization of the overall course of treatment. In addition, new traumatic events may arise, making the treatment plan more convoluted and complex. The targets, as explored in Chapter 8, may need to be selected to fit the child's current level of stability and overall regulatory capacities. When a child experiences a sudden new loss or adverse event, the reprocessing of trauma memories may have to be put on hold while stabilization work is reinitiated. Clinical decisions will need to be made if a recent traumatic event is present, and either the recent event protocol (Shapiro, 2001) or the Recent Traumatic Episode Protocol (R-TEP) (Shapiro & Laub, 2008) need to be incorporated into the overall treatment. Children with a compromised social engagement system and compromised ability to modulate affect experience everyday life situations like enormous traumatic events. As a result, they feel traumatized on a daily basis. Katie, a 7-year-old girl coming to therapy with a diagnosis of reactive attachment disorder, had an accident at school as she was trying to get to the bathroom and she urinated in her clothes. Her friends and other children at school witnessed this incident, and some of them actually made fun of Katie. Katie became so dysregulated and agitated that she ran out of the school building and jumped over the school fence. A search for Katie lasted for one hour, causing great turmoil in the school and also Katie's family system. This incident for most children would be considered a negative, upsetting event that most likely, with the help of teachers and parents, would be a negative but manageable situation. However, for Katie, this was an event that actually activated fight-flight responses leading her to escape from school. According to the mother, Katie could not go to school for a few days due to her heightened internal state. Nightmares and high anxiety filled Katie's days and nights after the incident. This incident, for most children, would not turn into an extremely traumatic event, but for Katie it was. As a result, I made the clinical decision to target it with one of the protocols that work with recent traumatic events. In fact, many times we had to target and process recent events as they arose in Katie's life.

Once past traumatic and adverse experiences have been assimilated into a larger adaptive memory system, the reprocessing of present triggers is initiated. Oftentimes, the present may not hold any disturbance once the past has been integrated. However, some current eliciting events may need to be targeted and processed separately. This may be due to an association established between the current trigger and the elicited negative affect linked to the past event (Shapiro, 1995/2001). These repetitive associations through conditioning may imprint disturbance and negative affect to the eliciting present events. Once the past and the present triggers have been processed and assimilated, the clinician reevaluates all the past and present memories to ensure complete integration and assimilation. Only then can the child embrace the future. Once the child can imagine the former triggering situations in the future through a new lens of positive beliefs, emotions, and somatic reactions, treatment is terminated.

Playful approaches are pivotal elements as we walk through the different phases of EMDR therapy. When children do reevaluations, they do "detective work." Some children actually like to wear their detective gear as we engage in weekly timelines or as we play with the dollhouse to find out what happened during the prior week at home or school.

When children report during reevaluation a positive experience resulting from the work they are doing in therapy, these mastery experiences can be installed. These experiences or acts of triumph are installed as resources to help children maximize their ability to experience positive affect.

Below is the script that may be used during reevaluation with children. This script is based on the EMDR Institute treatment manual (Shapiro, 2011).

Evaluate what the child and caregiver have noticed since the prior session:

- Dreams
- Changes in behavior
- New environmental triggers
- New thoughts, feelings, etc.
- Other aspects of the target memory
- Earlier associated memories

It is also important to check with parents and caregivers how they are following through with recommendations or instructions given in therapy. Any changes in the family's or parent's stress level may be at the bottom of a sudden increase in symptoms as well as changes in the routines or parenting strategies suggested in therapy sessions. In addition, any new event, positive or negative, occurring during the week prior to the therapy appointment should be thoroughly explored. Robert, a 4-year-old boy brought to therapy because he had been sexually abused at a domestic violence shelter, was showing improvement in his EMDR therapy sessions. The mother usually brought him to the therapy sessions, but his father was skeptical and even resistant to continuing to bring Robert to his therapy appointments. After a session where the memory of his molestation was reprocessed with EMDR therapy, the parents came back, especially the father, really upset, stating that the EMDR therapy session had caused Robert to have a really difficult week. I took the time to honor their feelings while exploring thoroughly the occurrences of the prior week. The parents reported that Robert had a bad throat and ear infection, but they stated that they did not think his illness had caused his emotional dysregulation. I continued to explore the situation by asking about the medications administered to Robert and how they actually administered it. The parents stated that Robert did not want to take the medication and they had to restrain him daily to get him to take his medication. When Robert was sexually abused, the perpetrator restrained him and he could not escape. The repetitive restraints that happened the prior week continued to activate and enhance this maladaptive memory networks associated with his molestation. Robert continued to relive the experience of feeling trapped and powerless. I carefully explained this to the parents without sounding accusatory and helping them see the importance of using other means to get him to take the medication. Without this thorough exploration, the reason behind Robert's sudden symptom increase would have been positioned in the wrong place, causing the parent to continue to re-traumatize Robert, as he had to keep taking his medications for one more week. A plan was established with both parents to stabilize Robert and avoid reinforcing these neuronal networks. The reprocessing sessions were reinitiated once Robert was stabilized and the parents were onboard, providing a greater sense of safety and security at home.

During the reevaluation with the child, you may say, *"Tell me about what happened since the last time I saw you. Did you have any dreams? Any changes in your behavior at school? At home? Are things at home or school getting better, worse, or are they the same? Is there anything in your journal that you would like to share with me?"*

You may also use a standard form that parents and children use on a weekly basis that measures symptoms using a 0 to 10 scale.

Resuming Reprocessing of an Unfinished Target

Target did not achieve SUDs = 0, VoC = 7, and clean body scan.

Accessing the Target

Image

"I want you to bring up the memory (or the thing that happened to you) we worked on last week or last session."

Subjective Units of Disturbance

Using the "Bothering Scale," put the foam numbers from 0 to 10 in front of the child. Give the child the helper or a small doll that can walk on the Bothering Scale.

"Now we are going to use the Bothering Scale again. When you think about the memory your brain has been working on, how bad does it feel now from 0 to 10? Remember that 0 means it is neutral and 10 means it bothers you a lot." Allow the child to "walk" the doll or helper on the Bothering Scale until he or she can provide the level of disturbance.

Body Location

"Where do you feel it in your body? Or where do you feel it inside? Or where is this hanging out in your body?" You could give the child the "feeling finder/detector" to assist him or her in connecting with the body.

Resume Desensitization

"Now, I would like you to just think about this memory, or focus on what you see in your mind. Notice where you feel it in your body, and follow the helper." State the helper's name or use the form of BLS agreed upon with the child. Initiate BLS.

If the prior session ended with SUDs = 0 and VoC = 7, the SUDs and the VoC will need to be assessed as well as part of reevaluation.

FUTURE TEMPLATE

The future template of the EMDR three-pronged protocol is a pivotal aspect of EMDR therapy. The future template is done with the goals of reprocessing future events that still elicit negative reactions. It is also done with the purpose of enhancing the child's capacity to respond adaptively in the future to formerly triggering events. Future events that were evocative of disturbance can now be embraced through the lenses of more adaptive memory networks and a renewed sense of self. In order to respond adaptively to future events, the EMDR clinician identifies the roots of the disturbance, if any, arising from these future events. Alternatively, the child may need to be taught a variety of skills to compensate for deficits in various areas, that may be at the bottom of the disturbance associated with the future event.

The future template is designed to stimulate the child's ability to utilize in the future new resources, practice new skills, and respond adaptively to past eliciting stimuli. As a result of trauma, many children get stuck in early developmental stages. They are unable to attain new abilities, achieve new developmental milestones, or they simply lose already acquired skills in the face of trauma. As a result, the future template is a fundamental part of EMDR therapy that can assist children with complex trauma in mastering what once was dysregulating. As they are able to successfully anticipate the future, this becomes an act of triumph and an empowering experience.

As children work the third prong of EMDR therapy, they can create a movie of the former triggering event using the sand box or the dollhouse. They could also draw a picture, use Play-doh® or create a puppet show. The EMDR clinician assists the child in identifying how the mind, the heart, and the body want to experience this event in the future. For instance, a child having difficulty with bladder control created a future template where he or she could successfully go potty. He stated that in his mind he wanted to have the good thought, "I like myself the way I am." In his heart he said he wanted to have happy and proud feelings. He identified how he wanted his body to feel and the posture that was in alignment with what his mind and heart were experiencing. He also identified the new behavioral responses, such as noticing when he wanted and needed to go potty, going to the bathroom, and even reading something fun as he enjoyed his "potty" experience. I have worked with children that could not read or write at an appropriate age level as a sequelae of repetitive traumatic and adverse life experiences. Once the disturbing events were integrated and assimilated, these children were free to learn. During the future template they could envision themselves reading and writing successfully with a new, empowered, and a healthy sense of self.

Emily, a 5-year-old girl, came to therapy after both of her parents were arrested. Police officers arrived at night and took both of Emily's parents. After this incident where she was separated from her primary attachment figures, Emily could not sleep at night by herself. Her maternal grandparents assumed custody of Emily and had Emily sleep with them. Emily could not sleep with the light off and this became very disrupting for the grandparents. The memory of her parents being arrested was reprocessed first using a protocol for recent events, followed by other past events. After the current trigger was processed, Emily created her future template using the dollhouse. Emily chose a doll to represent herself and labels with drawings of her good thoughts, emotions, bodily states, and behaviors were added to the scene.

Children may also visualize a "mind pocket," a "heart pocket," and a "body pocket" where they either write or draw pictures of how they want to anticipate to the future event in their minds, hearts, and bodies. The body pocket also includes the actions they wanted to perform. They can also draw their own body outline with actual pockets where they are encouraged to place thoughts, emotions, and bodily states. Children may also create the entire scene of the future template in the sand box, with figures around themselves representing the positive cognition, emotions, and sensorimotor reactions.

Drawings have long been used in EMDR therapy with children and specifically in the application of the three-pronged protocol (Adler-Tapia & Settle, 2008; Gomez, 2006, 2008; Greenwald, 1999; Lovett, 1999; Tinker & Wilson, 1999). Having basic small buildings, a school, house, hospital, etc., may help children create a more tangible future template experience.

SUMMARY AND CONCLUSIONS

The installation phase, body scan, closure, and reevaluation are extremely important phases of EMDR therapy. Enhancing positive and adaptive memory networks and scanning the body, complete the reprocessing of memory networks containing traumatogenic material. In addition, ensuring the overall stability of the child during treatment and treatment termination is pivotal. The closure phase is geared toward safeguarding the security and well-being of the child while he or she is undergoing the processing of traumatic and adverse events. The reevaluation phase, additionally, allows the clinician to explore and evaluate the progress made by the client, changes experienced between sessions, and overall level of functioning of the child as treatment is progressing. Furthermore, the future template provides the child with the opportunity to embrace former activating events with a new sense of personal power and a renewed sense of self. All eight phases of EMDR therapy contribute in such unique ways to the overall treatment outcome, and especially with children with history of complex trauma, a comprehensive treatment approach that thoroughly uses the eight phases of treatment is necessary.

11

EMDR Therapy and Sensorimotor Psychotherapy With Children

Pat Ogden and Ana M. Gomez

*E*ye movement desensitization and reprocessing (EMDR) therapy and Sensorimotor Psychotherapy are compatible treatment approaches that address the nonverbal, implicit components of traumatic memories that are so difficult to resolve for many people with trauma-related disorders. While each approach can and does stand alone, we propose that including interventions from Sensorimotor Psychotherapy into EMDR therapy with children suffering from complex PTSD can strengthen the somatic components of EMDR therapy. Even though EMDR therapy already addresses top-down as well as bottom-up information processing, (Shapiro, 1995/2001) including additional bottom-up interventions that target dysregulated arousal and other somatic symptoms of trauma can help to resolve symptoms, support affect regulation, and increase the capacity for adaptive behavior (Bakal, 1999; Ogden & Minton, 2000; Ogden, Minton, & Pain, 2006). Several authors have proposed how these two approaches can be integrated with adults (Fisher, 2000; Minton, 2009; Paulsen & Lanius, 2009); this chapter is the first attempt to integrate Sensorimotor Psychotherapy techniques into EMDR therapy for children with histories of complex trauma.

The main goal of this chapter is not to change, but to enrich the use of EMDR therapy with pervasively dysregulated children by integrating Sensorimotor Psychotherapy strategies that enhance working directly with the body. This is accomplished while preserving the core and essence of EMDR therapy and the AIP model (Shapiro, 1995/2001). In order to best integrate Sensorimotor Psychotherapy strategies into EMDR therapy, an overview of Sensorimotor Psychotherapy principles and techniques will be presented through the lens of the AIP model. In addition, specific body-oriented exercises developed by each of the authors that can be used with children during different phases of EMDR therapy will be presented. We will attempt to clarify treatment throughout the similarities as well as the differences between EMDR therapy and Sensorimotor Psychotherapy in child treatment throughout the chapter.

DYSREGULATED AROUSAL, ANIMAL DEFENSES, AND THE BRAIN

Dysregulated arousal and overactive animal defenses biased by traumatic experience are at the root of many symptoms and difficulties observed in traumatized children (Ogden, Goldstein, & Fisher, in press; Ogden & Minton, 2000; Ogden, Minton, & Pain, 2006). Traumatized children have a tendency to experience "too much" arousal (hyperarousal), or "too little" arousal (hypoarousal), and often oscillate between these two extremes (Ogden, Minton, & Pain, 2006; Post, Weiss, Smith, Li, & McCann, 1997; van der Hart, Nijenhuis, & Steele, 2006; van der Kolk, van der Hart, & Marmar, 1996). Hyperaroused children are typically hypervigilant, anxious, and emotionally reactive, while hypoaroused children may be numb, passive and emotionally unresponsive (Ogden et al., 2006; Ogden et al., in press). When the memories of trauma and adversity are ignited, the children's regulatory capacities become increasingly overwhelmed, leaving them unable to adapt effectively to their environment (Ogden & Goldstein, in press; Ogden & Minton, 2000; Ogden, Minton, & Pain, 2006; Shapiro, 1995, 2001). Behavior becomes impulsive or destructive in cases of hyperarousal, and difficult or impossible in cases of hypoarousal.

Trauma-related hyper- and hypoarousal correspond with dysregulated animal defenses of fight, flight, freeze and feigned death. When such defensive responses are ineffective in assuring safety, as in cases of childhood trauma, they tend to persist in exaggerated and altered forms (Herman, 1992). Traumatized children tend to repeat defenses that were stimulated during the original traumatic circumstances, and may be at the root of many symptoms (Ogden et al., 2006). Powered by the sympathetic nervous system, the mobilization defenses of fight and flight are often reflected in constricted musculature, aggressive or active avoidance responses and hyperactivity (Ogden, in press; Ogden et al., 2006). Children may be easily triggered by minor events, causing impulsive behaviors, such as aggressive outbursts or tendencies to take off and run, that put them at risk for injuries and accidents. On the other hand, children with overactive hypoarousal responses, governed by the parasympathetic dorsal vagal system, experience ongoing low arousal states and typically exhibit social withdrawal and a lack of motivation. Their caregivers may describe them as compliant, lazy, or socially withdrawn, and prone to "spacing out" and daydreaming.

According to Perry (2009), "the brain organizes itself from the bottom-up, from the least (brainstem) to the most complex (limbic, cortical) areas" (p. 242). If trauma and attachment injuries were inflicted during critical developmental time periods, which affects how lower, less plastic brain regions function, treatment needs to emphasize interventions that address these subcortical areas of the brain. MacLean (1985) described his concept of the triune brain as a "brain within a brain within a brain," and both EMDR therapy and Sensorimotor Psychotherapy are compatible with MacLean's work, which can elucidate contemporary theories of information processing. According to both Sensorimotor Psychotherapy and the AIP model, when memory networks containing traumatogenic material are ignited, not only cognitive and emotional materials are activated, but bodily states through the afferent and efferent branches of the autonomic system, as well (Ogden & Minton, 2000; Ogden et al., 2006; Shapiro, 1995, 2001). On line at birth, the reptilian brain is the most primitive, and first to develop evolutionarily. It is the seat of instincts and survival responses, and "correlates with the sensorimotor level of information processing, including sensation and programmed movement impulses" (Ogden et al., 2006, p. 5). Surrounding the reptilian brain, the limbic, or paleomammalian, brain is responsible for feelings, emotions and some social behavior, and thus for emotional processing. The neocortex is responsible for cognitive processing, self-awareness and conscious thought as well as for regulating the limbic and reptilian brains. However, the neocortex is immature at birth and depends upon emotionally responsive early parenting to develop regulatory capacity. Infants and young children are dependent upon their attachment figures to help them modulate arousal states. When parents consistently fail to respond to a distressed infant or young child, the pathways between higher brain and these lower brain structures can fail to develop. The amygdala, or "alarm system" residing within the limbic brain, may be chronically overactive, causing the child to be chronically hyperaroused.

While each of the three levels of the brain has its own "understanding" of the environment, they are mutually dependent and intertwined (Damasio, 1999; LeDoux, 1996; Schore, 1994), functioning as a cohesive whole, with the degree of integration of the upper levels dependent on those below. MacLean (1985) points out that the levels of the brain may not work in harmony, which prevents integrated information processing. These three levels of brain architecture are conceptualized as correlating with three levels of information processing—cognitive, emotional and sensorimotor, with sensorimotor processing laying the groundwork for the development of the upper levels (Ogden et al., 2006). "In many ways Sensorimotor processing is foundational to the other types of processing and includes the features of a simpler, more primitive form of information processing than do its more evolved counterparts. More directly associated with overall body processing, sensorimotor processing includes: the physical changes in response to sensory input, the fixed action patterns seen in defenses, changes in breathing and muscular tone, autonomic nervous system activation and so forth." (pp. 6–7)

Particularly in the aftermath of trauma, sensorimotor processing in the form of dysregulated arousal and overactive defenses drive a traumatized child's emotional and cognitive processing. When the lower brains are not well regulated, as is the case of children with complex, chronic and early trauma histories, it might be useful to extend the preparation phase of EMDR therapy in order to focus more on the body to teach regulatory mechanisms, and subsequently target emotional and cognitive processing (Fisher, 2000; Gomez, 2009b; Minton, 2009; Ogden et al., 2006; Ogden et al., in press; Paulsen & Lanius, 2009; Perry, 2009). For example, when regulatory mechanisms are underdeveloped, it is crucial to first find ways to promote affect regulation, in the hopes of positively affecting the functioning of the subcortical areas of the brain. Perry (2009) and Ogden (Ogden & Minton, 2000; Ogden et al., 2006) propose that in, these situations, working exclusively at cognitive or emotional levels of information processing exclusively may be less efficacious since these levels are dependent upon the sensorimotor level for optimal functioning. In a Sensorimotor Psychotherapy approach, targeting the sensorimotor level of information processing through working with the movement, posture, gesture and sensation of the body facilitates this goal. In EMDR therapy, greater focus on the body, especially when working with children with complex trauma, may in some cases optimize information processing by directly impacting the lower brain areas, and as a result have a positive effect on the overall outcome of EMDR therapy.

It is important to highlight that, in EMDR therapy, once the memory network is accessed during the reprocessing phases, the client's choice of information processing mode is targeted. However, when information processing is blocked, separating the sensory effects of the trauma from the cognitive laden affective interpretations, and focus on bodily states if the client has not already accessed them, may be one way of stimulating the adaptive binding and integration of memory networks (Shapiro, 1995/2001). In Sensorimotor Psychotherapy, the information processing at each level is assessed collaboratively with the client to determine together which level to target for optimal outcome on all three levels (Ogden et al., 2006). For example, when memory networks are accessed, a client may hope to resolve her immobility through emotional or cognitive processing, but be unaware that her slumped posture and flaccid musculature both reflect and sustain the immobility. Thus, the Sensorimotor Psychotherapist may suggest working with bottom-up processing (posture and movement) before addressing cognitive and emotional levels to develop a somatic resource that might support adaptive processing at the upper levels. Or, the Sensorimotor Psychotherapist (as well as the EMDR therapist) may work simultaneously with somatic, cognitive and emotional levels to foster integration and transformation at all three levels simultaneously. In any case, in Sensorimotor Psychotherapy, the body is consistently included in the therapeutic process; its reorganization is viewed as essential to therapeutic change.

Along with the three components of the triune brain, the two lateralized right- and left-brain systems also fulfill specific functions. The left hemisphere is primarily responsible for cognitive processing, verbal elaboration, reasoning, linguistic behaviors, and meaning making and represents a conscious, explicit self-system (Schore, 2011). The right hemisphere for emotional and body processing, intersubjectivity, unconscious affect regulation and responses to threat cues, and represents an implicit self-system (Schore, 2011). The right hemisphere is fully developed at birth, but the left hemisphere develops over time in the first years of life. Schore (2001) asserts that when synchronization between left and right hemispheres occurs, "the organization of the infant's right brain shows increased coherence, as the flow of energy between the hierarchically organized higher right cortical and lower right subcortical components increase their connectivity, allowing the right brain to act as a self-regulating integrated whole, and therefore capable of increasing complexity (p. 24)." The right brain is dominant over the left brain in governing human behavior, indicating the necessity of treatment approaches that can address implicit processing rather than only conscious, explicit processing in treatment.

Both Sensorimotor Psychotherapy and EMDR therapy directly target the physiologically stored memories that are viewed at the basis of pathology (Ogden & Minton, 2000; Ogden et al., 2006; Shapiro, 1995, 2001). The client's attention is focused on cognitive, affective and somatic elements during accessing and reprocessing phases in both. However, children with pervasive dysregulation may need to work initially during the preparation phase of EMDR therapy with activities that soothe, regulate and stabilize emotional systems before accessing memories of trauma and adversity. When accessing traumatic memories with children with compromised social engagement systems and hyper- and hypoarousal tendencies, the use of interweaves in EMDR therapy that encourage the child to focus on the somatic response and "uncouple" it from the associated cognitions and emotions can assist the child in reintegrating information while staying within appropriate windows of tolerance (Ogden et al., 2006).

BRIEF INTRODUCTION TO SENSORIMOTOR PSYCHOTHERAPY

Sensorimotor Psychotherapy is a body-oriented talking therapy developed by Pat Ogden. Drawing from principles of interpersonal neurobiology and the work of Ron Kurtz (1990), this approach is informed by contemporary research on trauma, dissociation, neuroscience, attachment, and development. Sensorimotor Psychotherapy integrates traditional psychotherapy techniques with body-centered interventions specifically developed to treat the effects of psychological trauma, attachment failure, grief and loss, and developmental arrest.

Sensorimotor Psychotherapy is founded on the premise that "the brain functions as an integrated whole but is comprised of systems that are hierarchically organized. The 'higher level' [cognitive] integrative functions evolve from and are dependent upon the integrity of 'lower-level' [limbic (emotional) and reptilian] structures and on sensorimotor experience" (Fisher, Murray, & Bundy, 1991, p. 16). By working with movement, posture, gesture and sensation as primary targets of clinical intervention, it directly addresses the more primitive, automatic and involuntary physical and physiological functions of the subcortical brain that underlie traumatic and post-traumatic responses. Working from the "bottom-up" rather than "top-down," sensorimotor experience becomes the main entry point for intervention, and new emotional expression, meaning-making and positive cognitions arise out of the subsequent somatic reorganization of habitual trauma-related responses. As the arousal level, sensation, posture and movement of the body changes, a more positive sense of self emerges, supported by these physical changes. Starting with the body, and integrating cognitive, emotional levels of information processing in an atmosphere of play and exploration, Sensorimotor Psychotherapy helps chronically traumatized children discover their natural instinct toward integration and healing through the body.

THE ADAPTIVE INFORMATION PROCESSING MODEL AND SENSORIMOTOR PSYCHOTHERAPY

Traumatic or adverse experiences are encoded in memory networks in the brain. Both Sensorimotor Psychotherapy and EMDR therapy encompass the activation of neural networks with its accompanying cognitive, affective and somatic material. Similar to Sensorimotor Psychotherapy, the primary focus of EMDR therapy is the integration of networks containing maladaptive material with other corrective and adaptive information. As a result, traumatogenic memories are assimilated into a comprehensive adaptive network (Shapiro, 1995/2001). Despite major differences in methodology and principles, EMDR therapy and Sensorimotor Psychotherapy share important goals and procedures. The main goal of EMDR therapy and Sensorimotor Psychotherapy is to promote integration of the self and resolution of past trauma. The three different levels of information processing are accessed in both EMDR therapy and Sensorimotor Psychotherapy (Ogden et al., 2006; Ogden and Minton, 2000; Shapiro, 1995/2001). EMDR therapy incorporates body awareness interventions ("What do you notice in your body? How do you experience that in your body?"). In addition to the cognitive and affective elements, EMDR therapy also encourages clients to notice when movement impulses occur spontaneously and to allow them to complete, particularly when spontaneous processing appears blocked. However, in contrast to Sensorimotor Psychotherapy, the body is not emphasized in EMDR therapy; rather, the client is encouraged to report cognitive, affective and somatic responses as they spontaneously arise and move to completion. As a body-oriented approach, Sensorimotor Psychotherapy underscores sensorimotor *processing* interventions in addition to body awareness and following movement impulses to deliberately change how information is *processed* on a bodily level, and to support information processing on upper levels. Sensorimotor Psychotherapy interventions are designed to directly target and change postural, movement and physiological patterns that reflect and sustain trauma-related issues to help accomplish these goals.

As stated, Sensorimotor Psychotherapy focuses first on working from the bottom-up to target the lower levels of the brain and affect dysregulation. However, once self-regulation is in place so that arousal can remain within a window of affect tolerance, emotional and cognitive levels of information processing are addressed and integrated with sensorimotor processing. EMDR therapy accesses concurrently all levels of information processing (Paulsen & Lanius, 2009; Shapiro, 1995/2001) and uses various procedures during the preparation phase to directly address stabilization and the window of tolerance (Siegel, 1999). It incorporates body awareness within the preparation, assessment and reprocessing phases rather than explicitly working to shift posture and movement habits, although these shifts may, and often do, spontaneously occur during EMDR therapy. Both Sensorimotor Psychotherapy and EMDR therapy clinicians work with the client to expand or constrict the amount of information and the level of information processing being accessed.

Both EMDR therapy (Shapiro, 1995/2001) and Sensorimotor Psychotherapy (Minton, 2009; Ogden, 2009; Ogden et al., 2006) initially focus on "slivers" or single-framed images of the experience or memory and not the narrative of the entire event. During the assessment phase of EMDR therapy, the client is encouraged to identify a single "image" that represents the event and, from it, different aspects of the memory are accessed: cognitive, emotional and somatic. This stimulates the information processing system, and during successive sets of bilateral stimulation, the shifting of the stored information is tracked on multidimensional levels. The client reports on spontaneous shifts in cognitive, affective or somatic domains.

In Sensorimotor Psychotherapy treatment for traumatic memory, a step-by-step approach is used. As the client accesses a sliver of memory by thinking about the trauma, or reporting either triggering images or resources available during the traumatic experience, the therapist and client both track how the client's body responds. When resources are reported, time is taken to embody these resources. When arousal approaches the regulatory boundaries of the window of tolerance, or when preparatory movements that indicate truncated defenses emerge, the focus shifts to attending to the physiology and movement impulses of the body. By using the memory content to evoke the trauma-related bodily experience, the Sensorimotor Psychotherapist attends first to how the body has "remembered" the trauma and helps the client to resolve these phenomena on a sensorimotor level, through the body. Thus, an emphasis is on physical action and following body sensation as it progresses through the body (see section on Sensorimotor Sequencing, this chapter), based on the knowledge that since trauma profoundly affects the body and nervous system, many trauma-related symptoms are somatically driven (Nijenhuis & van der Hart, 1999; van der Hart, Nijenhuis, Steele, & Brown, 2004; van der Kolk, 1994; van der Kolk & McFarlane, 1996). Subsequently, another "sliver" is discussed, and the process is repeated, integrating cognitive and emotional elements as they emerge. Trauma was described by Pierre Janet (1898; 1907) as a "failure of integrative capacity," and thus the primary focus in therapy is to increase the client's integrative capacity on all levels of information processing and expand the window of tolerance.

In EMDR therapy, when the client's arousal exceeds the windows of tolerance and dual awareness is compromised, the focus is on stimulating the client's integrative capacity through the use of interweaves (Shapiro, 1995/2001). Interweaves vary and are designed to activate different levels of information processing, "jump start" reprocessing and modulate affective states so the client's integrative capacity is restored. EMDR therapy does not necessarily focus on the bodily states to accomplish this goal, even though it is one of the avenues that may be used when reprocessing is blocked.

Both EMDR and Sensorimotor Psychotherapy place great importance on maintaining dual awareness and mindful observation of the experience. They do not *require* that the client "narrates" the disturbing episodes; instead, the client is encouraged to "notice" internal experience through mindful awareness of the present moment experience. Mindfulness is typically described as being receptive to "whatever arises within the mind's eye" (Siegel, 2007) without predilection; however, mindful attention is best guided in specific ways. In EMDR therapy, the client is instructed to "Just notice, and let whatever happens happen." Then he or she is asked to indicate what comes to mind (Shapiro, 1995/2001). This allows the client to report on whatever emerges as the memory becomes integrated within the more comprehensive adaptive networks. The goal is to allow spontaneous processing to occur in all manifestations of the stored memory. However, other times, the EMDR clinician may use an interweave and/or invite the client to have a more "internal directed focus" to a particular response (Shapiro, 1995/2001, in press).

In Sensorimotor Psychotherapy, "directed mindfulness" (Ogden, 2007/2009; Ogden et al., in press) guides a child's awareness toward particular elements of present-moment internal experience considered important to therapeutic goals. To illustrate: An example of nondirected mindfulness about the body would be a general question, such as: "What do you notice in your body?" An example of directed mindfulness might be, "What do you notice in your chest right now, when you tell me about this bully?" The second question is based upon the therapist's specific tracking of the child's physical response (tightening in his chest that restricts his breathing) to the traumatic material. In Sensorimotor Psychotherapy, drawing the child's attention to his chest paves the way, for interventions targeting the symptoms of constriction and restricted breathing.

In EMDR therapy, the phases with greater flexibility and where strategies from Sensorimotor Psychotherapy may be appropriate to use are the client history and treatment planning and the preparation phase. In addition, the use of interweaves, during the EMDR reprocessing phases that promote and stimulate sensorimotor processing may be suitable and appropriate as long as they are guided by the AIP model, and the implicit injunctions of the interweave strategies to intervene as little as possible, and to attempt to mimic spontaneous processing (Shapiro, 1995/2001). In EMDR therapy, as with Sensorimotor Psychotherapy, spontaneous processing is foremost honored and preferred. However, as previously stated, when information processing stalls, strategies that directly address bodily states may be highly effective (Shapiro, 1995/2001). In this chapter, the use of interweaves directed to stimulate sensorimotor information processing will only be covered during the desensitization and installation phases of EMDR therapy. However, these interweaves may also be used during any of the reprocessing phases.

PHASE ONE: CLIENT HISTORY AND TREATMENT PLANNING

Assessing the body at the first stages of treatment is essential in a Sensorimotor Psychotherapy approach. Doing so provides invaluable information about the impact of attachment and traumatic experience upon posture, movement, and gesture; implicit issues and processing that are not expressed verbally; and suggest potential avenues of somatic exploration and change. It should be noted that, oftentimes, children cannot speak of what happened for a variety of reasons: Language centers of the brain are not developed, they cannot formulate the words, are ashamed, fear retribution, and so on (Ogden & Goldstein in press). In these cases, the body still "tells the story" and thus the residue of trauma can be effectively addressed somatically. In EMDR therapy, besides all the customary information gathered during the initial phase of EMDR therapy, nonverbal assessment and accessing the "body story and records" can be similarly utilized to yield important data about how the parent's and the child's bodies have been shaped by experience (Gomez, 2009b; Ogden et al. 2006; Ogden et al., in press). In both approaches, observing the body provides useful information, of which neither the parent nor the child is explicitly and consciously aware, and thus are unable to report it verbally to the clinician. In order to assess the "body story and records," the clinician observes the child's posture, gestures, musculature, breath, energy level and movements, and so on, by somatically assessing both child and parent: "Does the child's or the parent's musculature appear rigid and tense, or, on the contrary, flaccid and limp? Does the child or the parent present with collapsed body postures and, if so, where are these collapses present in the body? As the child or the parent tell his or her stories, are there any changes in tension, breathing or body posture? How does the child behave in the presence of each parent? Does the child seek or avoid physical proximity with caregivers or display contradictory or stereotypical behaviors or movements that simultaneously or sequentially seek and avoid proximity?"

Presley, a 12-year-old girl coming to therapy due to experiencing extreme anxiety and fear, presented a wide range of body responses and postures that provided critical information for understanding this child's experience and designing her treatment plan. Her body changed dramatically depending on who was in the room with her. When her mother was present, her voice was louder and aggressive and her musculature appeared rigid. However, when her father entered the room, her body posture changed significantly. Her chest caved in, her body became visibly smaller and her voice faded. The child and the parents reported having an overall positive relationship. At no point during intake were issues verbally articulated that pointed to concerns that became evident later on, such as the father's perfectionism, angry outbursts and high standards placed on this child. However, the body presented a clear picture of the "unspoken" family dynamics and the story of this child.

Vertical integration—integrating lower and higher parts of the brain (Siegel, 2010)—is a guiding concept in meeting the goals of both EMDR therapy and Sensorimotor Psychotherapy. This goal can be supported by gathering information from the three different levels of information processing at intake. Most initial clinical intakes tend to focus on cognitive and emotional levels, leaving behind extremely important sensorimotor information that, if assessed early, will greatly enhance the treatment plan and outcome. In addition, tracking and addressing representations of left- as well as right-brain functions will allow us not only to start promoting horizontal integration (integrating left and right hemispheres; Siegel, 2010), but also to obtain a thorough picture of the clinical landscape. Since the right hemisphere and the "implicit self" (Schore, 2010) will unfold in therapy sessions nonverbally, having strategies that can capture the voice of the right part of brain will be fundamental throughout the eight phases of EMDR therapy.

PHASE TWO: PREPARATION

Traumatized children come to therapy with dysregulated autonomic arousal, compromised social engagement, somatic patterns of tension and collapse that reflect overactive animal defenses, a narrow window of tolerance, and often a host of primarily nonverbal memories. In addition, the presence of memory networks containing positive and adaptive information is scarce. According to Shapiro:

> "The Preparation Phase from an AIP perspective promotes stabilization through the incorporation and increased access to positive memory networks that will also facilitate later processing. For instance, in addition to the intrinsic calming effects, the affect regulation techniques also promote stabilization by increasing these positive networks with memories of control and mastery. The amount of preparation depends upon the degree of client debilitation. However, in many cases stabilization itself can be facilitated through processing the physiologically stored memories that contain a volcano of distressing affective responses." (Shapiro, in press).

The preparation phase of EMDR therapy (Shapiro, 1995/2001) is comparable to the first phase of treatment (Herman, 1992; Janet, 1898; Ogden et al., 2006; van der Hart, Nijenhuis, & Steele, 2006), that focuses on affect regulation, symptom reduction, and stabilization. Since most attachment trauma was inflicted when lower brain areas of the child were still developing, affective regulatory mechanisms have been compromised. Interventions that help to soothe and calm the subcortical brain regions should be the starting point for these children. Below are a variety of body-oriented approaches that can be employed at this phase of treatment, starting with psychoeducation.

Psychoeducation: The Triune Brain and the Alarm System

Besides customary information and education on processing procedures, during the preparation phase of EMDR therapy, providing information to the child and the parent on how the brain functions is useful. A child-friendly explanation of the triune brain and the alarm system of the brain may be helpful to parents and children in understanding dysregulation. These three layers of the brain are interconnected, but they each have their own language and subjectivity. As stated, how this language is spoken within the brain and how the different layers operate and interact with each other is shaped by environmental experiences. This model helps children and their parents look at their conflicts and problems and their own healing through a different lens of understanding. The following explanation and exercises (Gomez, 2009b) exemplifies how MacLean's model can be explained and utilized in treatment with children: *"Let me tell you a really cool thing that we have learned about human brains. We have almost three brains that work together in one brain. Each brain has its own chores, needs, music, and language. They communicate with each other to make sure we have all that we need. Let's start with the first layer of the brain, 'the crocodile brain.' We share this brain with all the reptiles and this is why we call it the crocodile brain. This brain speaks through the body, like when we are feeling scared and the body tells us we are scared by having butterflies in the stomach or a tingly feeling in some body part, or we feel like having spaghetti arms and legs. The crocodile brain is actually in charge of helping us survive, and deal with danger. The second brain is called "the horsey" brain. We share this brain actually with all mammals, like doggies and horses and cows. This brain speaks through our hearts and uses the language of feelings. This brain is very important, as it allows us to love and receive love, snuggle and cuddle. It also allows us to have a rainbow of feelings from happy to crabby, sad to mad, and from fearful to cheerful. The last brain is the "cool smart" thinking brain. This brain is the one that allows us to speak words,*

understand math, read and control our impulses. Sometimes the horsey brain may want some-
thing right away and the cool smart thinking brain tells the horsey brain to cool down and wait.
All the brains are very important and help us in different ways. However, when the crocodile
brain gets triggered or turned on, the cool smart brain may have a hard time cooling it down.
We are going to learn to recognize which brain is speaking. Are you ready?"

Following this explanation, the therapist and child can address experiences where the child exhibited high arousal and disorganized behaviors. Once the child remembers these experiences and the resulting behaviors, the therapist can invite the child to listen to the language of the lower brain. Listen to the "fast heart" and the "fast breaths," or any other physiological experiences resulting from the activation of lower parts of the brain. If the child tends to experience low arousal, the same procedure can be followed, with discussion of how the crocodile brain can make the body very quiet, like a motionless lizard on a rock. The child can be encouraged to listen and notice the voice of the crocodile brain, and describe what happens in the body, prompted by the therapist's use of menus for sensation vocabulary (see section on "Tracking," below, for more on menus). Similarly, the child is encouraged to listen to the horsey brain when emotions emerge or when the child gives or receives affection. When the child is thinking clearly, making sense of his or her world, or figuring out a problem, reference is made to the thinking brain. When the child feels calm and safe, invite the child to notice how all the brains are working together, using the metaphor of the three brains "holding hands" with each other.

Highlight how the goal is not to neglect any of our brains, but to support these three levels working together, holding hands and being in synchrony and in harmony with each other. Exploring the rhythms of each brain through the use of maracas and other musical instruments (Chapter 7) can also be useful by first finding a rhythm for each brain, then finding a rhythm that includes all three. This exercise can yield important information about the child's resources and experiences that promote calm and regulated states or, on the other hand, memories of trauma and hardship that in turn can be placed in the child's targeting sequence.

Helping parents understand the concept of the triune brain can facilitate the use of parenting strategies that may be effective in soothing and regulating the child depending on what area of the brain is in a state of activation, thus helping parents develop mastery and become effective psychobiological regulators for the child (Schore, 1994).

A first step in both EMDR therapy and Sensorimotor Psychotherapy is to help children identify arousal states and increase self-regulation. Initial psychoeducation about the marvelous "alarm system" of the body may be provided to the child as he or she learns about the brain. Assisting the child in identifying when and what turns the alarm system on may be a good starting point. Sensorimotor Psychotherapy's "Modulation Model" graphs the "window of tolerance" (Siegel, 1999) and illustrates hyper- and hypoarousal states (see Figure 11.1).

The Modulation Model$^{\copyright}$ can be a useful visual aid to help children understand their arousal. Below is an example of how it can be used.

> In the therapy office, increased awareness of arousal can begin with the therapist creating a window of tolerance on a magnetic board [or on paper or chalk board] explaining to children in age-appropriate language and metaphors what the higher and lower arousal levels mean. Choosing from a set of brightly colored, appealing magnets, children are invited to place their magnets on the

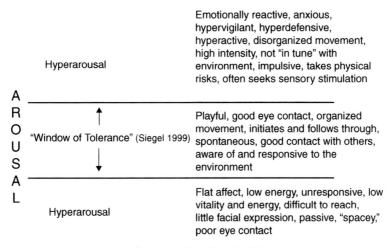

Figure 11.1 The Modulation Model$^{©}$.
Source: Adapted from Ogden (1995); Ogden & Minton (2000); Ogden et al. 2006; Ogden (2009/2011).

window of tolerance at the appropriate place to represent their own arousal. As arousal fluctuates throughout the session in response to different stimuli, the magnet can be moved accordingly, and children can be asked to show and describe how the level of arousal is reflected in their body. When one child was asked how he could tell his arousal was going up, he said, "Because I'm all excited in my tummy and my eyes are bugging out." Using these techniques, children can be helped to recognize the body cues that indicate fluctuations in arousal and then be invited to experiment with taking action to change arousal levels if they wish. (Ogden & Goldstein, in press.)

The child may be invited to bring up situations that turned the alarm system on in the past while the therapist tracks and describes the changes observed, such as the heart or the breathing "going" faster. These changes can then be written or symbolized on the window of tolerance graph, and contrasted with states when the child's arousal is within the window.

The child is taught to notice and observe this "wonderful alarm system" that allows us to protect ourselves from danger. It is important for the child to understand that *"when many 'yucky' things or one 'big yucky' thing have happened to us, it may change how the alarm system functions. The alarm system may go off all the time, even in situations that are actually safe, or it may shut down so we are not alerted when there is actual danger."* While the child continues to stay in a mindful and playful state, the clinician and child can investigate safe, situations where the alarm system tends to go off. An invitation is extended to the child to watch and follow any sensations by using the "feeling detector or finder" (Gomez, 2006), which is a magnifying glass that the child uses to explore the body and its special feelings and sensations. The child may also be encouraged to use the "internal camera" that navigates through the body. The child is invited to use the "zoom in" and "zoom out" features when a sensation is spotted (Gomez, 2009b/2010a).

Engaging in these activities may not only stimulate memories of trauma, but also provide an opportunity for the child to develop sensorimotor literacy and become familiar with EMDR procedural steps that include somatic awareness.

Safe Place

A first step in EMDR therapy is finding a safe place, which may be difficult for highly traumatized children. If the safe place is identified, when bilateral stimulation (BLS) is initiated, it may be hijacked by the activation of immature lower brain structures as other memories of trauma get ignited, typical of cases with children that are described as Reactive Attachment Disordered (RAD). When highly dysregulated children have difficulty identifying a safe place or it becomes contaminated once BLS is initiated, it is helpful, as stated in other chapters of this book (see Chapter 3), to have a "here and now" safe place or safe moment.

When using the EMDR calm-safe place protocol, utilizing playful and child-friendly approaches encourages the development of nonverbal resources that may help calm the child's affect and body. For example, finding songs and music the child experiences as calming or soothing may be used as a safe "here and now" resource instead of a visualized calm-safe place. The child may be asked to identify and bring a song or a sound that is calming and play it during the therapy session. Nature sounds of rain, water, creeks or the ocean may be played while the child is invited to notice the feelings and the bodily states associated with this safe and calming sound. The "feeling finder" (magnifying glass) the "body antenna" or the "internal camera" can be used to playfully assist the child in connecting with the body and finding its sounds and voices.

Sensorimotor Psychotherapy emphasizes the embodiment of positive states (Ogden et al., 2006). The therapist can track for when the child is experiencing a pleasurable sensation, indicated by a smile, increased engagement with the therapist; a deep breath; a spontaneous, integrated movement, and so on. During the child's journey through the body, when the child stumbles upon a positive body sensation, an invitation is extended to the child to investigate with the "feeling finder or detector" or the "body antenna" what the body is "saying" about this experience. Initially, encourage the child to express it without words, perhaps with movement, pretending to be an animal with such feelings or body posture. Later on, the child can be invited to find the words to label the experience. Once the emotional and bodily states are identified, the EMDR clinician can ask the child to notice them while engaging in BLS to enhance positive and adaptive memory networks (Gomez, 2009b/2010a/2011).

Musical instruments may be used as a means of nonverbal expression and as a way of giving a voice to the body (Gomez, 2009b; Ogden & Goldstein, in press). Throughout our western society, guitars, keyboards and drums may be ideal. However, other instruments from other parts of the world may also help the child express their experience and also honor the cultural heritage of these children and their families. Asking the child to bring a musical instrument that he or she is familiar with will be helpful because familiarity can promote a sense of safety. Drums have long been used in EMDR therapy to provide tactile bilateral stimulation (BLS) (Adler-Tapia & Settle, 2008; Gomez, 2006). However, drums and other musical instruments may also be used as a means of nonverbal expression of internal states (Gomez, 2010a/2011; Ogden and Goldstein, in press). Sensorimotor Psychotherapy uses drums to assist children to identify safety and competency, and other positive experiences, emotions, images, and so on, as well as to describe their experience of past trauma that they cannot or will not talk about(Ogden & Goldstein, in press; Ogden et al., in press). Using musical instruments helps children practice mindfulness to tune-in to the inner voices while also connecting to the outside world through the sounds emulated by the musical instrument. The child is invited to listen to the sounds or song that emulates positive emotions and use the selected musical instrument to reflect nonverbally the bodily and emotional states. The child then is encouraged to find the words for his or her emotions and bodily states. Sensation vocabulary menus are helpful since most children will not have a well-developed sensorimotor repertoire or literacy. (See section on "Tracking," below, for more on menus).

Highly dysregulated children with histories of early trauma may need to spend more time just connecting with the "inner sounds of the body" and expressing them nonverbally before the safe place or safe moment can be fully installed (Gomez, 2010a). The child is invited to let the body speak through the instrument. The child may be encouraged to alternate, or oscillate (Ogden et al., 2006; see "Oscillation Techniques" below) between the states associated with the safe place or moment and the minor disturbance. The child is asked to notice the difference, following regular EMDR calm-safe place protocol. Two "stations" may be created: The station where the calming, relaxing sound or song is played and the station where the minor disturbance is experienced (Gomez, 2009b).

In addition, when using the calm-safe place protocol, the child may be encouraged to find the place in the body that feels the safest and where the positive sensations and emotions feel the best or the strongest and bring the "safe moment" or the "safe song" into the body so it is always within reach if needed (Gomez, 2009b). In addition, the child learns to use the body as a resource, meaning that the child learns physical actions that he or she can perform to bring arousal into a window of tolerance, such as tuning into the safe place in the body (Ogden et al., 2006; Ogden & Fisher, in press).

DEVELOPING SENSORIMOTOR AWARENESS AND LITERACY

Most children do not have the vocabulary to describe and understand their sensorimotor reactions. During the preparation phase of EMDR therapy and the skill-building phase (Gomez, 2006), games to develop sensorimotor literacy might be used. In addition, Sensorimotor Psychotherapy techniques such as: Tracking, contact statements, boundaries, physical action, sensorimotor sequencing and the use of micromovements, among others, can assist EMDR clinicians working with children with affect dysregulation. The following is a description of interventions and strategies that honor the body. It is worth highlighting that these strategies are only needed in EMDR therapy when working with children that due to their limited regulatory and integrative capacities are not yet ready to move into trauma processing.

Tracking (Ogden et al., 2006)

In Sensorimotor Psychotherapy, tracking is a foundational skill that refers to the moment-by-moment observation of how experience is encoded in the body. Ogden,

Minton and Pain (2006) define tracking as follows:

> "Tracking refers to the therapist's ability to closely and unobtrusively observe the unfolding of nonverbal components of the client's immediate experience: movements, physical signs of autonomic arousal or changes in body sensation. Somatic signs of emotions (moist eyes, changes in facial expression or voice tone) and how beliefs and cognitive distortions that emerge from the client's narrative and history affect the body (such as the thought "I am bad" correlating with tension and looking down at the floor) are also tracked." (p. 189)

The clinician resonates and notices (tracks) the body throughout the session. Not only trauma responses, such as bracing, loss of postural integrity or the shaking of a dysregulated nervous system, but resources and physical evidence of proficiency and empowerment are noticed, such as a deep breath, lengthening of the spine, relaxation of the shoulders, etc.

The child is also invited to track his or her body from the inside by using directed mindfulness with the assistance of the therapist, which can increase the child's ability for focused attention (Ogden, 2009; Ogden et al., 2006; Ogden & Goldstein, in press). When teaching children to track their bodies, a playful atmosphere becomes an important element that not only facilitates tracking, but also activates the child's play and the social engagement systems (Ogden et al., 2006). The use of the "feelings detector" or the "body compass" may add a playful component to the mindful exploration of bodily states (Gomez, 2006). When using the "body compass" or the "internal camera" with "zoom in," "zoom out" and "slow down" features (Gomez, 2006), the child is invited to create one of these special imaginary devices inside to check what is happening in the body and detect any body signals. The "internal camera" can also "slow down" any movement or sensation as well as zoom in and out to experience it closer or from a distance. The child is invited to do "detective work", (Chapters 3 and 4), but this time the detective work is directed toward listening to the body. Once the child becomes aware of a somatic reaction, the child may be invited to track it internally with the feeling finder or the body compass, curiously following the sensation to see where it is going or where it wants to go.

The nonverbal tracking and expression of internal bodily states can be used to help the child develop body awareness. This initial work is followed by labeling bodily states and emotions, with the intention of engaging the cortex and left brain. Since most children will not have a well-developed sensorimotor literacy, the clinician can help the child develop his or her repertoire of sensation words by providing a "sensation vocabulary menu." We may say, *"I wonder what kind of feeling it is . . . maybe it's tingly, shivery, shaky, or warm. Or maybe it feels like a pressure pushing out or in."* This gives a child options to choose from, and, whether the clinician's guesses are accurate or not, they will spark the child's own words to describe his or her body (Ogden et al., 2006). As the child develops somatic and interoceptive awareness, information on resources, current eliciting stimuli and past experiences of adversity may surface that can be placed in the child's targeting sequence (Shapiro, 2010). The following list (Ogden, 1997; Ogden et al., 2006) provides examples of sensorimotor vocabulary that may be used with children:

twitch	dull	sharp	achy	smooth	jagged
frozen	airy	thick	tremble	shivery	chills
vibration	itchy	intense	mild	numb	flaccid
blocked	moving	congested	expanding	tight	puffy
bubbly	tingly	shaky	paralyzed	sweaty	moist
clammy	jumbly	frantic	energized	stringy	damp
electric	fluid	light	fuzzy	dense	cool
throbbing	faint	strong	pulsing	constricting	warm
radiating	shudder	bloated	flushed	prickly	buzzy
flutter	pressure	jumpy	tense	wobbly	tingly
nauseous	spinning	dizzy	tremulous	breathless	quake
quivery	suffocating	pounding	heavy	spasming	fuzzy
goose-bumpy	tightness of skin				

Children may also come up with their own words, as have children in treatment with one of the authors: spaghetti-like, needle-like, earthquake-like, butterflies.

Contact Statements (Ogden et al., 2006)

The therapist notices the changes in the body through tracking, and, subsequently, what is tracked can be communicated to the child in the form of a "contact statement" (Kurtz, 1990). The child will probably not notice his or her body experiences until the therapist brings attention to it through a simple descriptive statement, such as, *"Seems like your body is tensing,"* or, *"As you say those words, your hands come up to your heart,"* or, *"It looks like you are starting to tremble."* The therapist can track and contact the physical process communicated by the body, as well as the meaning-making and emotion evoked by the content (Kurtz, 1990). For example, in Sensorimotor Psychotherapy treatment, when Adam drummed his feelings about being molested, his therapist noticed the sadness in his face. Her contact statement *("I notice your face got very sad and still when you drummed your feelings")* helped bring this to his attention. She also tracked that his breath became very shallow. Her contact statements, *"You held your breath the whole time your hands told the story. It's hard to catch your breath when the story is so scary. I see what a hard time you're having breathing,"* helped him notice his body, and paved the way for a somatic resource of expanding his chest by extending his arms to his sides (Ogden & Goldstein, in press). It is important that therapists attend to both the traumatic reactions and the physical signs of mastery and well-being. When Adam was able to breathe as he extended his arms, his therapist's contact statement was, *"Wow, that was a big breath when you opened your arms,"* which helped Adam feel a sense of mastery.

By tracking and describing changes that occur in the body as they unfold in the moment, the therapist re-directs the child's attention to present bodily experience and helps him or her become curious about the body. The therapist does not try to interpret or make meaning of the client's physical phenomena, but rather simply observes and describes the sensorimotor elements in the simplest, most concrete terms possible. Concurrently with encouraging awareness of present experience, contact statements evoke and maintain social engagement. As Kurtz (1990, p. 77) has written: "Contact statements are not mandatory. They are optional. Creating a connection is mandatory."

Good contact statements should induce, maintain and increase social engagement between therapist and child.

The technique of making contact statements can be used during different phases of EMDR therapy. During the preparation phase, as information continues to be gathered to develop the EMDR targeting sequence (Shapiro, 2010), tracking and then contacting (Ogden, 2006) how the body participates and has participated in the child's experience will provide rich information as to how the body tells the story. During the reprocessing phases of EMDR therapy, when information processing is blocked, "somatic" interweaves may be one of the avenues the EMDR clinician takes to restore information processing.

Translating the Language of the Body (Ogden & Peters, 1990)

The meaning of physical experiences often remains unconscious until we translate these nonverbal habits into words, or "translate the language of the body" (Kurtz, 1990; Ogden, 1997; Ogden & Peters, 1990; Ogden et al., 2006). Sensorimotor Psychotherapy proposes that we can translate the language of the body by finding the verbal equivalent and meaning of physical experience. This technique assists children in connecting the body with verbal language and meaning making, thus bringing the unconsciousness to consciousness, and integrating cognitive, emotional and sensorimotor levels of information processing. The AIP looks at different components of the memory network: Cognitive, emotional and somatic. EMDR therapy and its eight phases access not only the cognitive aspects of the memory, but the affective and bodily states. Different avenues may be taken to access the memory networks. It may be accessed through the cognition, the affect or the body.

In working with children, microphones may add a playful approach to translating the body's language (Gomez, 2009b/2011). Using this technique, the clinician interviews body parts or sensations. For instance, the clinician tracks and contacts the body. "*I notice that your hands are making a fist.*" After the child is encouraged to notice the hands and track any movements or sensations, the hands may be interviewed by using a toy microphone. The hands may be invited to make a sound or a movement or use words or images if available. "*I wonder if there is a sound, words or something the hands would like to do or say. Let the sound, words or images come from your hands, not from your thoughts.*" The use of a microphone makes translating the language of the body playful, appealing and tangible for the child. The microphone is introduced as a special device that helps the body and its music be heard, seen and felt by the child and others with whom the child feels safe (Gomez, 2009b/2010a/2011). Listening to the inner sounds and inner music of the body can assist children in expanding their ability to focus attention, increase ability for mindfulness, develop affect regulation and later access traumatic memories. As stated above, these strategies may represent a road into the memory network as the somatic aspects are explored during early phases of EMDR therapy, and can also be used as interweaves during the reprocessing phases. During the preparation phase of EMDR therapy, the child develops important skills needed when reprocessing phases are initiated and the memories of trauma and adversity are accessed (Shapiro, 2001). By the time the memories are addressed, the child should have some familiarity with the tools and techniques used to explore the body mindfully.

The Freezing–Unfreezing Game

When teaching children about freeze responses, the following exercise (Gomez, 2010a, 2011) may be helpful. First, the child is invited to play the "freezing–unfreezing game," where the child and the therapist create a "freeze and unfreeze remote control." The therapist, the parent and the child take turns using the remote control. This exercise also helps children experience immobilization without fear, as they are in a playful state. The child is encouraged to study the body while immobilized and then later when it is mobilized. Directed mindfulness and translating the language of the body, as described earlier in this chapter, are encouraged with such questions as: *"What happens in the body? What is the body saying and/or communicating? How is the body communicating it? Is the heart saying something or the stomach? What are the legs or arms communicating to you?"* The child may also be invited to play with a pretend camera. The child is asked to freeze and pose before each photo is taken. The clinician can practice with short and long periods of mobilization and immobilization (Gomez, 2011).

Oscillation Techniques

Oscillation techniques (Ogden, 2006; also called "pendulation" by Levine & Frederick 1997) are also useful in helping children to shift their focus from dysregulated states to a more resourced experience, which supports flexibility in state shifting and increases awareness of different states. Oscillation techniques involve directing the child to repeatedly and mindfully first embody calm or resourced states and then states that are dysregulating or uncomfortable, and practice going back and forth between these two states. The following exercise (Gomez, 2009b) shows how oscillation techniques can be used with children: The therapist invites the child to identify something that is bothersome in the child's life. As the child identifies the current upsetting situation, ask the child to listen and notice how "the body is speaking" to him or her. Without words, invite the child to find an animal that best describes what the body is saying. For instance, if the body is communicating about feeling really small and scared, the child may pick an ant or a mouse. Then, ask the child to notice how he or she would like his or her body to feel, or to remember a time when he or she felt really good, and identify the animal that best represents this bodily state. Some children may choose a lion if they want to feel strong, an eagle if they want to experience a feeling of freedom, or an elephant if they want to feel big and powerful inside. Invite the child to embody the "elephant state" and the "elephant body posture" so that the child can embody the state of strength and empowerment symbolized by the elephant, such as having the child lengthen the spine and feel big inside. After the animal representing positive bodily states has been fully embodied, have two different stations or areas in the room and invite the child to move back and forth to experience and learn about the state change. In other words, therapist and child together create the "mouse station" and the "elephant station," where the child can experience each animal and its accompanying bodily state. When the child is in the "positive sate" station, the child may be encouraged to notice the positive states, verbalize them along with the accompanying emotion to engage the left hemisphere, and use slow and short sets of BLS (Gomez, 2009b/2010a/2011). Affect regulation includes flexibility and smooth transitions between states, and experiences of mastery are fostered when they successfully oscillate back and forth from one state to another (Ogden & Goldstein, in press).

Boundaries

Relational trauma indicates that a violation of the child's boundaries has occurred, shattering physical and psychological integrity, and leaving him or her feeling vulnerable and unprotected. Children with early trauma and thwarted attachment experiences lack the adaptive memory systems containing appropriate information about the self, other and the world. As a result, their sense of boundaries is compromised. During the preparation phase of EMDR therapy, interventions from Sensorimotor Psychotherapy may be incorporated to assist children in developing a somatic sense of boundaries and deepen their bodily experience. A *somatic sense* of a boundary is not the same as a cognitive understanding because it is based on the felt sense of one's preferences, wishes, and rights, as well as on the felt sense of safety" (Ogden et al., 2006, p. 226). A felt sense of boundary goes hand-in-hand with arousal that is within the window of tolerance, while hyper- or hypoarousal states indicate that the child does not have an adequate somatic sense of safety or boundary.

Reinstating a somatic sense of boundaries is facilitated by exploring actions such as pushing away with the arms, kicking away with the legs or walking away, thus setting distance between the individual and the unwanted intrusion of person or object. A variety of exercises teach children how the right personal distance can help them feel safe. Adam, 7 years old, was molested at school by an older boy, and refused to discuss what had happened or to return to school. With a collapsed posture, and weak, tentative voice, Adam was unable to say "no" or set his boundaries. Adam's treatment goals included learning about boundaries and practicing boundaries motions, such as pushing away. Many sessions focused on developing his somatic sense of boundaries; one such session is described in the following excerpt:

Sitting on the floor, Adam was invited to use a rope to create a "bubble" around him and then to push out what he did not want inside his boundary space. His older sister, who came to this session, role-played invading his boundary, and Adam discovered many ways to say "no:" "I'm in charge of me!" "You can't touch me unless *I* say!" "I get to decide." "I can be powerful, I *am* powerful!" His therapist helped him to find the pushing movements of his arms that best correspond to his saying "no." At first, he pushed his sister out of his bubble hesitantly and with little force, but, with practice, his push became more and more assertive and strong, as did his voice (Ogden & Goldstein, in press).

Instead of being unable to set boundaries, like Adam, some children set their boundaries through anger, dominance, and disruptive behavior. The following example illustrates using Sensorimotor Psychotherapy boundary exercises with a child who had learned to set his boundaries aggressively.

Jake, age 7, the youngest boy in a family of seven, slept in the living room with his three brothers. Jake was constantly picked on in his family and could not even complete his bowel movements privately without being taunted by his siblings. Extremely hostile, restless, and disruptive, with hunched, tight shoulders, Jake often aggressively said to other children, "I want to KILL you." In group therapy, these issues were addressed by asking Jake to make a boundary around himself with rope. He was encouraged to keep everyone out of his "bubble," his nomenclature for the circle of rope he created, and to use his voice and his arms to give the "get out" message. Jake experimented with telling others to come into his bubble, and then telling them to leave. Group members were instructed to do as he said and to get out of his boundary space when asked. With repeated iterations, Jake's procedural patterns visibly changed: his spine lengthened, his head came up, his eyes softened and his shoulders relaxed. These physical actions supported engagement with others, while his tense shoulders, squinting eyes, head down and compressed spine supported disconnection and aggression. Jake finally had control over his own boundary, something he never had in his family, and his aggressive outbursts lessened (Ogden & Goldstein, in press).

Another way of helping children connect with their bodies and their own sense of boundaries is by using an exercise in which the therapist assists the child in developing a felt sense of saying "yes" and "no" with his or her body rather than by using words (Ogden, 2006; Ogden et al., in press). The child is encouraged to embody the felt sense of "yes" as he or she walks around the room, and to share moments where he or she remembers saying "yes." The child and therapist may also explore moments where the body wanted to say "no" and instead the word that came out was "yes." The child can walk around noticing how the body says "no" but the word that came out was "yes." The child then can practice embodying a congruent state where the body, heart and mind are aligned, "holding hands" and saying "yes" or "no" versus when they are not aligned and they are "not holding hands." The therapist may ask the child what happens when the mind, heart and body are "holding hands," and invite the child's left brain to participate by asking the child to verbally identify the emotions and body sensations associated with being able to "congruently" say "yes" or "no." These "congruent" experiences can be enhanced with slow and short sets of BLS after the child identifies the emotions and body sensations associated with saying "yes" and "no."

Using Music

The following exercise (Gomez, 2010a/2011) capitalizes on children's natural love of music. It is also geared toward both enhancing the child's interoceptive awareness as well as developing and/or enhancing the child's capacity to access positive memory networks. The therapist explains to the child how we all carry music inside our bodies, and that this music is performed by our different parts and organs. Sometimes this music turns into noise if all the organs and parts of the body are going "too fast." Some other times the music shuts down and silences us when all the organs in the body are going "too slow." The child is encouraged to listen to just one organ or part of the body at a time; the therapist invites the child to listen to the organ or part of the body that is more accessible to him or her. Maracas can be used to help the child tune into the rhythm of the organ or part and play the internal rhythms externally. If the child chooses the heart, the therapist can encourage him or her to connect the heart to the maracas and create an invisible connection or "cord" from the heart and the maracas. The child is encouraged to listen to the music of his or her heart and let the maracas play this music. The therapist might also ask the child to think of an upsetting situation and notice what the heart is communicating to the maraca and again invite the maraca to be the voice of the heart. Both parents and child can be encouraged to listen and feel the rhythm of the child's heart through the maracas. Engaging the child in activities that increase and decrease heart rate provides the opportunity to notice the different rhythms of the heart. Other parts of the body (legs, arms, back, head, chest) and organs (stomach, lungs, etc.) can be explored in the same manner.

The following exercise (Gomez, 2010a) is designed to promote in EMDR therapy the development and or stimulation of memory systems that support a greater ability for affect tolerance, regulation and interoceptive awareness. It is also thought to promote integration between the right and left hemispheres when the child tries the maraca first with the left hand and then switches to the right hand, noticing how each side listens to the specific organ. Similarly, the child may be invited to notice the left foot while holding the maraca with the left hand, or experiment with the right hand holding the maraca while noticing the left foot. These exercises can be used during the reprocessing phases of EMDR therapy, as the child can let the clinician know more explicitly what is happening internally by allowing the maraca to be the voice of the body. Since the child has played the maraca during the preparation phase, he or she will already have learned to give a voice to his or her internal experience and arousal level through this instrument.

The use of sounds and chanting is yet another way of helping children attune to their own internal experience. The child can experiment with sounds that are low, medium or high in tone and pitch. The child may be invited to connect his or her voice to an organ, or a part of the body and give an "unworded" voice to this organ through sounds and words (Gomez, 2010a/2011). What is important is that the child learns to speak the language of the body, the heart and the mind. The therapist and the parent can join in if the child resonates with this idea, allowing them to share a moment through sounds and chants. Through this exercise, the child is provided with the opportunity to sense how his or her internal experience is felt, known and seen by the parent and the clinician. Using slow and short sets of BLS with the child may enhance these moments of regulation, attunement and connection during the preparation phase. The attuned clinician makes contact statements and describes what the body is expressing during this moment of connection. Using a voice that resonates with the bodily and emotional states of the child, the clinician can use a contact statement, such as, "*I can see how as you sing, your face gets really relaxed and your legs and arms get really calm.*" The clinician then provides slow and short sets of BLS to install this experience. Later on, the clinician may invite the child to label the feeling and where it is felt in the body as it is done in standard EMDR resource installation protocols. All these exercises in general increase the accessing and/or enhancement of positive and adaptive memory networks and can become mastery experiences for the child as his or her self-awareness and self-efficacy increases.

Actions of the Body

A Sensorimotor Psychotherapy exercise to be used with children consists of engaging in exploration what parts of the body can do (Ogden et al., 2006; Ogden et al., in press). The therapist invites the child to mirror movements and gestures, such as reaching out, holding, tightening, pushing or grasping, and notice which ones feel "new" and which ones feel "familiar." The child is encouraged to study and explore each movement and gesture and allow the body to "speak." Some children may recall positive and negative past experiences elicited by the body posture or movement as they engage in this exercise. The therapist may invite the child to find stories of events elicited by a movement or gesture and access memories of resources and mastery experiences as well as memories of adversity and trauma. The child can create a container or a "memory box" (see Chapter 4) where "negative or yucky memories" are placed and another container where "positive and good memories" are deposited (Gomez, 2006/2007b). If the story recalled by the child represents a resource or a mastery experience, the EMDR therapist can invite the child to connect with the emotions and bodily states while the therapist provides slow and short sets of BLS to install this resource and positive experience.

DESENSITIZATION PHASE

After the memories of trauma and adversity have been explored and accessed, the reprocessing of such events is initiated. Even though spontaneous synthesis and assimilation of memories are preferred and foremost encouraged, information processing may stall (Shapiro, 1995/2001). When this happens, the attuned EMDR clinician will need to skillfully utilize strategies to stimulate and reengage the child's information processing system (Shapiro, 1995/2001). Standard EMDR procedures to jump start reprocessing should be followed. For instance, changing mechanics should be considered before attempting to use an interweave. In addition, after each interweave is used, the child should be encouraged to engage in BLS followed by customary procedures and questions. However, children with chronicity in their trauma histories may need the active and attuned participation of the EMDR clinician. The interventions proposed in this chapter for the reprocessing phases of EMDR therapy should only be used when spontaneous processing is blocked.

Interweaves geared toward promoting assimilation at a somatic level are of extreme importance considering how so many traumatized children present with dysregulated arousal and truncated and incomplete defense responses and actions that could not be performed during the traumatic event (Ogden et al., 2006; Ogden & Minton, 2000). Overtly incorporating the child's bodily experience with his or her emotions and cognitions in the reprocessing phase, along with body contact from loving caregivers, can assist in the efficient reprocessing of the disturbing memories. Most of the techniques described above can be adapted as interweaves during the reprocessing phases of EMDR therapy. It is important to highlight that, in EMDR therapy, the assimilation and processing of cognitive, affective and somatic information may happen simultaneously. However, when information processing is blocked, child-friendly interventions that include the active participation of the body in EMDR therapy (Gomez, 2006, 2009b, 2010a/2011) and the inclusion of Sensorimotor Psychotherapy (Ogden et al., 2006; Ogden et al., in press) strategies to stimulate blocked processing may be successfully used.

Using Touch

The child's self-touch and the parent's touch may be used to develop new somatic resources, foster self regulation, and, when the parent's touch is used, foster connection between child and parent (Gomez, 2010a/2011; see also Wesselman, 2007). Children may learn to use touch to regulate themselves, capitalizing on utilizing his or her body as a resource. For instance, placing their own hand on their heart, touching their legs to feel grounded, and so on can teach children to self-regulate, fostering a sense of agency and empowerment (Ogden et al., 2006; Ogden & Goldstein, in press). During the desensitization phase and, in general, all the reprocessing phases of EMDR therapy, touch may be used as an interweave. When touch provided either by the child or the parent promotes positive states, it is thought to stimulate the development of adaptive neural networks and may be useful during the preparation phase, as well (Gomez, 2009, 2010a, 2011; Wesselman, 2007, 2010). According to Cozolino (2006), "Light touch and comfortable warmth leads to increases in oxytocin and endorphins that enhance social bonds through an association with a feeling of well-being" (p.103). Either the child may be invited to touch an area of the body where turmoil is being experienced, or the parent, if present, can provide the touch. For example, during the reprocessing of a disturbing event, when information processing gets blocked as the child reports fear and a tingling sensation in the chest, one possible way to stimulate information processing is by encouraging the child to stay with the sensation and to express what he or she needs (Gomez, 2009b/2010a/2011).

The clinician may provide menus that include touching the area experiencing turmoil in the way it wants to be touched to experience relief or to provide what it needs. Another interweave that may be offered to the child is to receive a "helping hand" (Gomez, 2009b). The sensation is invited to choose the hand of the parent or the child, and then to place the hand on the body where the sensation is experienced. In a Sensorimotor Psychotherapy approach, several interventions may be used with regard to touch: Find the kind of touch the area of the body needs, refine the touch so it is exactly right in terms of pressure, exact area touched, still hand or moving hand, fast or slow movement, translate the language of the body, translate what the hand is saying to the body and obtain reports from the child about "what happens inside when touch is used (Ogden & Goldstein, in press; Ogden & Peters, 1990; Ogden et al., 2006). When using the "helping hand interweave," directives such as: *"Let the 'sound,' 'sensation' or 'music' of your body tell the hand what it needs"* can "jump start" information processing through the use of a "somatic" interweave. Other interventions include, *"What would the 'sensation' like the hand to do? It may want the hand to stay still or to move while rubbing it. Let the 'sensation' show the hand how much pressure it wants and how fast or slow it wants it. Is this place being touched exactly on the right spot, or is it better higher up or to the side?"* The following questions may assist in translating the language of the body: *"If the hand could say something, what would the "sensation" like to hear from the hand?"* And *"What does this place in your body say back to the hand?"* Menus, as described previously, may assist the child to mindfully connect with the hand and describe what happens inside when he or she is touched. Tracking and contacting any bodily changes resulting from inviting a "helping hand" also aid the child in sensing his or her experience. These body-focused interweaves are used to restore information processing when it has stalled by disrupting the current manifestation of the memory network and promoting integration through the elicitation of positive affective and somatic states.

When using this strategy during the reprocessing phases of EMDR therapy, BLS is used after new information is accessed from the "sensation." BLS is also used while the parent is touching or rubbing the area of the body where the sensation is present. Basic EMDR therapy procedures are used after each set of BLS. These interventions are especially meaningful when the parent's touch is used (Gomez, 2009b/2010a/2011). The child is encouraged to observe what happens in the body as the hand of the parent who attunes with the child's bodily experience and provides exactly what the "sensation" is asking, thus promoting a connection between child and parent. If parents are involved during the reprocessing phases of EMDR therapy, as stated in prior chapters, enough preparation with the caregiver should have been achieved to warrant their participation during trauma processing sessions.

Creating Experiments

According to Ogden (2006), experiments occur within the context of social engagement, and elicit the exploration action system of the child. Conducted in an atmosphere of collaboration and curiosity, an experiment "invites exploration of new experiences without investment in a specific outcome, an attitude that renders 'right' and 'wrong' answers irrelevant, and is reflected in the phrasing of contact statements and mindfulness questions" (Ogden et al., 2006, p. 195). The wording that the therapist uses during experiments is a version of *"What happens when....?"* In treatment with Adam, his therapist suggested he experiment with pushing against a pillow with his arms, while she asked, *"What happens when you push?"* Adam was encouraged to report what he noticed inside his body. These experiments can also be proposed to bring arousal into the window of tolerance if the child becomes hyper-aroused or hypoaroused, as in, *"Let's see what happens when we stand up and walk around."* Even though, in EMDR therapy the spontaneous linkage and assimilation of information is preferred and usually accessed, when information processing is blocked, "experiments" may be used as a form of "somatic" interweaves. Movement, especially with children that tend to experience hypo- or hyperarousal states during EMDR reprocessing, can be used to bring the child back into appropriate windows of affect tolerance. Movement can make children's experience more tangible, concrete and thus more meaningful to them.

The child may be invited to experiment with executing a movement or gesture, or to focus on a sensation: *"How about if we just check that tingly feeling in your stomach with your "internal camera" and see what happens?"* Another interweave may be, *"I notice that as you say that your hands are making a fist, would it be ok to do it again and check it out? Let's do it again and just notice it or check it out with your internal camera and see what happens."* The child may be invited to use the "zoom in," "zoom out" or "slow down" features to study closely the hands and their physical sensations. The child may also be encouraged to exaggerate the movement so it can be studied. While the child is experimenting with executing the movement, he or she is asked to watch it through the "internal camera" and report what happens. The child may be encouraged to use the "slow down" feature and watch the movement slowly as it unfolds.

The therapist could also find incomplete actions and help the child execute them. The clinician assists the child in discovering the action that is naturally emerging from the body and moving it to completion (Ogden & Goldstein, in press; Ogden & Minton, 2000; Ogden et al., 2006; Shapiro, 1995, 2001). The therapist can also use objects to help the child complete the action, such as holding a pillow against the child which he or she can push. Other playful objects such as "marshmallows" made of toilet paper that the child can throw, or old newspaper that the child can break when held by the therapist, (Booth & Jernberg, 2010) are all playful ways of encouraging the child to execute empowering defensive actions. Exploring tempo and intensity of the movement is also helpful (Ogden & Goldstein, in press). The "body remote control" (Gomez, 2010a) with the "slow down" or the "slow motion" feature is used to slow down movement while the child mindfully studies the move-ments. The therapist playfully uses the remote control to invite the child to slow down movement and modulate arousal. Using the "volume button" to turn up or turn down the intensity of the movement and the effort needed to execute it is also helpful (Ogden & Goldstein, in press). The child, however, has all the power to use the volume button and the remote control to tests different speeds and intensity to find the speed and intensity that feels best.

Sensorimotor Sequencing

This is Sensorimotor Psychotherapy intervention that facilitates the completion of involuntarily bodily actions associated with traumatic memories (Ogden et al., 2006). Sensorimotor sequencing is described as "… slowly and mindfully tracking, detail by detail, the involuntary physical movements and sensations that pertain primarily to unresolved autonomic arousal, orienting and defensive reactions" (Ogden et al., 2006,

p. 253). The use of the "internal camera" (Gomez, 2009b) is an effective tool for kids during sensorimotor sequencing. With the "zoom in," "zoom out" and "slow down" features, the child can slowly and mindfully track micromovements and sympathetic arousal. Children are invited to notice and track involuntary micromovements instead of doing them voluntarily. The child is supported to stay with these involuntary movements until they are complete and the sensation in the body settles. (Ogden et al, 2006; Ogden & Minton, 2000; Ogden et al., in press). In EMDR therapy, when memories are accessed and reprocessing stalls, sensorimotor sequencing can be an effective somatic interweave. In the following exercise (Gomez, 2009b, 2010a, 2011), the therapist may say, *"Using your wonderful special 'internal camera,' let's just watch what is happening in your body right now."* Once the child identifies a sensation, the child is invited to keep observing while BLS is provided. The child remains in a curious observing mode, as the therapist says, *"Ok, just keep tracking and following where this body feeling is going or if it is staying in the same place. Is it a tingling, buzzing feeling?"* After the child reports what is happening in the body, the therapist can encourage tracking as BLS is provided: *"Just keep noticing that with your special camera."* Questions such as, *"Is it heavy or light or cold or hot? Just keep listening to the sounds, music or noise this feeling is making in your body. Are there any impulses as your body tells its story?"* can also be useful. If impulses arise, the child is invited to notice them and allow these impulses to continue to sequence through the body without trying to control them (Ogden et al., 2006). Safety and a sense of curiosity and self control are important: "The slowness of this microprocessing and the maintenance of social engagement with the therapist keep the experience safe and manageable, challenging the habitual re-experiencing of implicit emotions, sensations, and motor activity" (Ogden et al., in press).

INSTALLATION PHASE

At this point in EMDR therapy, the child has already achieved a level of disturbance of zero (0) or if ecologically sound, of one (1) (Shapiro, 1995/2001). During the installation phase of EMDR therapy, the main goal is the enhancement of positive memory networks as cognitive, affective and somatic information continues to be assimilated spontaneously (Shapiro, 2001). For instance, the positive cognition installed can be embodied through the use of Sensorimotor Psychotherapy interventions by helping the child identify and practice the physical posture and movement that reflects the positive cognition (Ogden, et al., 2006; Ogden & Goldstein, in press). Looking at the verbal and nonverbal cues the child provides during the installation phase and, in general, all the eight phases of EMDR therapy, may help the EMDR clinician see if changes and integration at different levels of information processing is happening. A child working with a positive cognition of "I am a good kid" while reporting a validity of the positive cognition (VoC) of a 7 is exhibiting a collapsed body posture and flat facial expression may not show how this positive cognition is fully integrated. Very often in EMDR therapy, these changes of procedural tendencies happen spontaneously. However, if they do not, the therapist might ask the child for the body posture that goes with the positive cognition or if he or she could "say" the positive cognition with movement and posture. For instance, If the positive belief is "I am strong," the child can be invited to notice how the legs, the arms and posture would express the positive cognition. It might be useful to remind the child of the special language that the body speaks: *"The body can say the same thing the brain or the heart says, but using a different language."* The child can be encouraged to speak the same positive cognition with all three "languages:" *"Let's say 'I am strong' with your body, your heart and your mind."*(Gomez, 2010a/2011). Since Jim's positive cognition was "I am strong," his therapist used interweaves like, *"How would your body say, 'I'm strong?'"* Embodying the new posture along with the positive cognition continues to stimulate the integration and assimilation of adaptive information. The same strategy may be used during the future template of EMDR therapy as the child identifies the positive cognitive, affective and somatic states while envisioning the adaptive future response in the presence of a former activating situation.

SUMMARY AND CONCLUSIONS

Children with complex trauma and pervasive affect dysregulation may require extended and more complex preparation and resource development during EMDR therapy. Because children may rapidly move out of their window of tolerance into hyper- and hypoarousal states, the reprocessing phases as well might be more complex and may require more active participation and interventions from the EMDR clinician. Children who have experienced early and chronic trauma oftentimes have poor interoceptive awareness and may feel disconnected from their bodies. The inclusion of additional interventions from Sensorimotor Psychotherapy may enhance the therapeutic work and overall treatment outcome when using EMDR therapy with children with complex trauma. Despite major differences between EMDR therapy and Sensorimotor Psychotherapy, they both share important treatment goals and procedures. The ultimate goal of accessing the three levels of information processing—cognitive, emotional, and sensorimotor—and promoting integration among them are common for both EMDR therapy and Sensorimotor Psychotherapy, although they achieve this goal by different means. This chapter intends to provide theoretical as well as practical approaches to the integration of Sensorimotor Psychotherapy techniques into a comprehensive EMDR therapy. The strategies provided throughout this chapter are not intended to change the core and crux of EMDR therapy and the AIP model, but instead to enhance and enrich its work with difficult to treat children while honoring the essence and heart of Sensorimotor Psychotherapy.

12

Using EMDR Therapy and Theraplay

Ana M. Gomez and Emily Jernberg

The main focus of this chapter is to present how eye movement desensitization and reprocessing (EMDR) therapy and Theraplay can be used together when treating children with a history of complex trauma. Thus, this chapter will provide an introduction to Theraplay, the ways it can be adapted to fit the needs of traumatized children, and how it can be added to a comprehensive EMDR treatment to enhance the healing process of these children. These two approaches work together so well because the areas they target complement each other:

- Theraplay focuses on the parent-child relationship as the healing agent that holds within it the potential to cultivate growth and security in the child.
- EMDR's main focus is on the stimulation of the adaptive information processing system of the brain in order to promote the integration of memories of trauma and adversity that lay at the core of the child's current suffering and difficulties.

When the parent-child relationship has been the wounding agent, the integration of such memories of attachment as well as the transformation of the parent-child present interactions are necessary to promote true healing. Often, insecurely attached and dissociative children have not had the appropriate developmental and attachment experiences. As a result, neural networks containing experiences of safety as well as congruent and unitary models of the self and other are nonexistent. These children will need the appropriate reparative experiences of healthy parent-child or adult-child interactions so new neural connections in the brain can develop. On the other hand, even when the parent-child interactions are repaired and healed, the memory networks formed during the times when trauma and adversity were experienced may remain unintegrated. As a result, these memories have the potential of being activated by present stimuli, causing the child to act in ways that are more consistent with the past (Shapiro, 2001). Children may continue to use the mechanisms of adaptation needed while trauma was occurring and respond to a safe environment as if they were still facing danger. Consequently, the implicit memories that remain unintegrated and fragmented will keep the child in the prison of the past. Moreover, if these memories of hardship are integrated and assimilated, but the parent engages in the present in wounding interactions with the child, the parent will continue to reinforce the same memories that the EMDR therapist is assisting the child in processing and assimilating. With this in mind, it is clear how these two approaches can work well together in cases where trauma and adversity have occurred within the caregiving system. It is important to highlight, though, that Theraplay is not an approach intended to directly work through the memories of trauma. Consequently, when using Theraplay with traumatized children, other approaches such as EMDR therapy need to be incorporated to directly process and assimilate the traumatic events. In order to integrate the two, a thorough review of Theraplay principles and procedures will be provided, followed by the specific phases of EMDR therapy where Theraplay activities may be incorporated. When and how to use Theraplay within the eight phases of EMDR therapy will be thoroughly described.

WHAT IS THERAPLAY?

Psychologist Ann M. Jernberg developed Theraplay, a therapeutic method based on attachment theory and modeled on the early parent–infant relationship in 1967. Jernberg turned to Austin Des Laurier's (1962) model of insistently engaging children in the here-and-now and Viola Brody's ideas of the therapist providing nurture to children (Brody, 1978, 1993). In addition, Jernberg was convinced that the healthy parent-child relationship held the key for growth and change. She drew on John Bowlby's newly emerging attachment theory for further confirmation (Bowlby, 1969). Although the very important elements of coregulation and attunement have been present from the beginning of Theraplay, in recent years Theraplay has been adapted to focus more on these important aspects. Current best practice of Theraplay focuses on security (Bowlby, 1973/1980), intersubjectivity (Trevarthan, 1989), social engagement system (Porges, 2011), and play and joy (Panskepp, 1998/2009).

Theraplay is an active, right brain, here and now playful therapy with a focus on health instead of pathology. The goals are to enhance attachment, self-esteem, joy and regulation. The relationship is the vehicle of change, and the therapist guides the therapy in a way that is empathic and attuned. The therapist also trains the parents (the word "parents" throughout this chapter will be used synonymously with "primary caregivers" or similar) to be cotherapists; they carry on the therapy at home whenever possible. Theraplay meets the child where he or she is developmentally, so if a child experienced difficulties at earlier stages of development, Theraplay treatment provides experiences that are relevant to the child's level of development. Theraplay is used for individuals at every stage of life, but it is used most often for clients from infancy to age 12.

Theraplay Theory and Basic Principles

Theraplay was modeled upon the normal, healthy parent-child interactions that enable a developing child in a nurturing, stimulating, attentive relationship to grow into a secure, resilient, satisfied and happy adult; the kind of relationship that leads to secure attachment. Parents in a healthy parent-child relationship will consciously or nonconsciously act in a variety of ways to help a child's development. The parents will help structure a child's experience when appropriate. They entice their children into relationships with them and give them the message that the world is an exciting place. Parents nurture a child so he or she feels secure, confident and loved. Parents can support the child in tackling appropriate challenges that will lead to the growth in ability and confidence. They can also help the child tolerate his or her frustration if the child cannot overcome a challenge. Healthy adult-child interactions vary from playful to somber, from quiet and peaceful to loud and rambunctious, from highly engaging to relaxed coexistence. Throughout these interactions, the parent is, ideally, highly attentive and attuned to the needs and the "place" of the child, and can adjust the activities according to what the parent knows that the child needs.

Thus, the basic components of the parent-child relationship that foster growth and security in a securely-attached child form the foundation of Theraplay. These are STRUCTURE, ENGAGEMENT, NURTURE, and CHALLENGE. Different children need activities from each of these components at different times and in different ways. The attuned mother of an 8-year-old girl who is tired and hungry and frenetically flying across the room will lovingly but firmly insist that she sits down for dinner and afterwards stick with a ritualized bedtime routine to help transition the fatigued girl into sleep (STRUCTURE). An infant and his father stare deeply into each other's eyes and smile and laugh in sync with each other (ENGAGEMENT). An attuned parent intuitively selects what is needed at the appropriate times. For example, a 4-year-old boy runs in the house, having scraped his knee playing in the yard. His mother cleans up the wound, puts on a Band-Aid® and blows a kiss on it (NURTURE). A father helps coax his tentative toddler to try throwing a ball just a little bit further by carefully taking a step farther away when he sees that his daughter has managed to successfully toss the ball to his current position (CHALLENGE).

THE FOUR DIMENSIONS OF THERAPLAY

Structure

Just as in a healthy parent-child relationship, the therapist, not the child, is in charge. The therapist's tone is firm and directive, while remaining positive. By providing clarity and organization, the adult helps reduce anxiety and uncertainty. For example, the therapist may greet the child in the waiting room with, *"I see you brought your strong legs with you. We're going to hold hands and hop together like bunnies to my playroom."* The therapist plans a sequence of activities within a session and each activity is structured with a beginning, middle, and end. There also may be a change of pace within the activity with the therapist leading the change. For example, during the activity "Row Boat," the therapist sits facing the child and clasping hands. As the therapist leads in the song of "row your boat" and rocks with the child, the therapist may do one verse in a calm way and then with a "storm coming," rock the boat faster and with "calm waters," slow the boat down. This change from quieter to active and back to quieter gives the child a chance to practice regulating arousal.

Although sessions are planned ahead of time, the therapist is always ready to modify the plan in response to the child's needs. The therapist may have planned for a session to emphasize structure and activities that target regulation for an overactive child. If the child arrives tired or sad over something that happened that day, the therapist would change the session to focus on nurturing activities. If a child feels fearful while doing an activity, the therapist may adjust the activity to reassure the child. The therapist paces the session according to the child's needs. An overactive child may be met initially at his or her fast pace and then slowed down. When doing "Row Boat" with such a child, for example, the therapist may begin with fast rowing and then have the waters become calm while child and therapist slow down and then end in a calm way. So, the adult is in charge but not rigidly controlling, instead attuned to what the child needs. No matter the child's reaction, the adult sets the session tone of accepting the child.

Structure in Theraplay, such as the activities described above illustrate, leads the child to feelings of safety and trust in the caregiver, and the experience of being well regulated. For traumatized children, it is particularly important that they experience not having to be responsible and instead being taken care of and able to have fun. The child gets an opportunity to feel that the world is predictable, which allows the child to enjoy the perhaps new experience of having fun while letting the adult take charge. This, in turn, helps the child to let his or her guard down.

Engagement

If you imagine the scene of a parent playing peek-a-boo with a baby, you can get an idea of the way that engagement in Theraplay is founded in healthy parent-child interactions. Carefully watching the baby's cues, parents woo and entice their babies into the game. They stimulate their child and draw them into a mutual gaze and a mutual sense of fun in the moment. The back and forth creates a powerful communication before the baby is even able to speak. As a result, the child feels that he or she has the power to attract others and is worth getting to know.

By the same token, engagement in Theraplay draws the child into an interpersonal world of adventurous play. Just as in an ideal parent-child exchange, in Theraplay the child feels joy and connection and that he or she has an impact on the therapist. In exploring the relationship with the other, the child comes to see himself or herself as fun, appealing, unique, and "felt." By the same token, the child learns to experience others as safe, exciting and fun. This translates into seeing the world as full of exciting opportunities.

While a game of peek-a-boo may on the face of it seem restricted to an audience of babies and toddlers, in the hands of the creative Theraplay therapist, play like this can be used with surprising success with older children. For example, the sullen and withdrawn 13-year-old who slumps half-covered by his jacket in the waiting room assiduously avoids the gaze, or seemingly any other interaction, with his or her therapist, until the therapist turns the very avoidance into a game. "I see you under there," elicits a first skeptical scowl, but the teen pulls the edge of the coat down to investigate what this odd adult is up to. Playing along, the therapist says, "You can't fool me. There you are!" The teen covers the face again with his or her jacket, but a reluctant smile is elicited, and eventually the teen cannot resist looking again, and after more rounds of this game, they are soon laughing together. It is important to remember that children with complex trauma may have needs consistent with a much younger emotional developmental level so a game that is normally used for infants and toddlers could be adapted to the child's chronological age to allow healing at those earlier developmental stages to occur.

The therapist monitors the intensity of the connection so that the child stays at a level of optimal arousal. A child who is easily keyed up may need more modulated engagement by slowing the pace or allowing for more breaks in the connection. For example, a child who feels intense shame may not be able to tolerate much eye contact, so a game of blowing a cotton ball between therapist and child may be done with more fleeting eye contact. Engagement is especially useful for children who have underdeveloped and compromised social engagement systems, and are withdrawn, avoid contact, dissociate, present with a flat affect, or have an autism spectrum disorder.

Nurture

Parents feed, rub lotion, rock, sing lullabies to soothe, and generally help their children to relax. Children sit on their parents' laps and parents comfort and dote on their children naturally without their children having to "work" for it. Therapists demonstrate some of the same activities in sessions to parents and then coach parents in taking over that direct nurturing role as quickly as possible. They soothe a child and convey the message that the child is special and cared about and that he or she deserves good things. The therapist begins each session with a "check-up" in which all the ways the child is special are noticed. *"I see you brought your chocolate brown eyes and your big smile with you today, and it looks like you even got some more freckles on you than the last time we saw each other."*

Hurts are attended to during a checkup, and the therapist or parent may put lotion around a child's "owie." A child may have her face painted during a session, while the adult uses imaginary "paint" on an empty paintbrush and comments, *"Now I'm painting your soft cheeks. You have the greatest dimple right here."* Often, toward the end of the session, the therapist has the child sitting on his or her parent's lap or next to the parent while the parent feeds the child. The child feels calmed and develops more abilities to regulate. When a child feels worthy and has the experience of having his or her own needs met, the child can look outside of him- or herself and recognize others' needs and feelings. Thus, when a child is nurtured, the child can eventually develop empathy toward others.

Many children with complex trauma assume an air of bravado that belies their inner feelings of vulnerability and fear. Getting the message that they are lovable just as they are, including their vulnerability, is a powerful force in their healing. Because many of these children fend off nurture, the therapist may adapt the nurturing activity so that the child can accept it more easily. A game in which a child tries to bite a pretzel off the adult's finger without breaking it is a way to allow a child to accept nurture while still saving face. Even adolescents rise to the challenge of biting the pretzel or guessing where and on which hand they are being touched with a soft feather. Thus, Challenge may be added to Nurture early in the therapy for a child with complex trauma until he or she becomes comfortable accepting nurture. Nurture is especially useful for children with histories of attachment injuries and early deprivation.

Challenge

Parents look in mock surprise when they help their young baby to a standing position and celebrate when their children learn to walk. The baby or child feels powerful and competent: "I can do things when I try. I have an impact on the world."

In Theraplay, the therapist also stretches the child to reach above what he or she thinks it is possible do. A child may be encouraged to do an activity: *"I wonder if you can jump off these 2 pillows into your parent's arms? Oh, that's good. Now, let's see if you can do 3 pillows. Oh my, look at that."* It is important to match the difficulty of an activity so that the child has to try but ultimately can accomplish it in the end.

As seen above in the nurture example, challenge often is added to allow a child to accept other elements in the interaction with an adult. Challenge can also be used to channel a child's resistance or high activity level. A child who is hitting may be told, *"See if you can punch a hole in the center of this newspaper if I hold it like this."* Often, children are enticed into the activity and, thus, accept adult guidance, which they may not have done without the challenge. What was a moment of dysregulation and defiance becomes an experience of self-efficacy.

Many traumatized and insecurely attached children have had to grow up too fast and often take the role of the adult. The therapist does not need to plan much challenge, for they turn most things into challenges. Underneath their bravado, however, they feel helpless. Challenge is the dimension least needed for children who have suffered from trauma and, therefore, is used least in sessions with these children. However, challenging activities can allow them to get clear about what they can and cannot accomplish at a level in touch with reality. For example, they could not have gotten their birth mother to take care of them but can jump a foot high. Challenge is especially useful for children who present as passive, helpless, withdrawn, and those who are afraid of their anger.

All children need all four dimensions in each session. Deciding which ones to accentuate in each session depends on what the child needs in general and in the session. Does the child need to develop strategies for self-soothing and regulation? A sense of self-worth? Joy in a relationship? Using attunement and empathy, often in addition to a formal assessment (Marschak Interaction Method, to be described later), the therapist determines the dimension, activities, the tone, and interactions that elicit these goals. Activities pull for certain dimensions, as Row Boat does for structure, for example. Some activities can draw on more than one desired dimension, as Pretzel Bite does with nurture and challenge.

CORE CONCEPTS: THERAPLAY IN ACTION

In addition to the original four fundamental "dimensions" that form the basis of Theraplay treatment, there are seven "core concepts" that help define and illuminate the application of Theraplay. These core concepts are always present regardless of which dimension is used at any given time.

1. **Theraplay is interactive and relationship-based.** As we have emphasized before, the therapeutic focus in Theraplay is on the relationship. It is this connection between the parent (or therapist) and the child that forms the very foundation of Theraplay's therapeutic action. The formation of a healthy relationship that compensates for any existing deficiencies in the four dimensions is the "magic" that allows for repair and healing to occur. In a normal Theraplay session, there is an active and often intense meeting of minds as the adult helps the child cocreate a play experience.

   A child's problematic view of his- or herself and others will emerge in the behavior within the relationship. The therapist's relationship-focused response presents the opportunity for repairing these views and behaviors.

2. **Theraplay is a direct, "here-and-now" experience**. Rather than cognitively exploring the past or the future, Theraplay focuses on what is happening in the moment. Change happens when a direct experience is felt in the moment. The emotional, physical, kinesthetic, and sensory experiences coalesce and the child's brain and body absorb what is happening that is so important to the child. When the therapist transitions from an engaging and challenging activity to a nurturing activity quickly, confidently and caringly, the child who needs to experience nurturance, but finds it unsettling, is less able to effectively set up defenses. When these defenses are bypassed, the child is then free to enjoy being comforted, rocked and fed. These new rhythmic, repetitive, relational, and reparative experiences can create new neural pathways in the child's brain.

3. **Theraplay is guided by the adult.** Just as a parent provides structure to the child, the adult in Theraplay guides the therapy session, allowing the child to feel safe and secure. If a child becomes oppositional, the adult continues to set the tone as one of acceptance and, if appropriate, playfulness.

4. **Theraplay is responsive, attuned, empathic, and reflective.** Attachment research has demonstrated that responsive parenting is a determining factor of secure attachment. In Theraplay, the adult leads the session while being attuned to the child and ready to change the interaction to respond to the child's needs. It is this responsiveness that allows the child to feel seen, felt and heard, and to experience adults as trustworthy and caring. For example, the therapist "beeps" the young child's nose and the child turns slightly away. The therapist reflects to himself or herself "maybe the 'beep' was too intrusive because it was on the child's face." The therapist may "beep" the child's knee or foot to verify this hypothesis. If the child appears upset by the nose "beep," the therapist may say, "that beep was too much. I'll do it over here and see if that feels better."

5. **Theraplay is preverbal, social and right-brain related.** The limbic system, intimately connected to the right brain, is responsible for managing emotions, responding to emotions in others, allowing a person to have empathy, and regulating interactions and the relationship between self and other. The wiring of these emotional circuits is influenced by the interactions with the caregiver, the emotional tone of voice, eye contact, and body gestures (Trevarthen, 1990). The regulation or dysregulation of these early communications determines how the baby attaches to the caregiver and, ultimately, how the internal working model, which is housed in the right brain's limbic system, is formed. Thus, it is important to go to an earlier level where the imprinting of these experiences went awry to create new internal working models. In the application of Theraplay, our goal is to "speak the language" of the right brain. We do this by focusing on preverbal interactions (such as rhythm, tone of voice, movement) rather than on cognitive processing. Often, this will manifest as the frequent use of rhythm in a session, such as introducing a song or a handclapping game. If a child is dysregulated, and is, for example, looking away, we may turn it into a game such as "peek-a-boo." We wait for a glimmer of interest, and then repeat it until we get a rhythm going, and the child can get regulated again.

6. **Theraplay is multisensory.** Just as a parent with a baby uses touch, eye contact, and voice to connect with his or her baby, so does the Theraplay therapist use these modalities with children in treatment. We are speaking to the right brain when we do this. There is sometimes anxiety in this day and age about inappropriate contact with children. While mindful of these concerns and knowledgable about the child's trauma history, the therapist seeks to provide appropriate, respectful, reparative experience at a pace that the child can accept and benefit from. In Theraplay, we believe children should get to experience good, healthy touch and we find ways to experience this primarily between the caregiver and child. We may use smell and taste, as well. We often include a food treat in sessions and we may use soothing smells like lavender lotion to help a child soothe.

7. **Theraplay is playful.** The foundation of change happens through play for children. Our play has an upbeat, optimistic quality to it. We convey through play that the child is fun, appealing, and a joy to be with and that his or her behaviors are appropriate. With these messages in mind, the child can experience the world as joyful, enticing and an exciting place to be.

ADAPTATIONS TO COMPLEX TRAUMA

Theraplay is often used to treat children who have suffered relational trauma. It offers exactly what these children are missing:

- Focus on relationships as reparative (which is the opposite of the child's previous experience in relationships).
- Emphasis on regulation for children who become too easily dysregulated.
- Emphasis on attunement and empathy for children who have little experience of being truly seen and felt by their caregivers.
- Communication in right brain "language" for children exposed to incongruent and multiple models of the self and other.

Yet these children, for whom Theraplay is often such an appropriate fit, are at the same time one of the most difficult populations to treat. This is because their history of trauma typically has seriously compromised their capacity to trust both the world in general and their adult caregivers in particular. These children are too often frightened at the prospect of adults being in charge. The need-for-control characteristic of many traumatized children and children with disorganized-insecure attachment gets in the way of attempts to reestablish trust in their parents.

The challenge for the therapist is to guide children who are often on a "hair trigger" and ready to collapse into dysregulation, to move into play activities that both stretch and reassure. We want to respect children's fears but also entice them into as much fun, engagement, and nurture as they can tolerate. Striking the right balance is a delicate matter. Too much caution or reassurance may jeopardize the process. The therapist must remain carefully attuned so as not to exacerbate the existing wounds of trauma too fast too soon when the child's regulatory capacities are overtaxed.

As difficult as all this is, Theraplay has been adapted to address ways to walk this line. A first principle is that the child must feel safe. One step in this direction is predictability. If a child can predict how the future will go, he or she will feel safer. The therapist can, for instance, show the child a schedule of what the planned sequence is and have play materials visible to the child rather than have them in a bag of surprising activities. The therapist can do the activity to the parent first or have the child do the activity to the parent (Booth & Jernberg, 2010).

Engagement is modified so the child is not overstimulated. In a game typically played with direct eye contact, the child may hide his face under a sheer scarf and voices may be quieted, slower, and gentler. Closeness can come about more as the child gets more comfortable.

In addition, the therapist needs to be highly sensitive to when a child may be experiencing fear, which may sometimes appear as subtle body signs, such as widened eyes. The therapist may offer more explanations and reflections so that activities make sense to the child as well as explaining the child's own reaction to him or her. For example, a child may not know what he or she is feeling and may need the therapist to articulate it.

Since these children are already trying to take care of themselves and since challenge promotes feelings of autonomy, we want these children to feel relaxed and cared for, and we do not want to reinforce their striving. By using challenge, the children may be drawn into accepting activities that are harder for them to enjoy due to their past trauma memories being activated.

Since these children reject their parents often, and might instead turn to the therapist as a parent figure, it is especially important to work on healing the parent–child relationship and empowering the parent. When working with children with complex trauma, parents are in the sessions from the beginning. Needless to say, the therapist should obtain the parents' permission early in the therapy.

An example of empowering the parent is to arrange experiences where the child can be shown the parents' awareness of the child. The therapist can ask, "Mom, does Susie like orange or apple juice better?" If the mother says the child likes apple juice and then the child happily drinks apple juice, the therapist can say, "Your mom really knows the things you like. Your mom really knows lots of things about you."

In conclusion, even though Theraplay was not initially indicated for traumatized children, current adaptations have made it an important form of therapy that can help traumatized children heal. However, it is important to highlight that Theraplay is not designed to directly address trauma. As a result, other therapeutic approaches that deal with trauma, such as EMDR therapy, need to be utilized once the child has developed appropriate regulatory capacities and is ready to address the memories of the traumatic and adverse events.

THE AIP MODEL AND THERAPLAY PRINCIPLES

Now that a clear review of basic Theraplay principles has been provided, we need to look at EMDR therapy and the AIP model in conjunction with Theraplay and Theraplay core values. The AIP model is founded on the premise that the brain and human beings are geared toward health, integration and wholeness. When trauma or adversity occurs, the ability of the brain to process and integrate information is thwarted, causing these memories to remain unprocessed and unintegrated (Shapiro, 2001). Children who have experienced attachment traumas and injuries have not had appropriate parent–child interactions, and as a result these experiences have not been integrated into a healthy sense of self. The AIP model looks at the impact of these earlier experiences that are held in the nervous system in a state-specific form as the core of present dysfunctional characteristics and symptoms (Shapiro, 2001). For children growing up in chaotic, traumatizing, emotionally impoverished environments, memory networks containing adaptive and positive information are usually scarce. Due to the limited internal and external resources of these children, promoting reparative parent-child experiences should be an important part of the initial stages of EMDR therapy.

EMDR preparation phase with children at its core is geared toward fostering stabilization; homeostatic states and the expansion of windows of affect tolerance. This is partially but fundamentally done by assisting caregivers in increasing their ability to synchronize, attune and resonate with the brain and the nervous system of the child. Before processing memories of disturbing life events, the presence of adaptive memory systems in the brain is pivotal. During the reprocessing of memories of adverse events, synthesis appears to happen in the brain (Shapiro, 2001). Linkage of memory systems, connections, assimilation of information and, ultimately, the integration of disturbing memories are at the core of EMDR therapy. For the assimilation and transmutation of experience, positive memory networks need to be present in the child's system. Some children with complex trauma initially may not respond to protocols such as the calm-safe place due to the absence of experiences that foster a sense of safety and security. Theraplay activities in the four different dimensions provide children with the appropriate experiences of touch, connection, play, structure, boundaries and nurturance. Theraplay challenges representations of the self and other that are imprinted in the brain in the form of neural networks. These new reparative experiences provided in Theraplay sessions, in turn, can create new patterns of neural firing in the child's brain. The reparative experiences during Theraplay sessions challenge the brain to develop new positive and adaptive memory systems that are noncongruent with what the child has come to expect in relationships ((Booth & Jernberg, 2010). Theraplay can assist the caregiver in providing the experiences that can help the child in repairing and rebuilding the trust in others, especially adults. Oftentimes, the child may be reluctant to process memories of adversity due to the lack of trust in others, including the therapist. Adverse and traumatic experiences may have also hindered the child's capacity to experience hope. As a result, the child may approach EMDR processing of traumatic material with a sense of hopelessness and helplessness. After repetitive experiences where the caregiving system has failed to meet the needs of a child, new experiences will be approached with a sense of disbelief and distrust. Theraplay works at helping the child experience what it is to be in a relationship where safety and trust are at its core.

Theraplay treatment is also geared toward promoting attunement and facilitating the parent's ability to meet the child's deepest needs for connection, boundaries, nurturance, trust and regulation, among others. On the other hand, the goal of EMDR therapy is to access, reprocess, integrate and assimilate disturbing memories that lay at the core of current problems and symptoms. However, the reprocessing and integration of these memories needs to be done in a safe and contained therapeutic environment. The child can experience the relationship with the therapists and caregivers as a strong safety net that provides a sense of security and containment. Within this net, the child can safely access, process and assimilate the memories of adversity that continue to shape the present life of the child. EMDR therapy is also focused on promoting and enhancing neural networks containing positive and adaptive information about the self and other.

Each of the eight phases of EMDR therapy contributes to the final treatment outcome in very specific ways. The ultimate goal is, however, the assimilation, integration and adaptive resolution of memories of adversity and hardship. Nevertheless, EMDR therapy accomplishes this goal while promoting stability and regulation of the biological systems. The preparation phase is dedicated to supporting the expansion of affect tolerance and regulation. The goal of promoting the augmentation of positive affects and the creation of new neural pathways containing positive and adaptive information is a critical one during this phase of EMDR therapy. However, throughout the eight phases of treatment, fostering stability, regulation and the development and enhancement of positive memory networks is foremost cultivated. Since Theraplay is an attachment-based psychotherapy that stimulates connection, regulation and positive affective states, its addition to a comprehensive EMDR treatment can greatly facilitate and enhance the outcome of therapy with complex trauma cases.

EMDR THERAPY AND THERAPLAY: WHEN AND HOW

Knowing when and how to integrate Theraplay with EMDR therapy will help clinicians maintain adherence to EMDR therapy and the AIP model as well as to preserve the essence and heart of Theraplay. To better integrate EMDR therapy and Theraplay, EMDR clinicians should pursue formal training in Theraplay (www.Theraplay.org). In order to assist the clinician in better understanding the appropriate use of EMDR and Theraplay, each EMDR therapy phase where Theraplay activities may be incorporated will be addressed. The following may serve as general criteria to incorporate Theraplay:

- The child experienced early trauma and grew up in relationally impoverished environments.
- The current parent or caregiver continues to engage in maladaptive parent-child interactions and lacks the ability for attunement. As a result, current attachment needs are not being met.
- The child presents with attachment injuries and traumas, is unable to find a safe place and shows limited relational resources. When using the calm-safe place and RDI protocols they become contaminated with negative affect once engaged in BLS. This is due to the lack of positive attachment experiences as well as experiences of safety in the child's life.
- The child has developed an insecure pattern of attachment with past or current caregivers and reparative parent-child interactions are needed.
- The current parents show dismissing, preoccupied or unresolved states of mind with regards to his or her own attachment experiences and, as a result, his or her mentalizing capacities and reflective function are compromised.
- The parent clearly exhibits the lack of emotional attunement, synchrony and resonance with the child. As a result, the needs for connection, nurturance and boundaries are lacking in the parent-child transactions.
- The child is unable to explore memories of adversity and shuts down or becomes hyperaroused. The clinician finds chaotic family environments and dysregulated parent-child interactions in the present or the past.
- The child presents with co-morbid disorders to trauma, such as disorders from the autism spectrum. In addition, the child displays serious impairment of the social engagement system as it is seen in reactive attachment disorder.

PHASE ONE: CLIENT HISTORY AND TREATMENT PLANNING

After a thorough assessment and information gathering has been attained, the EMDR clinician can map the areas in need of intervention. During the initial interview, gathering information related to attachment history and current parent-child dynamics will determine the need for Theraplay. A child with a parent identified as having dismissing, preoccupied, or unresolved states of mind with regard to his or her own attachment experiences will benefit from having Theraplay as an adjunctive approach to EMDR therapy. A child with avoidant, anxious-ambivalent or disorganized patterns of attachment with the current parent or prior caregiver will also benefit from having Theraplay. Keeping in mind that the major foci of Theraplay are attunement, regulation, parent-child interactions and the attachment system will help the EMDR clinician know the children that will benefit from having Theraplay as an adjunctive approach. In addition, children that are highly dysregulated and have great difficulty exploring adverse experiences will greatly benefit from having Theraplay sessions during the initial phases of EMDR therapy. It is important to highlight the need for attunement

and the ability to resonate with the child's system. The EMDR and Theraplay clinician will benefit from thoroughly understanding the strategies the child has utilized
to accommodate not having his or her attachment needs met. A child using avoidance as a strategy will need a gradual introduction to receiving and accepting nurturance, since the mechanism of adaptation has been to actually detach from his or her
own needs for connection and nurturance. The child with disorganized strategies has
most likely experienced the interactions with the caregiver or parent as frightened or
frightening. As a result, the clinician using Theraplay activities without appropriate
attunement may activate memory networks associated with connection to others as
frightening and dysregulating.

During the initial phase of EMDR therapy, data is collected about earlier history
going back to the parents' relationship and history specific to symptoms. The use of an
interactive assessment that corresponds to an instrument used by Theraplay therapists
may be also useful for EMDR clinicians. In Theraplay, the therapist carefully assesses the
child and the relationships with parents or primary caregivers by using an interactive
assessment, the Marschak Interaction Method (MIM). The MIM allows the therapist to
watch the parent or caregiver interact with the child in a controlled setting. The parent
and child sit alone in the room, with instruction cards given to the parent and specific
materials (e.g. toy animals, dress-up hats, blocks). The interpretation and implementation of the written tasks helps reveal the strengths and challenges of the individual
adult and child, and of the parent-child relationship. One example of an MIM task is
"parent and child feed each other," with the associated envelope containing predeter-
mined parentally approved snacks. Sometimes the parent invites the child to sit closely
and gently places a cracker in the child's mouth. If the child has problems accepting
the cracker and instead rejects the food or tries to instead feed the adult (common in
children with attachment issues or trauma), the therapist will note that one of the treatment goals will include allowing the child to become comfortable accepting nurturing
from a well-meaning caregiver. Based on the results of the initial interview and MIM (if
administered), the therapist will plan a series of Theraplay sessions.

The use of the MIM can provide a baseline in terms of assessing the parent's capacity to be playful and engage in playful transactions; establish appropriate boundaries;
regulate, care and comfort the child; and motivate the child to attain developmental
milestones (Booth & Jernberg, 2010).

The practical application of Theraplay involves carefully assessing the specific
needs of the child. This is done particularly in terms of what components of a healthy
relationship might be deficient with this specific child. The interactive Theraplay sessions are tailored to repair the particular dimensions found in this child to be missing that would normally be present in a healthy child and in the relationship with a
primary caregiver. Since Theraplay is relational, an assessment of the parents is part
of this process. Once the baseline has been established, the clinician can identify the
resources and deficits in the parent-child relationship: what works in the relationship
that can be enhanced and stimulated, and what is not working that needs repair?

With this in mind, the EMDR clinician can either make a referral for the child to
receive adjunctive Theraplay sessions or, if the formal training in Theraplay has been
received, Theraplay sessions within a more comprehensive EMDR treatment can be
provided. Once the clinical landscape has been developed, and the strengths and deficits have been mapped, a treatment plan is created and designed to meet the child's
needs. If a referral is made for Theraplay therapy, this chapter will assist the EMDR
clinician in having a better understanding of the goals and activities used in Theraplay

so the communication with the Theraplay therapist will be more efficient. Clear goals need to be created based on the initial clinical landscape developed by the EMDR clinician. Close and frequent communication between the EMDR and the Theraplay therapist should occur. The following strategies and specific use of Theraplay within EMDR therapy are designed for EMDR clinicians already trained in Theraplay.

PHASE TWO: PREPARATION

Children with early and complex trauma usually require multifaceted and extended periods of preparation. When Theraplay has been identified as an adjunctive approach to EMDR therapy, Theraplay sessions are initiated during the preparation phase. The parent and the child receive information on EMDR and also the use of Theraplay. The parent should receive enough clarification so an informed decision can be made and appropriate authorizations can be obtained.

EMDR Preparation Phase: Theraplay Sessions

During Theraplay sessions, the child is engaged in a playful series of interactions that are determined by the therapist. The therapist is safely and comfortingly in charge of every activity in the session, but not rigidly so. The intended composition of each session is carefully planned ahead of time; however, a child's mood or energy level at the time of a particular Theraplay session can sway the planned itinerary to more empathically match the child's need at that time.

For a child who has experienced significant trauma, there are several adaptations that may be incorporated. Although physical touch is an essential component of standard Theraplay sessions, in the case of a child who has experienced trauma, touch is used cautiously and respectfully. The use of touch should be thoughtfully administered throughout each session in order to avoid activating the child's memory networks containing traumatic material. Touch should be used judiciously to help establish a sense of security and nurturing for the child. We do not want to deprive children who have been traumatized of healthy touch. However, in a child with a history of trauma who might be further traumatized by physical connections or intense experiences, the therapist "checks in" frequently with the child to ensure that the child feels "safe" with the activities and that his sense of personal space and privacy are respected. The therapist does not ask for permission, since that would burden the child with being in charge, but instead reflects what the therapist sees, makes a brief reflective comment, and makes sure the child feels comfortable with the touch the therapist uses. For example, if a child shuts down when the therapist touches him or her in a nurturing or playful way, the therapist would reflect, *"You seemed scared when I put my hand on your shoulder. I think maybe it reminded you of the way your grandpa sometimes touched you."* If the child resonates with the therapist's statement, the therapist would say, *"That must have been hard and scary. I am going to work on finding a kind of touch that would feel better and safer for you."* Thus, gradually, and with careful attention to the child's level of comfort, safe and gentle touch is used to convey that the therapist (and, subsequently, the parent) is aware of the child's needs and can provide healthy, relationship enhancing, nurturing touch. When information about traumatic or adverse events are disclosed or tapped into during Theraplay sessions, the therapist takes notes so this information can be added to the child's targeting sequence and comprehensive clinical landscape.

EMDR Preparation Phase: Theraplay Strategies With Parents

Early in its development, Theraplay integrated parental involvement into its therapeutic model. Although Theraplay can still be effective in instances where parental participation is unlikely or impossible, we have found that participation of the parent in Theraplay sessions markedly accelerates and solidifies the therapeutic process. Having the parent intimately involved with close supervision and encouragement from the therapist is fundamental. In addition, helping the parent learn how to meet the child's needs and also helping the child learn to transfer his or her trust and engagement from the therapist over to the parent is critical in Theraplay. With the carefully coordinated participation of parents in the Theraplay sessions, parents learn how the therapist guides activities as determined by the child's needs in different situations.

For Theraplay with children who have not been traumatized or with parents who are not ready to be in sessions, perhaps due to their own dysregulation, initially, from behind a one-way mirror, or by viewing videos of the Theraplay sessions, the parent observes the child interacting with the Theraplay therapist. This often happens while the parent's own therapist is helping the parent reflect on what is happening in the Theraplay room. They discuss why the therapist structures the activities as seen in the next room, or why he or she reacts to certain behaviors of the child. Also important in the observation room, the therapist comments on what the child might be thinking and feeling and elicits different emotions and insights in the parents at particular behaviors or activities.

In some cases, the parent is brought in sooner. With adopted and foster children, and other children who have been traumatized, the parent is in the session from the very first meeting. If the parent has not been present from the beginning, when the parent is ready, at the end of the first few sessions, the therapist invites the parent into the room for part or all of the session. Before seeing the child individually, the therapist prepares the parent for what the parent will be doing when joining the session. The therapist engages both the parent and the child in specific Theraplay activities designed to teach the parent how to supply those dimensions necessary for the development of a healthy relationship between parent and child and for healthy growth of the child. Frequently, we find that the parent can use some emotional support, and in these situations, often one therapist will sit behind the mother and one behind the child as the mother and child face each other or snuggle together. In the absence of another therapist that can work with the parent, the sessions may be videotaped and watched later on with the parent or caregiver. The parents learn to understand healthy and not-so-healthy dynamics and how to relate in a way that benefits the child and empowers healthy parenting. Through guiding and coaching during parents' participation in the Theraplay sessions, parents acquire the essential skills and emotional perspectives that will help them be more effective caregivers and, along the way, gain an enhanced sense of personal fulfillment in their parenting.

By participating actively in Theraplay, parents come to better understand their child. Consider, for example, a child with heightened auditory sensitivity who puts his hands on his ears or gets angry after a parent sings a song. The therapist, either by advising the parent directly or by modeling for the parent, may encourage the parent to respond like this: "*Bobby is letting us know that singing is too loud for him. Mom, sing it again but more quietly this time,*" or, "*Bobby, I think my singing was too loud for you. I will sing more quietly so it will not hurt your ears.*" Such an interaction provides an opportunity for the parent to become more attuned to the child and to develop ways to respond more empathically.

An important component of parental participation is helping the parent understand the etiology of the child's "bad behavior." During an observation, the therapist stimulates the parent's reflective capacity when looking at the child's actions and discusses the parents' reactions to their child's behaviors. For example, in the case of a girl referred for aggression and a history of trauma, the therapist adds this reflective comment in an aside to the parent: *"See how scared she looks right before she hits? She may be aggressive in this case because she is scared. She may need us to move more slowly and predictably and to tell her more clearly what we are going to do."* Thus, misbehavior becomes an opportunity. As Phyllis Booth (2010) writes:

"We create moments of excitement that suddenly shift the child into a moment of joyful connection. We challenge the child's negative internal working models by responding to his behaviors in ways that are noncongruent with what he expects, e.g. we take a child's negative behavior and see it in a positive light, and in so doing we organize a behavior that might typically get a negative response into one that is positive, and create a moment of shared, playful activity. Rather than talking about new meanings, we create them in the interaction."[1]

Enabling the parents to understand where the child "is coming from" also allows the parents to become experts on their children. In a partnership with the therapist, parents come to see the child differently, and also understand and become competent and comfortable with their important roles as protectors and adult caregivers in charge of helping the child.

In addition, if parents' own psychological vulnerabilities arise in the course of this intense and often intimate process, the therapist and parent can explore them together. The parent can receive EMDR therapy (see Chapter 5 for strategies on working with parents) and work through the memory networks activated by the child. In the case of a father who was emotionally triggered by some of his child's regressive behaviors during a session ("don't talk baby-talk, you're too old for that"), the therapist was able to detect, and at a later time (not in front of the child) to explore with the father his own childhood experiences which had given rise to these feelings. It turned out that the father had felt that he was forced to "grow up too fast" himself, and in being enabled to process and integrate the memories containing feelings of resentment and frustration about his past, he became better able to be patient with his child's occasional babyish behaviors. Without this level of work, the father's emerging guilt and shame about his own past might have undermined the parent-child connection.

The Theraplay therapist's necessary attunement to what is arising in the parents, as well as the child, is even more essential when it comes to children who have suffered trauma. In addition to the more or less typical ways in which a parent may be triggered during a session, parents of traumatized children are vulnerable to a more profound layer of emotional exposure. The experience of trauma teaches children that they are not safe and must be ever watchful for real or imagined sources of danger. As a result, they become adept at knowing their parent's "weak spots." Because these children tend to vigilantly scan their parents' emotional landscape, they know exactly how to push their parents' buttons. As a result, the parents find themselves drawn into a power struggle; they may even find themselves not liking their child and then feeling guilty and ashamed about that. Parents may also be grieving over what they could not provide for their children during the time their children were traumatized and feel helpless that they could not prevent the trauma.

---

[1]*http://theraplay.org/downloads/core_concepts.pdf, p.2 originally published in The Theraplay Newsletter, p. 7, 2010*

The EMDR and Theraplay therapist must therefore support the parents and explore their histories around attachment and trauma to identify the memory networks that the interactions with the child continue to activate. The therapist must also educate parents about the child's experience, *"When he was in the orphanage he had to keep his guard up, and he has not yet learned that it is safe to let his guard down...."* so that they can empathize rather than taking it personally. Parents can be led to even celebrate that their child's admittedly exasperating behaviors were part of a strategy that helped the child survive. The parents' experience of receiving empathy and feeling safe with, and psychologically held by, the therapist can allow the parents to provide that same experience to their children. In situations like this, the trauma is so deeply embedded that it can demand sometimes heroic levels of patience and empathy on the part of the parents until trauma memories can be accessed and integrated.

Since, ultimately, children need to securely attach to their parents, an important goal of Theraplay is to restore the family system hierarchy to a positive footing, where children trust their parents and where parents, in turn, feel confident and competent in sustaining that trust. The transition from a fearful or frustrated relationship to an "in sync" and thriving relationship can actually engender a self-sustaining delight of the parent and the child in each other's company. The goal is to give parents the opportunity to change their relationship with their child by direct interaction, first under the guidance and support of the therapist and then through practicing at home. These new interactions in the AIP model of EMDR therapy have the potential to promote the development of new neuronal pathways in the child as well as the parent.

Using Theraplay Activities as State Change Strategies

Theraplay has a wide variety of activities that promote homeostasis in the child's system through the use of touch, laughter, connection and play. If the child has not been able to identify a safe place or once BLS is initiated, the safe place or other resources become contaminated and negative, Theraplay activities can be used as state change strategies. The EMDR therapist can enhance positive emotional states experienced during Theraplay activities. The clinician could identify moments when the child is experiencing positive affect, regulation and connection while engaged in Theraplay activities and provide slow and short set of BLS. The clinician may ask for what the heart and the body are saying about this moment and install it as a resource. Even though Theraplay's primary goal is to engage the right-brain, by labeling affective states, the left-brain is also engaged. These activities become state change strategies that can be used at home by the parent or by the clinician after a session where disturbing material has been accessed and the child needs to regain balance and equilibrium.

If the EMDR clinician is not directly providing Theraplay, the clinician may ask the child for the Theraplay activities he or she enjoys the most and invite the child to either think about them or draw pictures of them. The clinician then can proceed to assist the child in identifying the feelings and location in the body and provide slow and short sets of BLS to install them as resources. These positive feelings of Theraplay moments can be stored inside the "heart-helping box," so the child can always carry them inside and access them when needed. The child is invited to go to his or her "heart-helping box" whenever things do not go right and the child is in need of getting the good feelings stored in this box.

Promoting horizontal and vertical integration in the brain is an integral and intrinsic component to the EMDR treatment. Many children with high activations of lower brain areas as well as the right-brain may benefit from the soothing that the labeling of affect may bring. In a study conducted by Cresswell et al. (2007), it was found that labeling negative affect enhances prefrontal cortical regulation of affect. Even though Theraplay offers the door and the key to enter into the right-brain, with a finesse for timing, the EMDR therapist may work on inviting the left-brain to participate. This "therapeutic artwork" may hold the key to promoting horizontal integration and balance.

PHASE FOUR: DESENSITIZATION

During the reprocessing phases of EMDR therapy, Theraplay can be very helpful in providing different avenues for emotion regulation and for the repairing of the attachment system.

Using Theraplay Activities as Interweaves to Heal the Attachment System

When working with insecurely attached children, repair is necessary to fully assimilate and integrate adverse and traumatic attachment experiences. An innovation of the use of Theraplay activities, ego state therapy and EMDR has been developed by Gomez (2009b, 2011). Once the current parent-child interactions have been positively affected and changed, the repair of past attachment experiences can go forward. Traumatic or adverse repetitive experiences, despite the positive environmental changes experienced in the present, may still remain frozen in the nervous system in a state-dependent form. One element of the dysfunctional storage of these memories is that they are stored in isolation, unable to link up with any adaptive information. Consequently, these state-dependent memories continue to be activated by the present stimuli, despite the positive changes achieved by the current parents or caregivers. For example, children adopted by parents that have been providing positive attachment experiences of connection and safety continue to feel like the parents do not love them. Despite the constant expressions of love and care, these children still feel abandoned and rejected. In these cases, when these memories remain unprocessed and unintegrated, the use of reparative interweaves (Gomez, 2009b, 2011) to help children meet unmet developmental and attachment needs can be very powerful. Keep in mind that this strategy is used for traumas or adverse events happening within the caregiving system.

From an AIP perspective, a "part" or "ego state" is a manifestation of the unprocessed, isolated, unintegrated memory network that contains the information from previous adverse life experiences. Therefore, during the EMDR reprocessing session, the child and the parent are invited to meet, nurture and engage with the "inner child," the "little me," or the "baby or little part of me." All these represent the part or ego state that contains the information related to the memories of abandonment, rejection, neglect or abuse experienced earlier in life. A good way of accessing these memory systems is by either visiting in the past or bringing into the present the younger self during the exploration of these early memories of adversity. Theraplay activities can be encouraged, but this time they are not directed toward the child, but the younger self. A baby doll may represent the younger self, or the child can imagine the "little me" inside the heart. During Theraplay sessions, the therapist invites the parent and the child to nurture and connect with the younger self. The child can ask the "little me" to be present while the parent engages in nurturing and engaging activities. Considering how reprocessing sessions need a fair amount of planning and organization, the EMDR clinician should identify the potential need of meeting past unmet attachment needs. If this is the case, the younger self should be already identified and invited to Theraplay sessions during the preparation phase. For example, after singing a song to the child, the clinician either sings or asks the caregiver to sing a song to the younger self. If the parent is putting lotion on the child's scars, hurts, and special freckles, the parent should be invited to also put lotion on the doll that represents the "little me." By the time the memory containing information about early trauma is accessed, the child is already familiar with the concept of the "little me" and the need for nurturing this part of the self in need of healing. Initially, the child may not have much emotional connection with the younger part of the self, but with time, the child's compassion and care for the part of him or her that suffered and experienced hurt and pain will grow. It is important to highlight that the "little self" should be introduced after the child has found some level of comfort with the clinician and the Theraplay process itself. If the child shows great levels of dysregulation, oppositional behaviors and resistance to relinquishing some level of control, the concept of the younger self should not be introduced. In addition, how each child responds to the concept of a younger self tends to be very much connected to the strategies used to cope with not getting deep attachment needs met. Many children with avoidant patterns of attachment will tend to reject and not like getting closer to the "little me." For these children, being small and younger is associated with shame; as a result, they want to grow up quickly and be treated like an adult or older child. Sometimes children with disorganized strategies may want to hit or hurt the younger self, or may say that they hate the "little me." However, as they start to accept themselves and greater levels of connection with the therapist and the parent, the younger self may be introduced and accepted by the child. Analogies that explain the multiplicity of the self are presented in prior chapters in this book. These analogies may be used to introduce the concept of the different colors of the self.

Once the clinician has selected a target of early rejection, abuse or neglect, the clinician will plan the session to have the younger self present. The younger self is invited so the child can have the doll that represents the younger self present. First, the memory is accessed by doing a full assessment with the younger self. All the questions about the memory that are asked during the assessment phase are directed to the doll representing the "little me." After the desensitization phase has been initiated, the clinician will look for a "stalling point" to use reparative interweaves and meet attachment and developmental needs using Theraplay activities. For example, when the opportunity comes, the EMDR clinician may ask the "little me" what he or she needed that he or she did not get. The younger self may say that mom did not feed him or her or that mom did not take good care of him or her. If this is the case, the caregiver can be invited to feed the doll as well as the child. The caregiver, under the direction of the clinician, can have the younger part sit on his or her lap while singing, playing or providing nurturing touch to the doll representing the younger self. The child can also be invited before or after the parent, to nurture, play or sing to the younger self. Keep in mind that these are interweaves provided during the reprocessing of early adverse experiences and, as a result, they should be followed by BLS. The clinician should continue to use these reparative interweaves until all the needs of the "little me" are met and the younger self reports feeling loved, full, taken care of and happy. If the child chose to imagine the "little me" inside the heart, the parent and or the therapist will engage in Theraplay activities with the child, but this time making it clear that they are directed to the younger self. The child may be fed, have the face painted, rocked or sang to, but the child is invited to have the "little me" look through his or her eyes.

PHASE FIVE: INSTALLATION

During the installation phase, a positive belief about the self is enhanced and with it a new arising sense of self. Theraplay activities can assist in amplifying this positive experience for the child and the parent. Using Theraplay to further enhance the installation of a positive cognition during the installation phase of EMDR therapy can give the child a deeper and more expansive experience. For example, when a positive cognition such as, "I deserve love," "I am strong," "I am safe now," or "I deserve good things," has been installed, an enhancing Theraplay activity can be incorporated at the end of the session. A Theraplay nurturing activity that enhances the child's positive belief about being loveable further anchors it cognitively, affectively and somatically. The EMDR therapist can also ask the parent to whisper the positive cognition "I am safe" or "I deserve love" as the parent is painting the child's face. BLS can be provided as the positive cognition and the associative affect are further enhanced.

A Theraplay challenging activity can be incorporated after the installation of a positive belief, such as "I can be happy now," or "I am strong." In addition, if the child, during the traumatic event, could not complete defensive responses due to moving into submission or a freeze response, Theraplay activities that incorporate movement could further enhance the installation of the positive cognition. With this, the positive belief is embodied and felt at different levels of human experience.

When reparative interweaves have been utilized and the "little me" has been involved during the desensitization phase, the installation of the PC should involve the "little me" as well. The "little me" is instructed to think about the adverse event and the good thought while the clinician provides BLS. Then, the caregiver and the child are invited to create a song, or simply sing the PC to the "little me." For example, using any of the background music of children's songs, repeat the positive cognition over and over again while the caregiver and the child are holding the "little me." These are creative, child friendly and developmentally appropriate ways of installing the PC using Theraplay activities that will facilitate the involvement of the child during the installation phase of EMDR therapy. It is important to note that, even though creative and child friendly interweaves are used, adherence to EMDR procedures is still possible and encouraged.

PHASE SIX: BODY SCAN

When moving into the body scan phase of EMDR therapy, if the "little self" has been participating, the younger self is invited to scan the body from head to toe. "The feeling finder," explained in prior chapters, may be used to add a playful component. If the session is incomplete and ends with a body scan that is not completely clear, the younger self is invited to assist the child in identifying where in the body the disturbance is still present.

Another set of interweaves that contain Theraplay activities is connected to soothing bodily states through Theraplay. For example, when the child reports negative somatic reactions, the therapist communicates with this area of the body and the bodily state. What does it need? How can it be soothed or released? For a child that expresses having tingling in the stomach, the therapist may say, *"Can I communicate or talk to this tingling feeling? Miss Tingling Feeling, how can we help?"* Menus can be provided so you can say, *"We can sing a song or use a 'loving brush' and brush this part of your body."* The therapist or the parent can sing a song to this sensation or hurt experienced in the body. If it is appropriate to touch this area of the body, the parent or the therapist may do pretend painting with a 'loving' or 'soothing' color over the part where the negative sensation is experienced. The parent may also put some lotion on or touch it with a special "caring cotton." Needless to say, each time the clinician intervenes by using interweaves that include Theraplay activities, basic EMDR procedures are used. *"Take a breath, let it go; what do you notice or what comes to you? Okay, just notice how mom is "brushing" or "painting the 'hurt' with a 'loving color'."* The BLS is provided as the parent or the clinician is using the Theraplay activity. It may also be provided after the Theraplay activity is used and the clinician follows up with a question, such as, *"What happened as mom was touching the tingling feeling?"* The child is then invited to notice whatever came up while engaging in BLS.

PHASE SEVEN: CLOSURE

The use of Theraplay can continue as an adjunctive approach during the phases where trauma memories are accessed and processed. Each session where disturbing and maladaptive material have been accessed should follow appropriate closure procedures. Theraplay activities can be used during the last 10 to 15 minutes of the session with the purpose of bringing the child back to balance and equilibrium.

During the closure phase of EMDR therapy, Theraplay activities should be selected according to the work done by the child during the EMDR session. If the session is incomplete and the child is emotionally drained, nurturing or engaging activities may be appropriate. If the child completed a reprocessing session and the child is invigorated by the work accomplished, a challenging or engaging activity will be best suited. The age of the child should be taken into account when selecting activities to close EMDR sessions. In order to stimulate the social engagement system and promote physiological balance in the child's system, play, nurturance, and laughter are really good ways of ending sessions. Feeding activities may also be helpful as the attachment system is soothed and the digestive system is activated. With the activation of the social engagement system, and the digestive system, the parasympathetic ventral vagal system comes alive.

CASE 1: EMDR THERAPY AND THERAPLAY WITH A TRAUMATIZED CHILD

A summary of this case is presented as we walk through the EMDR therapy phases where Theraplay was also used. Since this represents a summary of the case, only the most salient aspects and the phases where Theraplay was used will be presented.

Phase One: Client History and Treatment Planning

Vladimir, age 6, had a history of complex trauma and was diagnosed with Reactive Attachment Disorder. He was adopted from a Bulgarian orphanage when he was 3 years old. There had been ongoing medical trauma. The adoptive mother was told that, when he arrived at the orphanage, he used to look out the window for hours and scream for his mother to come back. He had several placements in the U.S. and two of the initial potential adoptive parents let him go after a few months due to his extreme rage, as well as controlling and oppositional behaviors. There were allegations of sexual abuse in his first foster placement, but they were never substantiated.

Vladimir was highly dysregulated, oppositional, and hypervigilant. He had some indiscriminate attachment and he felt like a "garbage boy" in his own words. He fiercely needed to be in control at almost all times. The slightest misattunement on the part of adults could lead to wildly destructive behaviors. The peers in his first grade class feared him because he "stalked" one child and attacked any others who were in the proximity of his targeted or chosen friend.

This child was referred for EMDR therapy after receiving three years of unsuccessful therapy. A thorough initial assessment was performed as all the history of the child and the current parents was gathered. The adoptive parents were having great difficulty dealing with Vladimir's behaviors. The MIM was used, and it was discovered that the mother exhibited great difficulty attuning to Vladimir's needs and setting boundaries when needed.

The following were key aspects of the clinical landscape created for Vladimir:

- A potential targeting sequence was developed using the information provided by the mother.
- Deficiencies in the parent's ability for attunement and reflective capacities to understand the child's behaviors were identified.
- Deficiencies were found in the areas of engagement and an ability to accept structure and nurture.
- Absence of positive and adaptive attachment and developmental experiences and great difficulty to regulate states were identified.
- In contrast to the difficulties Vladimir and his family faced, the MIM also led the therapist to identify strengths. Specifically, Vladimir and his parents shared high intelligence and some playfulness, such as humor, in addition to high motivation to resolve their problems.

Phase Two: Preparation

The EMDR therapist started to work just with Vladimir and attempted to use the calm–safe place protocol. Vladimir could not find a calm-safe place and became agitated throwing the crayons and paper away. He started to run around the office and the therapist had great difficulty regulating Vladimir.

Within an EMDR perspective, the goal for Vladimir was to reprocess the memories of attachment trauma and adversity experienced in his relationships with important caregivers. All the memories of abandonment, sexual and physical abuse and medical trauma were placed in his targeting sequence and treatment plan. Developing affect tolerance and the ability to regulate affect as well as enhancing his capacity to accept connection, nurturance and structure were identified as important goals. However, considering the absence of positive and adaptive attachment and developmental experiences, the EMDR therapist decided to focus on providing reparative experiences that could stimulate the creation of new and adaptive memory networks. The EMDR clinician decided to incorporate during the preparation phase experiences that could soothe lower parts of the brain and start to promote vertical integration and regulation of Vladimir's system. In order to accomplish this goal, Theraplay was included as an adjunctive form of treatment in order to provide the reparative experiences that could promote attachment security and self-regulation.

Theraplay goals for Vladimir were to develop a more secure attachment to his mother, become more regulated overall and, particularly, during interactions with others, allow an adult to take charge, and increase empathy for others. With these goals in mind, the therapist decided that Theraplay for Vladimir would focus on structure and nurture. For his part, Vladimir resisted structure vehemently and allowed nurture only on his terms. Happily, the exception to this is that he allowed it from his mother when he was hurt. The therapist used challenge as a way to draw Vladimir in, so Vladimir could allow himself to accept nurture and structure.

Part of a Theraplay Session

The therapist greeted Vladimir and his mother in the waiting room down the hall with an appealing, "We haven't done a crab walk race before." Vladimir looked happily surprised. "You remember how to do a crab walk. Here we go down the hallway to my playroom."

The therapist had planned some structuring activities: check up; make a foil impression of Vladimir's hands and feet and have mom guess which parts of Vladimir's body they came from; blow a feather back and forth; and feed. When they got to the office, the therapist had Vladimir sit on his mother's lap and went over the list of activities the therapist had planned. This was a visual schedule so that Vladimir could understand it with his right-brain as well as his left. When the therapist moved on to the check-up, Vladimir squirmed off his mother's lap and ran across the room. The therapist quickly changed her plan for the session to begin with a challenging activity for the purpose of capturing Vladimir's focus and helping him to regulate. Once he was ready to join in, they could then move to the reparative dimensions of structure and nurture that Vladimir needed. The therapist said, "*Vladimir, I'm so glad you brought your strong, fast legs with you today. Do you think we could keep this balloon* (quickly pulling the balloon out of his play cabinet) *up in the air with your feet? Here it comes. Get ready to kick it.*" Vladimir, always on the lookout for a challenge, joined in and soon was playing with gusto. The therapist had Vladimir's mother count out loud the number of times he kept it up in the air. After some rounds of Balloon Kick, Vladimir was more regulated and willing to sit down. The therapist then showed Vladimir the foil and explained what they would do with it. Predictably, Vladimir demanded that mom make the foil prints first, and that Vladimir would guess. If Vladimir's behavior had not been driven by his adaptation to complex trauma, the therapist may have had decided that Vladimir would benefit from following the therapist's structure and would continue with the original agenda while allowing Vladimir to save face; for example, "*You have some good ideas. Right now, this is just for you.*"

Because of the role trauma had played, the therapist hypothesized that Vladimir was afraid of the foil. Was it the sound or texture? Or was having the adult in charge intolerable? Or because this activity was new, that may have led Vladimir to not be able to predict how it would unfold and Vladimir may need to see how this activity looks before he feels safe enough to go along with it. While never treating Vladimir with kid gloves, the therapist briefly reflected, "*You wanted to know how this feels; I'm glad you could let me know what you needed*" and went along with Vladimir's wish.

During "check ups," the therapist looked for "hurts" and put lotion on them. Quickly, the therapist invited the mother to join in and put lotion on Vladimir's hurts and special freckles. Vladimir accepted the nurturance from his mother and gazed at his mother, stroking her face. This session was videotaped, so the following session the therapist and the mother could watch it together.

The following session, the therapist and the mother watched the video while the therapist stimulated the mother's reflective capacity and attunement. The therapist worked on guiding the mother to notice Vladimir's responses and reflect on them while attuning to the physiological changes in Vladimir's system, the underlying needs and the triggers. Several sessions with the mother and the father were scheduled thereafter.

Beginning Bilateral Stimulation

After twelve Theraplay sessions, Vladimir was more accepting of nurturance and structure within the session. He often engaged easily in the activities the therapist brought up. The therapist spent time with the mother and Vladimir explaining EMDR, and showing the different forms of BLS. During the session, the therapist noticed moments where Vladimir seemed calm and joyful and used slow and short sets of BLS. At this time, the therapist is purposefully not asking the child yet to label the emotions and location in the body, as these moments of joining in and connection are still nonverbal and housed in the right-brain. The mother was also invited, at the direction of the therapist, to provide slow and short sets of taps. The therapist invited the mother to put lotion on Vladimir's feet. While the mother was massaging Vladimir's feet, the mother was instructed to provide the massage bilaterally, going from one foot to the other, while the therapist reflected on Vladimir's state, "*I can see that this feels nice and soothing. It feels really safe huh?!*" Vladimir resonated with the reflections of the therapist and the mother was invited to reflect on Vladimir's emotional and bodily states. "*Your body is really calm and safe, this really makes you feel good.*"

During another Theraplay session, the therapist found multiple opportunities to playfully provide BLS. While counting Vladimir's fingers, the therapists went from one finger of the right hand to the other of the left hand while saying how Vladimir had brought all his special fingers to the session.

As the sessions were progressing, the mother was also using on a daily basis some of the Theraplay activities at home so Vladimir was receiving patterned, repetitive, daily reparative stimulation to enhance the formation of new and adaptive neuronal pathways and promote affect regulation.

During the latest sessions of Theraplay, when Vladimir had negative reactions, he started talking about the "scary things" he went through at the hospital and the orphanage. The therapist honored Vladimir's bravery and validated how hard that must had been for him. The therapist created a special space for the memories of negative events to come and "land" in the office. Vladimir agreed to put all these "things" he was remembering in a box that the therapist created for Vladimir. Every time Vladimir had a "yucky" or "scary memory" he was invited to take a piece of paper and draw a symbol of the memory and put it inside the box. After that, he was able to resume Theraplay activities. The memories were invited to come freely without any prompting on the therapist's part. The therapist reassured Vladimir that the memories could safely visit the office when they need to come.

Developing a Safe Place

After approximately eighteen sessions, the EMDR therapist decided to use Vladimir's favorite Theraplay activity as a safe place. He experienced great joy when his mother gave him "back stories." During "back stories," the mother told him tales while drawing the stories on Vladimir's back. During the session, the mother was invited to use this activity for some time while Vladimir identified his feelings and bodily states associated with this wonderful activity. The therapist installed this special safe moment and place by using BLS. This time the labeling abilities of the left-brain were invited as Vladimir identified and labeled his emotions. He also identified the location in the body and, without resistance, he engaged in eye movements by following a puppet labeled as one of his EMDR helpers.

Inviting the "Little Me"

The therapist started to talk to Vladimir about the "rainbow and the bright shiny me" we all have inside (see Chapter 7 for a thorough explanation of this analogy). Vladimir chose a little baby doll to represent his "little self." The younger self was invited to the sessions and started to be the recipient of Theraplay activities that involved nurturing and engaging. For example, when Vladimir was fed, so was the "little me." When "check ups" were done, the younger self also had lotion put on special freckles and "hurts." The younger self was also invited to share any "yucky" memories where he felt scared, sad, or where he was not treated well, or where he did not have what he needed. The therapist started to assist Vladimir in developing emotional, sensorimotor and cognitive literacy by involving Vladimir in games about thoughts, feelings and sensations (see Chapter 4). Slowly, the left-brain was also involved, as well as higher parts of the brain.

Phases Three, Four, Five, and Six: Assessment, Desensitization, Installation, and Body Scan

As Vladimir was attaining greater levels of stabilization, and the parents were developing attunement and the ability to promote attachment security, the therapist decided to move into the reprocessing of traumatic material. The therapist spoke with Vladimir about starting to help the brain "chew up" the "yucky stuff." A memory where an orphanage worker hit Vladimir was the first target. The "little me" was invited to tell the story through Vladimir. The assessment phase was done, and Vladimir, with the cognitive, emotional and sensory literacy previously developed, was able to identify the negative beliefs, emotions and location in the body. During the reprocessing of this memory, several reparative interweaves were used to assist the younger self to meet attachment needs. The mother was invited to provide to the "little me" what he requested or reported needing or wanting that he did not have in the orphanage. The younger self sat on the mother's lap, and was protected, defended against the worker, sang songs, fed and, ultimately, loved through the process. Each time the younger self expressed an unmet need, and the mother provided what was needed, it was followed by BLS. Standard procedures for using interweaves during the reprocessing phases of EMDR were followed.

During the installation phase, the "little me" asked for a song, so the therapist, the mother, and Vladimir created a song containing the positive cognition, "I am safe now." Vladimir and his younger self were invited to think about the target memory and at the same time sing the song containing the positive cognition. In all the sessions where trauma was explored or processed, Theraplay activities were used as state change strategies to close the sessions.

Following treatment, Vladimir was calmer and took pride in his strengths. He only occasionally felt like "garbage boy" and he enthusiastically described his "sparkling" blue eyes and strong legs. He did occasionally cheat at basketball when "garbage boy" feelings arose. He now had several friends and, because of his "big heart," in his words, his teacher put his desk facing a boy with Asperger's Syndrome in his classroom so that he could help this other child. Both parents found Vladimir easier to understand and a joy to play with. He let them snuggle him and easily accepted affection. Vladimir and his parents agreed that he generally followed household rules and that family life was "fun and funny."

SUMMARY AND CONCLUSIONS

Children wounded and traumatized within the caregiving system present with compromised social engagement systems, profound difficulties in affect regulation, and memory networks containing multiple and incongruent representations of the self and other. The regulatory capacities of the parents of these children are usually strained, which interferes with their capacity to attune, synchronize and resonate with the systems of their children. Due to the scarcity or absence of patterns of neural firing containing adaptive information, reparative experiences that involve play, laughter, nurturing touch and connection, while being cared for by an attuned and safe adult, is pivotal. Theraplay is a relationship-based, playful approach where the adult guides the therapy in a synchronous and attuned way. Theraplay core values and principles are guided by attachment theory, regulation theory and current brain research. It promotes change by focusing on healing the parent-child relationship and promoting attachment security, emotion regulation, and self-esteem through attuned dyadic interactions between the child and the parent and or the therapist. Theraplay is not designed to address directly the memories of trauma and hardship; instead, it focuses on providing restorative experiences of connection, touch, and play while staying within an appropriately structured environment. Theraplay, for traumatized children, is usually used with approaches that directly work through the trauma. This chapter presents how Theraplay can be effectively used within the framework of the eight phases of EMDR therapy. Furthermore, guidelines are presented so EMDR clinicians can identify the children to whom Theraplay may be an important addition to the overall EMDR treatment. Efforts are made to maintain fidelity to the AIP model and the EMDR standard procedures, and at the same time preserve the crux and essence of Theraplay.

13

EMDR Therapy and the Use of Internal Family Systems Strategies With Children

Ana M. Gomez and Pamela K. Krause

The main goal of this chapter is to integrate elements and strategies of internal family systems (IFS) psychotherapy into eye movement desensitization and reprocessing (EMDR) therapy with complexly traumatized children. It is worth highlighting that this chapter represents the first attempt to combine these two approaches with children. The integration of these two approaches is done first by identifying their commonalities while honoring their differences. Examining the parallels of both approaches, when looking at human suffering and healing, can shed light into the appropriate and effective use of IFS strategies into a comprehensive EMDR treatment with children. This chapter will present an overview of IFS principles and procedures as well as the view of these principles through the lens of the AIP model and EMDR therapy. The phases of EMDR treatment where IFS strategies can be utilized to enhance its effectiveness with child complex trauma cases will also be thoroughly addressed. It is important to highlight that the overall adherence to the AIP model and EMDR methodology is foremost honored. However, the treatment of children and families with histories of complex trauma may benefit from the use of additional complementary therapeutic strategies that can enhance the overall treatment outcome.

OVERVIEW OF IFS: BASIC PRINCIPLES

IFS model of therapy was developed by Richard Schwartz more than 20 years ago. It is a client-centered approach that can be broadly classified as an ego state model, as one of the model's basic assumptions is that it is normal for the mind to be subdivided into "parts" or sub-personalities. However, the IFS model also incorporates an additional component beside the parts, this is the concept of the 'Self'. Within this model, the Self is defined as a whole, undamaged, healing entity that exists in everyone. It is posited that everyone has a Self, no matter how much trauma or neglect they have experienced in their lives, and that it has the ability to heal any wound present in the internal system. Therefore, it is designated as the healing agent in the IFS model.

BASIC ASSUMPTIONS OF THE IFS MODEL

First Assumption

The first assumption of IFS is that it is the natural state of the mind to be subdivided into "parts." In this model, parts are viewed as multidimensional beings, little people if you will, with a range of thoughts, feelings, and belief. Each part has a function or preferred role within a system. Examples of some roles include parts that are good at planning and organizing; parts that are playful or creative; and parts that are contemplative or quiet.

Since every part is multi-dimensional, each contains a full range of thoughts, beliefs and emotions. This means that there is not one part that is sad and or one part that is angry, etc., but, rather, that every part can feel sad, angry and any of a number of other emotions.

It is postulated that people are born with parts either manifested or in their potential to manifest, and these parts will emerge as a child grows and interacts with others in the world. As parts emerge, they form a system of interaction not unlike a family, thus the name of Internal Family Systems therapy.

Second Assumption

The second important assumption of the model is that, in addition to parts, everyone also has a "Self." The Self is not a part, but the essential, undamaged core of who we are. The Self cannot be damaged, no matter what a person experiences in his or her life. However, it can be obscured, making it appear as if there is no Self.

Defining the Self is difficult, as it is often experienced as a "felt sense."

Richard Schwartz describes the Self as the " 'I' in the storm" (Schwartz 1995). The Self is often described as containing the qualities of: calm, curiosity, compassion, confidence, courage, clarity, connectedness, creativity, patience, presence, perspective and perseverance.

While the Self is meant to be the leader of the internal system, it does not demand leadership and can only take leadership if the parts allow it.

Third Assumption

As stated above, each part enters the world with a function or preferred role in the system. With "good enough" parenting and a safe enough environment, parts will grow and thrive in their preferred role. As parts grow and thrive, the Self will emerge and take leadership of the internal system. This is referred to as a Self-led system.

In a Self-led system, all parts are connected to the Self and with each other. Each part is honored and respected for its contribution and the system is balanced and harmonious.

However, most people do not experience either "good enough" parenting and/or a safe-enough environment. Most children with complex trauma experience rejections, betrayals, loss of love or affection, harsh criticism, either physical or emotional punishment, shaming and even sexual assault. When this happens, parts are hurt and can become wounded or "burdened." Burdens are defined as "extreme ideas, behaviors, or feelings derived from extreme events or interactions with others in a person's life" (Schwartz, 1995 pp. 52). Parts carry these ideas, behaviors, or feelings like transferred burdens.

When a part is burdened, it begins to organize itself around the burden, requiring it to shift from its preferred role and take on the new, more extreme role. An example can help illustrate this point. Parts can enter the world filled with joy and curiosity wanting to explore the world around them. Parts like this can feel lovable, full of enthusiasm and curiosity with a desire to explore their world. What might happen if a part like this is met with criticism *("you're so nosey")* or verbal and physical punishment as it explores its environment? The criticism and/or punishment could feel shocking, frightening, and painful to the part, and it is likely to begin believing there is something wrong with its curiosity. It might believe there is something wrong with it for being curious and feel flawed, defective, or not good enough. Or, it may decide that the best way to avoid criticism or punishment is to stop being curious. It might become docile, withdrawn, or even detached.

Burdened parts do not grow and thrive in their preferred roles. When they are forced into extreme roles, the Self is unable to emerge as the leader of the internal system and may become obscured. In an internal system without Self-leadership, parts are left to jostle for control of the system. Parts develop different beliefs about how to best protect the system and develop *polarizations* with each other, thus creating a system with conflict and strife without harmony or calm.

Nature and Classification of Parts

Schwartz describes three categories of parts (Schwartz, 1995): Managers, firefighters, and exiles. Managers and firefighters make up a broader category of protector parts.

Exiles are the parts that hold any painful feelings or memories from traumatic events. These are the thoughts and feelings that are deemed too intense for the system to bear. Before they are wounded, these parts are often the most joyful, sensitive, and creative parts. However, once wounded by the outside world, they begin to believe they are unlovable, worthless, stupid, or flawed in some way. Exiles feel intense emotions like loneliness, emptiness, despair, sadness, shame, embarrassment, and humiliation. In an attempt to protect the system from these thoughts, memories, and feelings, these parts are forced from of conscious awareness, or exiled, by protector parts.

Schwartz (1995) defines two categories of protector parts: Managers and firefighters. Managers are proactive in their attempt to keep exiles from being hurt. They have a "never again" philosophy meaning, "I will never again let anything happen that makes me feel that way." Managers try to prevent feelings like shame, humiliation, embarrassment, or worthlessness.

Managers have strategies like, "If I'm just smart enough...nice enough...pretty enough....achieve enough....I'll never feel hurt again." These parts can be hard working, organized, great at planning, attentive to detail and nuance, an internal "Homeland Security."

However, no matter how skilled and diligent manager parts are, they cannot predict every eventuality. Invariably, something will occur that wounds an exile(s) again releasing its feelings into the system. Once the exile is triggered, firefighters step in to numb or suppress the unwelcome sensations. These protectors are called firefighters because their priority is to put out the flame of emotion; they react, giving little thought to possible collateral damage from their action.

Firefighters utilize a variety of approaches to suppress exiles, including some that are classically described as addictive behaviors (e.g. alcohol, drugs, sex, gambling).

However, firefighters also employ other strategies, such as cutting, bingeing, disso-ciating, rage, and even suicide. It is easy to understand why the common reaction to these parts is to try to manage, contain, minimize, eliminate, or re-direct their behavior. However, in the IFS model, a different approach is taken with not only firefighters, but also managers and exiles. This healing approach is outlined below.

The IFS Approach to Healing

As we understand the nature and origin of parts, it becomes clear that there are no bad parts, only parts that have been forced into extreme roles due to wounding. The more severe or intense the wounding (nature and degree of the trauma), the more burdened the parts will be. The greater the burden, the more intense or extreme parts will be.

We know that protectors (managers and firefighters) utilize strategies they believe will: 1) prevent the system from being injured again; and, 2) keep painful feelings at bay. As a result of these strategies, some parts are exiled from the system.

When managers and/or firefighters are interviewed we find that most do not rel-ish their extreme roles. However, they feel compelled to adhere to their role while there are vulnerable parts to protect. For this reason, it is often difficult, if not impossible, to permanently alter or modify the behavior of managers or firefighters while exiles are burdened. But, if the exiles were no longer burdened, there would be no need for the managers and or firefighters to continue to protect is extreme ways.

Therefore, it seems clear that if exiles can be relieved of their burdens (unbur-dened) then protectors could be free from their extreme roles and behaviors. This is how IFS therapists approach the healing process. The work begins by gaining clarity about the role of the protectors (managers and firefighters) in the system; the ways in which they attempt to create safety or limit pain. We also offer them hope; hope that the exiles can be unburdened thus relieving the managers and firefighters of their responsibility to protect. Once the responsibility is lifted, both managers and firefight-ers are free to assume a role they prefer, rather than the extreme role they had been forced to adopt.

THE SIX STEPS TO HEALING A PART

IFS therapy is equally effective with adults and children. What follows is a description of healing a part using *in-sight* with a child. *In-sight* "involves having the client look inside to find and work with parts that he or she sees or senses and describes to the therapist" (Schwartz, pg 95, 1995)

Step One: Create a Trusting Relationship Between the Client's Self and Part

As with any model of therapy, the initial goal is to create a safe, trusting and hopeful environment in which healing can occur. The IFS therapist starts by ensuring the cli-ent's external environment is safe and supportive of the therapy. At the same time, the IFS therapist helps the client feel safe and comfortable in the therapeutic setting. An IFS therapist does this by welcoming all of the client parts with curiosity and compassion. In other words, the therapist relates to the client from his or her own Self-energy.

The therapist helps the client begin to identify his or her own parts by "nam-ing" them as they arise. Parts can manifest in a variety of ways, including: thoughts, emotions, feelings, images, or body sensations. So, for example, a young client tells the therapist about a part that manifest as a feeing by saying that, "my friend made me so mad that I hit him." The therapist could respond, *"So, part of you got mad and hit your friend. I wonder what made you so mad."* With this kind of response the therapist embodies curiosity and compassion, not reaction to the feeling.

The therapist would remain curious and compassionate about any part that was revealed and begins to introduce the concept that everyone has parts and it is normal to have parts. For example, the therapist might say, *"You know, everyone has parts that get mad, even me. Our mad feeling isn't all of who we are, it's just part of who we are."*

As the child feels more comfortable, the therapist can offer the child a chance to get to know his or her parts so they can feel better. When the child is curious, the in-sight can begin. The first step of in-sight is to help a part differentiate or *unblend*.

Unblending

Before any part can be known, it must be differentiated from other parts and the Self; without differentiation it is impossible to know where one part ends and another begins, and/or where parts end and the Self begins. Once differentiated, a part can develop a relationship with the Self, which is fundamental to the healing process. Remember, in this model the healing relationship is between the client's Self and the client's parts.

Differentiation occurs through a process called "unblending." Richard Schwartz writes, "if I asked clients to separate from extreme and polarized parts, . . . most of them could shift quickly into a compassionate state of mind. In that state, they knew just what to do to help their parts" (Schwartz, 1995 pp 37). Unblending or differentiation begins by locating the part as a thought, emotion, body sensation and/or image in the body including the torso, limbs and/or head. Once a part has been identified and located, it is invited to unblend from the Self so a relationship can begin. Unblending is initiated by asking the client, *"How do you feel toward the part?"* The answer to this simple question reveals whether the client's Self or another part is present.

If the answer is something resembling one of the 8C qualities of the Self (calm, curiosity, compassion, confidence, courage, clarity, connectedness, or creativity) the Self is present. Clients need not respond precisely with one of the 8C's; they may say something like; *"I'd like to get to know it,"* or, *"I'm interested in it."* With this kind of response, the therapist knows the part is unblended, the client's Self is present, and a relationship between Self and part is possible.

However, if the answer is not one of the qualities associated with the Self, it indicates that the Self is not present. It could indicate that another part is present, so a part-to-part relationship is occurring. Some examples that indicate a part-to-part relationship include; *"I don't like it,"* or, *"I wish it would stop acting that way."* All parts must be unblended before a Self-to-part relationship is possible. It may be necessary to unblend many parts before the Self is present.

Once a client is able to respond to the question in some way that sounds like the Self, a relationship between the part and the Self can begin. The relationship starts by simply asking the part about itself. The part might reveal its current function or job in the system, how or where it learned to behave in the way it does, and/or what it likes and does not like about its job, among other things.

The part's responses will indicate whether the part is a protector (either a manager or firefighter) or a wounded exile. Protectors will describe behaviors that try to ward off or minimize painful feelings. Exiles hold the painful feelings and/or sensations so they can appear as frightened, tearful, meek, or quiet.

If the part is a protector, the focus is to gain clarity about its role in the system and offer hope that exiles can be unburdened and healed. In general, protectors appear first and require reassurance and hope before they will allow access to exiles.

The initial process with exiles is similar to that with protectors; the part must be unblended to establish the Self-to-exile relationship. Once connected with the Self, the exile can reveal its story about how it was wounded and burdened. This process, called witnessing, is the second step in the healing process.

Step Two: Witnessing

Protectors exile vulnerable parts in an attempt to keep them from being hurt again and from feeling their pain because they believe it is in best interest of the system to do so. This strategy can provide temporary relief, but the exile is still filled with strong, painful emotion and memories, frozen in the time and places where the wounding occurred. Exiles long to tell their stories and be understood, *witnessed*, so they can be free of their pain and released from exile.

Once the Self-to-part relationship is established, an exile can be witnessed in a variety of ways, including; memories in the form of visual images; feelings and emotions; and or with physical sensations in the body (somatically). Each exile knows exactly how to convey its story to the client's Self. The Self and exile are connected during witnessing, allowing the client's Self to be with the feelings, not "in" or overwhelmed by the feelings. Witnessing continues until the exile feels understood by the client's Self.

Because of their intense longing to be witnessed, some exiles may rush forward and flood the system with feelings and thoughts. When this occurs, it means the part has blended with the Self and must be unblended before witnessing can continue. One strategy for unblending is to ask the exile not to overwhelm the system with emotion; to just share the minimal amount of sensation required to express what it feels. This allows the exile to unblend and reestablish a relationship with the Self. Since exiles long to be witnessed, they are generally open to any suggestions that can facilitate the process.

Step Three: Retrieval

As indicated above, exiled parts are frozen in time at the point of their wounding. In cases of more severe trauma, these scenes can be extremely intense and dangerous. Frequently, parts need to leave the scene, or be *retrieved*, before they can feel safe enough to be witnessed or unburdened. If this is the case, the client's Self can enter the scene and either stay with the part until it is ready to leave or take it out of the scene to a place where it feels safe to tell or show what happened. All parts know whether or not they need to be retrieved and can indicate that to the client's Self and the therapist.

Step Four: Unburdening

Once the exile feels understood by the client's Self, it can release the burdens it acquired (*unburdening*). Burdens come in many forms, but all contain beliefs (I am worthless, I am unlovable, I am stupid) and feelings (loneliness, grief, emptiness, shame, humiliation, etc.). Some will also include body sensations (pains, constrictions, etc.). When a part unburdens, it does not give up the memory of the event(s), only the pain and wounding associated with the event(s).

To begin the unburdening process, the part is asked to locate the burden, either in or around its body. Burdens take many forms and can include: Masses of some kind in the gut, heart, head, etc.; heavy clothing like coats or cloaks; and unwanted energy or emotion, to name a few. This list is by no means exhaustive, it is just meant to give a few common examples.

Once the part has located the burden, it is invited to release it or let it go. Parts often choose to release their burdens to one of the five elements (earth, water, wind, fire, or light), but they are not limited to these choices. Just as with witnessing, every part knows exactly how to release its burden.

Step Five: Invitation

Once the burden is released, the part is asked to invite into itself any qualities that it wants or needs at that moment or in the future. These qualities include a range of possibilities too numerous to name, but a short list of examples includes: Love, joy, playfulness, competence, strength, or courage. Again, the part will have a clear sense of what qualities it needs and wants.

Step Six: Integration

After an exile unburdens, it no longer needs to be exiled and is free to take on a new role in the system. The client's Self interacts with the part to help it find its new place in the system. Parts often want ongoing contact with the client's Self as they assimilate into the system.

Obviously, other parts will be affected by this change, so it is important to find those parts and help them adjust to the new reality. Some protectors may be fearful about the change and what it means to them and their role. These parts need attention and reassurance from the client's Self and help to find their new, less extreme role. Other protectors may be relieved or happy about the change and may spontaneously shift to less extreme roles. Still, others may need to be witnessed and unburdened in the way exiles are unburdened.

Integration may take only a few minutes or many sessions. This is dependent on each individual system.

A Self-led System

Most people have more than one exile, so the healing process may have to be repeated with other exiles. As exiles unburden, they are no longer cut off from the Self or other parts; more and more parts have a relationship with the Self and with each other. This allows the Self to emerge and assume leadership of the system (a Self-led system). A Self-led system is one in which each part has a relationship with the Self and has a voice in the system. In a Self-led system, polarizations are absent or greatly diminished, leaving more harmony and balance.

When parts have a relationship with the Self, they are no longer so vulnerable to wounding from the outside. Life is full of rejection and loss and it is likely to impact everyone. Unburdened parts can still be hurt, however, once connected with the Self, the result of the wound is different. When a part is hurt, the Self can comfort the part so the pain no longer needs to be stored as a burden; it can be felt, acknowledged, and released. Helping people achieve a Self-led system is the ultimate goal of IFS therapy.

IFS WITH CHILDREN

Externalizing Parts Into Objects

The IFS model of therapy can be easily applied to children and adolescents. It is possible to use the model with children as young as 3 or 4 years of age. However, some children and younger adolescents have difficulty conceptualizing parts and benefit from having concrete representation of their parts. Those clients can utilize the model by externalizing their parts into objects. Parts can be externalized into: Dolls, puppets, animal figures, drawings, creations made from clay, and inanimate objects like stones or seashells. No one object is more preferable than another; the selection should be based on what feels most comfortable to the client.

Incorporating Parents or Caregivers Into the Therapy

As with other models of therapy, it is important to incorporate the parents or caregivers in the therapeutic process. Unfortunately, many children who enter therapy have been wounded and burdened by their parents or guardians. Therefore, therapy with the adults in the system can minimize the possibility of the child being wounded again.

Some IFS therapists work with the adults and the children together in the room, others work with them separately. There are benefits to both approaches but there are some caveats that should be considered when making the decision.

It can be beneficial for parents and caregivers to silently witness their child's parts unburden. It can help adults have a clearer understanding of their children and minimize tensions between them. Before allowing this to happen, the therapist should make sure that the adult is able to witness any or all of the child's parts with caring and curiosity. If the adult cannot be caring and curious, the child's parts are at risk of being wounded by the adult either during or after the session. If this happens, the therapy office may no longer be a safe place for the child, thus hindering the healing process. Therefore, the parent's ability to be caring and curious during a therapy session must be carefully evaluated before allowing them to witness their child.

This is especially important if the parent or guardian has been responsible for wounding the child. The adult's presence could activate the child's protectors, making it difficult and or impossible to gain access to exiles fearing they will be hurt again. In this situation, it is better to work with the child separately allowing him or her to heal some parts before inviting the adult(s) into the room. At the same time, the adult(s) should engage in their own therapy to heal any parts that have wounded their children.

THE ADAPTIVE INFORMATION PROCESSING (AIP)
MODEL AND IFS PRINCIPLES

IFS is founded on the premise of the existence of the Self as a wise, compassionate leader that exists in all human beings from birth. However, when and how the Self is formed may be seen and conceptualized through different lenses in AIP-EMDR and IFS. IFS view of the Self converges into the spiritual realm that is neither denied nor addressed in the AIP model. However, the AIP model recognizes the presence of an innate system in the brain that is geared towards health and healing. A central aspect of the AIP model is the drive of the human organism toward wholeness and integration. IFS therapy as well as other ego state approaches holds a multiplicity-based notion of the mind. IFS theory proposes the existence of exiles, firefighter and managers. To use an analogy, the IFS model sees the family system and its parts as a "bulb of garlic," holding several "cloves" within. Each system is self-contained with its own exiles, managers and firefighters. Once a new "bulb with its own cloves" is identified, the process of unblending, unburdening and integrating is repeated until greater and greater levels of integration are achieved within a Self-led system.

As we hold this analogy in mind, let's explore how the family system is seen through the AIP model. According to the AIP model, the human brain and biological systems are shaped by the environmental experiences they encounter. These experiences create maps and patterns of neural firing that are encoded in different forms of memory, implicit and explicit.

The memories of traumatic and adverse events will follow a path into implicit encoding and isolation from other adaptive and positive information imprinted in the brain. These networks, like the "bulb of garlic and its cloves," contain their own emotions, thoughts, sensory reactions and meta-perceptions such as: I am unlovable; I am not good enough; etc. They also include the coping mechanisms and defensive responses the human organism has come to use to defend against the affect, somatic reactions and negative beliefs encoded in these memory maps. When these neural nets are repeatedly activated by environmental stimuli, neuronal maps containing information about specific perceptions of the self, the other, and the future will emerge. With this in mind, we could say that the different memory networks that have become strengthened by traumatic or negative repetitive experiences become, in IFS theory terms, the different parts of the internal family system.

Exile parts hold the experiences of unresolved trauma and adverse experiences (burdens). According to Twombly & Schwartz (2008), the exiles carry the emotions, sensations and beliefs associated with traumatic and disturbing events. When looking at exiles from the AIP model (Shapiro, 2001), they represent the parts of the memory networks containing the emotions, thoughts, sensations and meta-perceptions of traumatic and adverse events that have not been integrated into a coherent autobiographical memory.

According to Twombly & Schwartz (2008), the presence of flashbacks, anxiety and somatic complaints, among others, indicate that the exiles have taken over the system. Based on EMDR and the AIP model, flashbacks, anxiety and other symptoms are manifestations of the past experiences of unresolved trauma and adversity that remain unprocessed and unintegrated (Shapiro, 2001).

Firefighters seen from the AIP model represent the activation of animal defenses fight, flight and dissociative responses. They embody the self-destructive coping mechanisms used to protect and modulate affect resulting from the activation of memories systems containing traumatogenic material. These mechanisms have been developed to modulate overwhelming high and low levels of physiological arousal elicited by the activation of maladaptive memory networks. It is important to highlight that these coping strategies have also become embedded in memory.

On the other hand, managers in the AIP model constitute channels within the neural networks that contain the mechanisms of adaptation that have been utilized by the individual to suppress, manage and avoid the existing memories of trauma (exiles). This is accomplished by using avoidance and keeping the memories of trauma and adversity away, compartmentalized and contained. The avoidance of any stimulus that could activate the memories containing disturbing information (exiles) is one of the primary goals of the managers. Children may have developed a number of ways of adapting and adjusting to hardship and adversity: Controlling behaviors and role reversing, avoiding feelings, pleasing and perfectionism, among others. These strategies (managers) have allowed the system to maintain some level of internal and external control and safety.

One of the main goals in EMDR therapy would be to access, process and integrate the trauma memories and their associated affect (exiles) as well as the mechanisms of adaptation (managers), while maintaining an appropriate level of stabilization and emotion regulation (firefighters stabilized). EMDR therapy promotes the synthesis, assimilation, binding and integration of maladaptive memory networks into a healthy and coherent sense of self. In IFS terms, we are unburdening, integrating and reconfiguring the internal family system (Twombly & Schwartz, 2008). Despite major differences in case conceptualization and methodology, EMDR and IFS share the primary treatment goal of helping individuals arrive at a place where love, connection and healthy, fulfilling relationships can be experienced. EMDR therapy works to achieve this goal through the use of an eight-phase model where individuals are assisted in assimilating and binding the memories that lay at the core of their suffering while maintaining appropriate levels of stabilization. This is accomplished by stimulating the innate information processing system of the brain while accessing and moving these memories of hardship to an adaptive resolution. On the other hand, IFS works to achieve this goal by witnessing and unburdening parts of the internal family system, thus allowing the Self to emerge as the leader, creating a more harmonious and well-balanced system.

EMDR THERAPY AND IFS PSYCHOTHERAPY WITH CHILDREN: WHY, WHEN, AND HOW

Children with chronic traumatogenic histories come with great deficits in affect regulation. As a result, the exploration, accessing and processing of these memories might be overwhelming. IFS therapy strategies can enhance the process of stabilizing the child's system and providing enough distance so maladaptive memory networks can be accessed, integrated and assimilated, while keeping the child stabilized, regulated and in a homeostatic state. The use of IFS strategies and language in EMDR therapy with children with multiple traumas and attachment injuries makes the memory networks more tangible. The neural network is no longer an abstract concept but it is tangible as we pick a horsey or a giraffe to represent it. When using objects or toy animals to represent the memory networks containing maladaptive information, this is not done with the purpose of enhancing division in the child's system but with the goal of making the information encoded in memory more concrete, tangible and accessible to the child. For instance, the "doggie" chosen by the child is the object that represents the trauma memory, the mechanisms of adaptations or the dysregulated responses of the child. Highly dysregulated kids find it overwhelming to deal with their traumas and current affective states, so the parts language, when used in EMDR therapy, helps them titrate what otherwise may be overwhelming material. In addition, it provides distance to facilitate the exploration of disturbing material. The "rainbow analogy" (see Chapter 7) may be used to help children understand the concept of the multiplicity of the self. When using the "rainbow analogy," children learn that we are like a rainbows, with many different colors. We are one person with "many colors" or parts. We emphasize oneness but also highlight the many colors of the self. In addition, highly traumatized children tend to over identify with their negative reactions and traumas. "I am just a victim" or "a bad kid." when we see ourselves as the beautiful rainbow we are, with many different colors, we see ourselves bigger and greater than the trauma itself, and the parts that suffer and have become dysregulated. We also see and access the "bright shiny me" and the positive aspects of who we are.

The incorporation of IFS strategies within EMDR therapy with complex trauma cases can:

- Facilitate the exploration, processing and assimilation of memory networks containing traumatic material, as well as the mechanisms children have used to defend and adapt (accessing the internal family system).
- Access mechanisms of adaptation used by children that may prevent them from fully participating in EMDR therapy. Children that use avoidance and, as a result, object doing EMDR, may benefit from exploring and dealing with such mechanisms by using IFS strategies. Accessing and talking directly to the part (manager, firefighter) that is not allowing access to the trauma memory offers a direct but titrated approach for dealing with mechanisms of adaptation that may interfere with the child's willingness to fully embrace EMDR therapy.
- Provide an excellent avenue to titrate, layer and promote appropriate distance so the memories of trauma and adversity can be explored, accessed and processed while maintaining optimal levels of stabilization.
- Assist in accessing the positive attributes of the Self and using the Self as a resource throughout the eight phases of EMDR therapy.
- Facilitate the work during the reprocessing phases of EMDR therapy by assisting in accessing adaptive information and linking it to the material being reprocessed. For example, when the child can witness and honor the mechanisms of adaptation he or she used to survive, adaptive information is accessed and linked to the networks containing maladaptive material.
- Facilitate the process of providing corrective experiences to promote the formation of new, positive and adaptive neural networks. For example, a child that did not have appropriate nurturing parenting experiences can now have the neglected young part be seen, heard, nurtured and felt by the child's Self, the parents (if present) and the therapist's during EMDR sessions.

IFS model can effectively be utilized throughout the eight phases of EMDR therapy. All the phases with the exception of phase one will be thoroughly covered in this chapter. Standard EMDR procedures should be used during the initial phase of EMDR therapy (see Chapter 2).

Phase Two: Preparation

How to Introduce EMDR and IFS to the Child

When utilizing both EMDR and IFS, it is probably best to introduce the EMDR process as described in previous chapters of this book. However, it may be too overwhelming to the child to introduce the IFS model at the same time. It seems more appropriate to introduce the IFS model as parts of the child begin to arise and need to be addressed. However, the use of the "rainbow analogy" (see Chapter 7) may be helpful in assisting the child in understanding the many colors we all have.

Accessing the Family System: Creative Strategies With Children

Once a thorough history has been identified, the preparation phase of EMDR therapy is in motion. During the preparation phase, the internal family system can begin to be identified and accessed.

Playful strategies can be used to assist the child in accessing the different parts and find his or her own Self-energy. The use of puppets, clay, body outlines, wooden faces, and/or sticks as well as sandtray figures can facilitate this process. Parts can be identified using a wide range of nondirective and directive approaches. The language of parts offers a great opportunity for children to access disturbing material in a gentle and progressive manner. As a result, the child can explore, access and reprocess material while staying within optimal levels of arousal. Needless to say, it is emphasized that the puppet or animal only REPRESENTS the part in a playful way. In addition, even though, like the rainbow, we have many different colors inside, we are still only one person. We access the system with the purpose of promoting integration not to reinforce division and fragmentation.

As indicated early, the six basic steps of the IFS model can also be applied to children and younger adolescents by using externalizing techniques. Parts can be "invited" to unblend into objects (such as animal figures, puppets, drawings, clay). For example, when a child has noticeable feelings (such as, anger, sadness, anxiety) the therapist can invite the child to notice where this sensation is located in the body or where it is hanging out in the body. You can use the "feeling finder" (see Chapter 4) so the child can identify the location in the body. Once it is located, the child can be invited to get to know the part (memory network) by letting it pick an object to represent itself. The key point is that the part (memory network) picks the object to represent itself. This can be done by using a miniature, animal, and puppet or by asking the part to create a figure with clay or draw a picture that represents it. Once a part (memory network) selects a representation of itself it can be unblended into that object and the therapist can help facilitate a relationship between the Self of the child and his or her part. After the part selects an animal to represent itself, the therapist asks how the child feels TOWARD (not about) the part. If the answer is something that sounds like the Self (such as, I want to know it, I wonder who it is, I'm curious about it, I like it) the therapist can invite the part (animal) to tell the child what it wants the child to know about itself. This kind of answer would indicate that the part has unblended and that there is the beginning of a relationship between the Self of the child and the part of the child. If the answer is something that does not reflect the Self (such as, I hate it, it's stupid, I wish it would go away) that indicates that there is not the beginning of a Self to part relationship. It means another part is present that may be polarized with the original part, so that part must be located and unblended before a Self to part relationship can occur.

If the part is a protector (a manager or firefighter) it must be understood and reassured before it will allow access to the exile(s) it protects. The protector (mechanisms of adaptation or defenses) may need to be reassured that the feelings and memories held by the exile are not too much for the system or, that once released, the child will not be permanently stuck with those feelings of terror, shame, humiliation, worthlessness, etc., but will be able to release the feelings and heal the exile. Once the protector is reassured, it will step back and allow the exile to come forward to be witnessed and healed.

Identifying the responses of the firefighters and managers and getting clarity about their role in the system should be an important goal of the preparation phase of EMDR therapy when using IFS strategies. Since the firefighters constitute the lower brain animal defenses such as fight or flight, freeze and dissociative responses, greater levels of stabilization in the system may be promoted by working with the firefighter. The IFS language, when used during EMDR therapy, gives the child a tangible and concrete way of seeing and meeting their "physiological alarm and defense system." It also concretizes for children the view and understanding of trauma memories (exiles), the body's alarm system (firefighters) and the homeland security of the body and mechanisms of adaptation (managers).

It is important to take into account that the goal of accessing the protectors during the preparation phase of EMDR therapy is to honor the work these parts have been doing to protect the exiles (trauma memories) and allow access to the exiles so EMDR processing can be initiated.

Most protectors have felt unappreciated and even criticized in the way they have been required to protect the exiles. An important first step is to really listen to what the protector is trying to do. For example, if the child has a part full of rage, it is likely this part has gotten the child in trouble with parents, teachers, other kids and adults. However, no one may ever have asked what the part was trying to do. If you ask an angry part to describe its job, it frequently says something like: *"I'm trying to help you feel powerful and not so weak and vulnerable (the exile), I am trying to keep mean people away from you."* So, the first important question is what is the role of the part in the system. It can be asked in the following ways: *"What's your job for 'the child?' How do you try to help 'the child?' What do you want 'the child' to know about yourself, and what you do for him or her?"*

Once the function of the part is revealed, the part may also want the child to know, 1) how it learned to protect in the way it protects, 2) how old it is, 3) things it likes about its job, and 4) things it does not like so much about its job. These questions most likely will yield negative beliefs and metaperceptions held in the child's memory systems as well as emotions and other relevant information that can be placed in the child's targeting sequence and overall EMDR treatment plan.

As these parts are understood and appreciated, they are likely to step back and allow access to the exile. Hearing the firefighters, appreciating their attempts to minimize the impact of the exiles (trauma memory), asking for their cooperation in not overwhelming the system and allowing access to the exiles are IFS strategies that can be incorporated during the preparation and the reprocessing phases of EMDR therapy. It offers a gentle, honoring and even playful way to enter memory networks without causing so much dysregulation in the system.

Once the protective parts have granted permission to access the exiles (trauma memories), they are encouraged to tell their stories as the Self witnesses with compassion. The child's exile may be invited to tell the story by talking, drawing a picture, creating the story in the sand box or using Play-doh®. If the child has history of multiple developmental traumas, encouraging the part to convey his or her story by putting it into a book, a time line, a memory box or a memory wand (see Chapter 4) may make the process more playful. The EMDR clinician can place this information in the child's targeting sequence. As the child's Self develops relationships with his or her parts, the child will begin to identify the Self as "me" or "I."

The child will also notice what the presence of Self-energy feels like in their bodies. Children often describe it as (1) openness in the heart, chest, or around the heart or (2) a calm feeling.

Throughout the different phases of EMDR therapy, the clinician can install acts of triumph. If protective parts step back or are successful in dealing with a trigger, these mastery experiences can be enhanced and installed as resources. In this case, the part, in the presence of the child's Self, is encouraged to notice "the act of triumph" and draw a picture of it or just thinks about it. Then, the part is invited to notice the positive feelings associated with this experience, where they are located in the body and engage in slow and short sets of BLS. *"Let the part show you what it feels as it thinks about . . . and where these feelings are in the body."* In addition, a part may be invited to create a safe place. The part is invited to create any kind of place or room the part needs to feel safe. *"What kind of place does it want? Let's create it any way it wants it. It could be a fort, an open space, a place up in the mountains, etc."* Invite the part to notice the feelings associated with being in this safe place and where they are experienced in the body and use slow and short sets of BLS to install the safe place. The full calm-safe place protocol may be used by inviting the part to participate in identifying the safe place, making a sensory picture of the safe place, identifying the feelings, location in the body and engaging in BLS. The RDI protocol may also be used if needed when greater levels of stabilization are needed.

Phase Three: Assessment

Once appropriate stabilization of lower brain physiological responses has been achieved (the protectors have granted access to the exiles), and the trauma memories have been explored and accessed (exiles have been able to tell their stories while feeling the acceptance and understanding of the Self), the reprocessing of memories can be initiated (releasing the burdens is on the way). In IFS therapy, the burdens carried by the exiles (trauma memories) can be released to one of the five elements. However, in EMDR therapy, this release is accomplished by the processing, assimilation and integration of memories with specific protocols and procedures. When preparing for the reprocessing of a specific memory, the figure (animal, clay, toy) the exile selected to represent itself may be present as well as important protectors and without a doubt, the Self. Once the memory has been selected and the exile and protectors have agreed to participate in a reprocessing session, full assessment is done with the exile. Continuing to use IFS language allows the child a level of distance that facilitates the process of accessing and assimilating such memories. This language should continue to be used during the assessment and reprocessing phases of EMDR therapy.

During the preparation phase, the child has already chosen a figure or puppet to represent each part or "color." As you move into the assessment phase, start by inviting the exile and the figure that represents it to select the form of BLS and the helper it would like to have for eye movement or tapping (Elizabeth, Mario, David or Robbie). Ask the child,*"Is it okay for the part or color to show you what helper it wants? Does it want to move the eyes, use tapping, etc.?*

We are going to start by helping the part or color tell its story. Is it okay for the part to show you what it needs you to know about what happened? While we are doing EMDR, I will ask the part or color to show you anything it sees, feels and thinks. There is no right or wrong way to do EMDR. Any way you and the part do it is fine. You can use your stop signal when you need it, so let's practice it (practice the stop signal).

1. Image:

   "What does the part or color want to show you about what happened?" You can also use the figure or puppet chosen by the child to represent the part. If the child chose a "doggie" to represent the part, you may say, *"What does the doggie part of you want to show you about what happened? Let the part show you the picture or image that most matters to it. It can draw a picture or create it using the sandtray."*

2. Negative Cognition (NC):

   "When it thinks about (repeat the picture reported by the part), *let the part or color tell you what mixed-up thought it has about itself now. Let the part or let the "doggie" part of you* (repeat the name of the animal or puppet representing the part) *know that cards, cubes and balls with mixed-up thoughts are available if it wants to use them."* See Chapter 4 for the use of cards, cubes and balls.

3. Positive Cognition (PC):

   "When it thinks about (repeat the picture reported by the part), *let the part tell you what good thought it would like to have about itself. Let the part know that cards, cubes and balls with good thoughts are available if it wants to use them."* Have the cards and other tools available in front of the child.

4. VoC (The "Thought Scale"- Validity of the Positive Cognition): Use the "Thought Scale" and put the foam numbers from 1 to 7 in front of the child (see diagram below). Invite the part to use the thought scale and place the card with the PC by the number 7 and say:

   "Now we are going to use this cool thing called the 'Thought Scale'. The 'Thought Scale' helps kids check how true the good thoughts feel to them. Let me show you how it works. The 'Thought Scale' has numbers that go from 1 to 7. The number 1 means that the good thought does not FEEL true and the number 7 means that it FEELS really true. Now, let's invite the part (using the figure or puppet selected by the child's part) *to practice using the 'Thought Scale' with the good thought that it picked. Let the* (repeat the name of the animal or puppet that represents the part, such as the horsey or the wolf) *show you. When it thinks about* (repeat the image that represents the memory reported by the part), *how true do those words* (repeat the PC) *feel to (the horsey, the wolf) now? Remember that 1 feels completely false and 7 feels completely true."*

5. Emotions:

   "When (repeat the name of the puppet or animal) *thinks about* (repeat the image that represents the memory or show the drawing), *and the words* (repeat the NC), *what feelings does it have now?"*

6. SUDs (The 'Bothering Scale"- Subjective Units of Disturbance):

Using the "Bothering Scale," put the foam numbers from 0 to 10 in front of the child (see diagram below).

"Now we are going to use this cool thing called the 'bothering scale'. The 'bothering scale' helps kids check how much things bother them or make them feel bad. Let me show you how it works. The 'bothering scale' has numbers that go from 0 to10. The number 0 means that it does not bother you or that it feels neutral and the number 10 means that it bothers you a lot. Now, let's practice using the 'bothering scale' with the (repeat the name of the animal or puppet representing the part). *When it thinks about* (repeat the image that represents the memory or show the drawing) *and the mixed-up thought* (repeat the NC) *how much does it bother it now or how bad does it feel now? Remember that 0 means it is neutral and 10 means it bothers the part or color a lot.*

7. Location of Body Sensation:

"Let's have the "doggie" part of you (repeat the name of the animal or puppet that represents the part) *help you find where this is felt in your body."* Have the "feeling finder" available for the child to assist in locating the body sensation.

"I would like to invite (repeat the name of the animal or puppet that represents the part) *to think about or notice* (repeat the image that represents the memory or show the drawing), *the mixed-up or negative thought* (repeat the NC), *and the feelings and where they are in your body and follow the helper or my fingers* (repeat the helper's name or use the BLS selected by the child)." Begin desensitization.

Phase Four: Desensitization

During the reprocessing of traumatic memories, other exiles (memories) may come up as new associative channels are accessed. If the emergence of new exiles or protectors stall reprocessing, interweaves that include the six steps to healing parts can be used. Inviting the child once again to notice where they feel it in their bodies, asking the child to externalize the part by using objects, inviting the Self to notice the feelings towards this part, etc., constitute very effective and powerful interweaves. After each step, the EMDR clinician invites the child to notice what is coming up, and then engages in BLS. For example: When the child is invited to notice a part, the clinician could ask the child to follow the object that represents the part and engage in eye movement. After BLS is provided, customary questions are asked: Take a breath, let it go; what do you notice now? When the child reports compassion, empathy or positive feelings toward the part, invite the child to again engage in BLS.

When reprocessing memories of adversity and trauma, the processing of such memories may get stuck. Following the steps to first develop a relationship with the part that may be blocking the process can jump start reprocessing. Moreover, inviting the Self to witness the part and its story or memory, as well as unblending the part, may be used as interweaves.

After receiving the responses from the child's Self and or the part, invite the child to notice and continue to use BLS. These can be very effective interweaves that promote integration and adaptive resolution.

The following represent potential "stalling points" during the desensitization and other reprocessing phases, and the potential interweaves that may be used using IFS strategies:

1. Identifying if the part is still stuck in the past or it is in the present: Ask *"Are you here in the present or are you 5 years ago?"* If the part is still in the past, ask the part if there is more it needs the child to know about itself. Ask, *"Is it okay for the part or color to show you what it needs you to know about itself? Or is it okay for the 'doggie' part of you to show you what it needs you to know about itself?"* Invite the child to witness the part or color in any way the part wants to be witnessed. *"See what it wants you to see, feel what it wants you to feel or know what it wants you to know. Does the part have any words or noises it wants you to make? Is there any movement the part wants you to make?"* Ask, *"Is it okay for the part to show you how it wants to move?"* The child does not necessarily have to move; the movement could happen inside as long as the part is witnessed. According to the IFS model, every part knows how it wants to be witnessed. If the child refuses to witness the part, there is another part that needs to be identified and unblended. Keep in mind that the questions described above do not need to be asked all at the same time. Ask one and wait for the child's response and then invite the child to "go with that" or "notice that" while engaging in BLS. Once these channels are accessed and integrated, ask a new question until the part has been able to fully communicate its needs, wants, fears, etc. A child with a history of severe neglect and food deprivation identified the part that had suffered deprivation. The child chose a puppet of a dolphin to represent it. When the "dolphin part" was asked what it needed, it expressed the desire to be fed. The child was asked to witness the needs of this part while engaging in BLS. The part was encouraged to let the child know what and how it wanted to be fed, as well as who it wanted to be fed by. I (Ana Gomez) showed the part a variety of toy food so it could choose what it wanted. The child and I fed the part until it let us know it was full enough and it was feeling satisfied. As the part was being fed, the child was encouraged to notice what the part was experiencing and feeling as the child engaged in BLS. Customary procedural steps for the use of interweaves were used.

2. Inviting the Self to step into the scene: When working with trauma memories where there are unspoken words and defensive responses that could not be completed, the clinician can invite the Self to step in to help the part. For example, *"If you want, and if this feels okay with the part, you can step into the scene to protect the part in the way it wished it had been protected at that time."* The clinician may also offer to go in with the child's Self, *"If you want I can come in with you. I will come if the part wants. Now that we are here, ask the part how it wants you and I to protect it."* *"If the part wants, you can step in there and take care of it, however it longs to be taken care of."*

3. Meeting attachment needs: IFS strategies offer a wonderful way to assist children in meeting unmet attachment needs. When meeting a younger part that experienced neglect or abuse, the part can be invited to share what it needed and wished that it did not get. For example, children that did not get to experience

nurturance, affection, appropriate care, etc., can be invited to ask the younger part to share these unmet needs. A part may say it did not get held or it did not get love. The part is then invited to tell the child's Self how it wants to be held or rocked and how it wants to be loved. The part can also be invited to let the child's Self know if it wants the Self, the therapist, or the parent (if present) to participate in meeting the needs of the part. If the part wishes to be held, rocked, fed or played with, the parent, therapist or the child's self will be invited to play, hold, rock or feed the part. This is done until the part feels that the need(s) has been completely fulfilled. Keep in mind that BLS and customary reprocessing EMDR procedures follow each action directed to meet the need of a part. The child's Self and the part are invited to notice what happens as these needs are being met while engaging in BLS.

Working with Caregivers

When using EMDR therapy and IFS, the parent may be invited to witness the work of the child. If the child wants the parent to come in, it is suggested that the parent also does some level of work so the parent's wounded parts do not continue to injure the child. This is especially true if the parent has been responsible for the wounding. If parents have not done their own healing, their presence may inhibit the child's ability and desire to reveal his or her most vulnerable parts, thus, slowing or stopping the internal work. However, once the parent has begun his or her own work, very powerful sessions can be done with the parent as an accompanying healing agent. The parent can then participate in helping and accompanying the child in meeting the needs of a part if this is what the part is choosing or asking the parent to do. The participation of the parent should be explored with the child's parts, so the parent's involvement honors the parts or part and, in general, the child's internal system.

Phase Five: Installation

Once the part reports reaching a SUD level of 0, invite any part that protected the exile (trauma memory) to witness the healing that took place with the former exile. If different animals or puppets have been identified to represent the family system, then all these figures or ways to represent each part should be present. A circle may be created with the animals or puppets representing the system around the child while working with the exile during the installation phase. This is done with the purpose of having the managers and firefighters witness the healing taking place as the memory of trauma or adversity is moving to an adaptive resolution. The exile part is invited with the child's Self to check if there is a better "good thought" or if a new positive thought has emerged. The Validity of the Positive Cognition (VoC) is assessed, followed by the installation of the positive cognition while the protector part(s) witnesses. A song may be created with the positive cognition. The exile part (trauma memory) can let the child know if it wants to sing it just with the child's Self or if it wants to ask the other parts, the parent and the therapist to sing it together while the therapists performs BLS to install this positive cognition. Children's tunes (such as "Twinkle, Twinkle Little Star" or "Old McDonald had a Farm," etc.) may be used as the main melody while integrating the lyrics containing the positive cognition (such as, I am safe now ... E-I-E-I-O).

Phase Six: Body Scan

When accessing residual traumatic material held somatically, the part is invited to help the child find any sensations and somatic reactions experienced in the body while thinking about the memory of trauma or adversity.

You may say to the child, *"As the part, color or* (repeat the name of the animal or puppet that represents the part) *thinks about or notices that yucky thing that happened, let's have the part, color or* (repeat the name of the animal or puppet that represents the part) *help you check your body form head to toe to find any feelings or sensations in your body?"* Have the "feeling finder" available for the child to assist in locating the body sensation.

If the child reports any negative or positive sensations, invite the part and the child's Self to notice them while engaging in BLS. If the part reports experiencing a negative feeling in the stomach, say, *"I would like to invite the part, color or* (repeat the name of the animal or puppet that represents the part) *to notice the stuff in the stomach and follow my fingers or the helper* (initiate the BLS selected by the child)." Standard procedures for completing the body scan phase should be followed.

Phase Seven: Closure

Closure activities involving IFS strategies can be beneficial in helping the child attain emotional homeostasis before ending the session. If a part was unburdened during the session or exile material (trauma memories) has been accessed, appropriate closure activities should be implemented. The clinician should highlight the wonderful work done by the child and the part. Remind the child and the part that new or known parts may show up during the week. Invite the child to draw pictures or write down any "stuff" that comes up, along with new or known parts that may appear.

The clinician can ask the child to listen to anything the part needs before ending the session. Invite the part to let the child's Self know what it needs. It may need to feel safe again, so at this point the part is invited to bring up the safe place or any other resource or state change strategies installed during the preparation phase. Each part can choose how it wants to be "tucked in" at the end of the session so balance and equilibrium is reached before the session ends. If the child chose a puppet to represent the part, the part is invited to find a place for the puppet in the clinician's office. Remember that you can always use the language of "colors." Where would this color feel safe in your body? Once the part(s) and the child go back to a homeostatic state, the session can be appropriately ended.

Phase Eight: Reevaluation

During the reevaluation phase, a follow up is completed to find any changes in the child's life following the prior session. Have any firefighters or managers been present or activated since the prior session? Have new exiles (trauma memories) been activated recently? An important part of the reevaluation phase is to identify if the trauma memory (exile) has been adequately assimilated and integrated.

When resuming reprocessing of an unfinished target, the exile (trauma memory) is invited to come forward and let the child's Self know how disturbing the traumatic event is experienced now.

Accessing the target:

1. Image:

   "We are going to start by inviting the part, color or (repeat the name of the animal or puppet representing the part) *that was present last week or last session to be here again so we can continue to help this part tell its story."*

2. Subjective Units of Disturbance:
   Using the "bothering scale" put the foam numbers from 0 to 10 in front of the child.

   "Now we are going to use the 'bothering scale' again. Remember that the 'bothering scale' has numbers that go from 0 to 10. The number 0 means that it does not bother you or that it feels neutral, and the number 10 means that it bothers you a lot. When the part, color or (repeat the name of the animal or puppet that represents the part) *thinks about the yucky stuff that happened, how much does it bother it now or how bad does it feel now for the part, color or* (repeat the name of the animal or puppet that represents the part)?"*

3. Body location:

   "Let's have the part, color or (repeat the name of the animal or puppet that represents the part) *help you find where this is felt in your body."* Have the "feeling finder" available for the child to assist in locating the disturbance in the body.

   "I would like to invite the part, color or (repeat the name of the animal or puppet that represents the part) *to think about this and where it is felt in your body, and follow the helper or my fingers* (repeat the helper's name or use the BLS selected by the child)."* Continue reprocessing.

A thorough reevaluation should be performed at the end of treatment. Parts that have participated in reprocessing sessions should be invited to revisit their memories and stories to assess if any level of disturbance still remains. The puppets or animals used to represent the parts should be used, as the parts report to the child's Self how disturbing the memory or the traumatic event is now. If any disturbance is still present, the reprocessing of such memory (exile) should be initiated until complete integration and assimilation of the memory is attained.

SUMMARY AND CONCLUSIONS

The work with children carrying attachment wounds and traumas as well as dissociative tendencies may be more convoluted and intricate. As a result, they may need a "village" of strategies to achieve greater levels of integration and healing. Strategies and techniques borrowed from IFS psychotherapy may facilitate for many children the exploration, accessing and processing of memories of trauma and hardship. Children with limited regulatory capacities and sensitized lower animal responses may be able to gently access these defenses (firefighters) through the use of IFS strategies so access to the traumatic material (exiles) is granted by the system. Through the initial work with firefighters during the preparation phase, stabilization of the system is achieved before memories of trauma and adversity are accessed and activated. Moreover, the mechanisms of adaptation (managers) used by children that may be preventing them from fully participating in EMDR therapy could also be witnessed, unblended, invited to participate and ultimately integrated. This chapter is the first attempt to incorporate IFS strategies into a comprehensive EMDR treatment with children. Special care has been used to preserve adherence to EMDR therapy and AIP basic principles and procedures and at the same time honor the heart and soul of IFS theory and practice.

References

Abidin, R. R. (1995). *Parenting stress index: Professional manual* (3rd ed.). Odessa, FL: Psychological Assessment Resources.

Achenbach, T. (1992). *Manual for the child behavior checklist/2–3 and 1992 profile*. Burlington, VT: University of Vermont Department of Psychiatry.

Adler-Tapia, R. L., & Settle, C. S. (2008). *EMDR and the art of psychotherapy with children*. New York, NY: Springer Publishing.

Aduriz, M. E., Bluthgen, C., & Knopfler, C. (2009). Helping child flood victims using group EMDR intervention in Argentina: Treatment outcome and gender differences. *International Journal of Stress Management, 16*, 138–153.

Ahmad, A., Larsson, B., & Sundelin-Wahlsten, V. (2007). EMDR treatment for children with PTSD: Results of a randomized controlled trial. *Nord Journal Psychiatry, 61*, 349–354.

Ainsworth, M. D. S., Blehar, M., Waters, E., & Walls, S. (1978). *Patterns of attachment*. Hillsdale, NJ: Erlbaum.

American Psychiatric Association. (1994). *Diagnostic and statistical manual of mental disorders* (4th ed.). Washington, DC: Author.

American Psychiatric Association. (2000). *Diagnostic and statistical manual of mental disorders* (4th ed., text rev.). Washington, DC: American Psychiatric Association.

Andrews, T. (2011). *Animal speak: The spiritual & magical powers of creatures great & small* (2nd ed.). Woodbury, MN: Llewellyn Publications.

Armstrong, J. G., Putnam, F. W., Carlson, E. B., Libero, D. Z., & Smith, S. R. (1997). Development and validation of a measure of adolescent dissociation: The adolescent dissociative experiences scale (A-DES). *Journal of Nervous & Mental Disease, 185*, 491–497.

Badenoch, B. (2008) *Being a brain-wise therapist: A practical guide to interpersonal neurobiology*. New York, NY: W.W. Norton & Co.

Badenoch, B. (2011). *The brain-savvy therapist's workbook: A companion to BEING a brain-wise therapist*. New York, NY: W.W. Norton & Co.

Bakal, D. (1999). *Minding the body: Clinical uses of somatic awareness*. New York, NY: The Guilford Press.

Barach, P. M. M. (1991). Multiple personality disorder as an attachment disorder. *Dissociation, 4*, 117–123.

Baradon (Ed.). (2010). *Relational trauma in infancy: Psychoanalytic, attachment and neuropsychological contributions to parent-infant psychotherapy* (pp. 180–193). London, UK: Routledge.

Barrowcliff, A. L., Gray, N. S., Freeman, T. C. A., & MacCulloch, M. J. (2004).Eye-movements reduce the vividness, emotional valence and electro dermal arousal associated with negative autobiographical memories. *Journal of Forensic Psychiatry and Psychology, 15*, 325–345.

Becker-Blease, K. A., Deater-Deckard, K., Eley, T., Freyd, J., Stevenson, J., & Plomin, R. (2004). A genetic analysis of individual differences in dissociative behaviors in childhood and adolescence. *Journal of Child Psychology and Psychiatry, 45*(3), 522–532.

Becker-Blease, K. A., Deater-Deckard, K., Eley, T., Hulette, A., J. Freyd, J., & Fisher, P., (2011). Dissociation in middle childhood among foster children with early maltreatment experiences. *Child Abuse & Neglect, 35*, 123–126.

Benjamin, L. R., & Benjamin, R. (1992). An overview of family treatment in dissociative disorders. *Dissociation, V, 5*, 236–241.

Benjamin, L. R., Benjamin, R., & Rind, B. (1996). Dissociative mothers' subjective experience of parenting. *Child Abuse and Neglect, 20*(10), 933–942.

Bisson, J., & Andrew, M. (2007). Psychological treatment of post-traumatic stress disorder (PTSD). *Cochrane Database of Systematic Reviews 2007*, Issue 3. Art. No.: CD003388. doi: 10.1002/14651858.CD003388.pub3

Blader, J., & Carlson, G. (2006). Increased rates of bipolar disorder diagnoses amongst US child, adolescent and adult inpatients 1996–2004. *Biological Psychiatry, 62*, 107–114.

Bleuler, E. (1911). *Dementia praecox or the group of schizophrenias* (J. Zinkin, Trans.). New York, NY: International Universities Press. (Original work published 1911).

Bliss, E. L., Larson, E. M., & Nakashima, S. R. (1983). Auditory hallucinations and Schizophrenia. *Journal of Nervous & Mental Disorders, 171*(1), 30–33.

Bokhorst, C. L., Bakermans-Kranenburg, M. J., Fearon, R. M., van IJzendoorn, M. H., Fonagy, P., & Schuengel, C. (2003). The importance of shared environment in mother–infant attachment security: A behavioral genetic study. *Child Development, 74*, 1769–1782.

Booth, P., & Jernberg, A. (2010). *Theraplay: Helping parents and children build better relationships through attachment-based play.* San Francisco, CA : John Wiley & Sons.

Bowen, M. D. (1978). *Family therapy in clinical practice.* Northvale, NJ: Jason Aronson.

Bowlby, J. (1973). *Attachment and loss, vol. 2: Separation, Anxiety and anger.* London, UK: Hogarth Press.

Bowlby, J. (1980). *Attachment and loss, vol. 3: Sadness and depression.* London, UK: Hogarth Press.

Bowman, E. S., Blix, S. F., & Coons, P. M. (1985). Multiple personality in adolescence: Relationship to incestual experience. *Journal of the American Academy of Child & Adolescent Psychiatry, 24*, 109–114.

Bradley, R., Greene, J., Russ, E., Dutra, L., & Westen, D. (2005). A multidimensional meta-analysis of psychotherapy for PTSD. *American Journal of Psychiatry, 162*, 214–227.

Braun, B. G. (1985). The transgenerational incidence of dissociation and multiple personality disorder. In R. P. Kluft (Ed.), *Childhood antecedents of multiple personality disorder* (pp. 127–150). Washington, DC: American Psychiatric Press.

Bremner, J. D. (2005). Effects of traumatic stress on brain structure and function: Relevance to early responses to trauma. *Journal of Trauma & Dissociation, 6*(2), 51–68.

Bremner, J. D., Vythilingam, M., Vermetten, E., Southwick, S. M., McGlashan, T., Nazeer, A., Khan, S., Vaccarino, J. S., & Charney, D. S. (2003). MRI and PET study of deficits in hippocampal structure and function in women with childhood sexual abuse and posttraumatic stress disorder (PTSD). *American Journal of Psychiatry, 160*, 924–932.

Bretherton, I., & Munholland, K. A. (1999). Internal working models in attachment relationships: A construct revisited. In J. Cassidy & P. R. Shaver (Eds.), *Handbook of attachment: Theory, research and critical applications* (pp. 89–111). New York, NY: Guilford press.

Briere, J. (1996) *Trauma symptoms checklist for children: Professional manual.* Lutz, FL: Psychological Assessment Resources.

Brody, V. A. (1978). Developmental play: A relationship-focused program for children. *Journal of Child welfare, 57*(9), 591–599.

Brody, V. A. (1993). *The dialogue of touch: Developmental play therapy.* Treasure Island, FL: Developmental Play Training Associates.

Brown, S. (2009). *Play: How it shapes the brain, opens the imagination, and invigorates the soul.* New York, NY: Avery.

Cassidy, J. (2008). The Nature of the Child's Ties. In J. Cassidy & P. R. Shaver (Eds.), *Handbook of Attachment: Theory, Research, and Clinical Application* (3rd ed., pp. 3–22). New York, NY: The Guilford press.

Cassidy, J., & Shaver, P. (Eds.). (1999). *Handbook of attachment: Theory, research, and clinical applications.* New York, NY: Guildford Press.

Chemtob, C. M., Nakashima, J., & Carlson, J. G. (2002). Brief-treatment for elementary school children with disaster-related PTSD: A field study. *Journal of Clinical Psychology, 58*, 99–112.

Christman, D., Propper, R. E., & Dion, A. (2004). Increased interhemispheric interaction is associated with decreased false memories in a verbal converging semantic associates paradigm. *Brain and Cognition, 56*, 313–319.

Christman, S. D., Garvey, K. J., Propper, R. E., & Phaneuf, K. A. (2003). Bilateral eye movements enhance the retrieval of episodic memories. *Neuropsychology, 17*, 221–229.

Christman, S. D., Propper, R. E., & Brown, T. J. (2006).Increased interhemispheric interaction is associated with earlier offset of childhood amnesia. *Neuropsychology, 20*, 336–345.

Chu, J. A., Dill, D. L. (1990). Dissociative symptoms in relation to childhood physical and sexual abuse. *American Journal of Psychiatry; 147*, 887–892.

Coons, P. M. (1985). Children of parents with multiple personality disorder. In R. P. Kluft (Ed.), *Childhood antecedents of multiple personality disorder* (pp. 151–165). Washington, DC: American Psychiatric Press.

Coons, P. M. (1996). Clinical phenomenology of 25 children and adolescents with dissociative disorders. *Child and Adolescent Psychiatric Clinics of North America, 5*, 361–374.

Courtney, D. (2009). *The EMDR journey.* Author.

Cozolino, L. (2006). *The neuroscience of human relationships: Attachment and the developing social brain.* New York, NY: W.W. Norton & Company.

Cozolino, L. (2010). *The neuroscience of psychotherapy: Healing the social brain.*(2nd ed.). New York, NY: W.W. Norton & Company.

Cresswell, J. D., Eisenberger, N. I., & Lieberman, M. D. (2007). Neurobehavioral correlates of mindfulness during social exclusion. *Psychosomatic Medicine, 69*(6), 560–565.

Crisci, G., Lay, M., & Lowenstein, L. (1998). *Paper dolls and paper airplanes:Therapeutic exercises for traumatized children.* Indianapolis, IN: Kidsrights.

Crowell, J. A., Treboux, D., & Waters, E. (1999). The Adult Attachment Interview and the Relationship Questionnaire: Relations to reports of mothers and partners. *Personal Relationships, 6*, 1–18.

Damasio, A. (1999). *The feeling of what happens.* New York, NY: Harcourt, Brace, and Company.

Damasio, A. (2010). *Self comes to mind: Constructing the conscious brain.* New York, NY: Pantheon Books.

Davies, D. (2011). *Child development: A practitioner's guide.* (3rd ed.). New York, NY: The Guildford Press.

de Roos, C., Greenwald, R., den Hollander-Gijsman, M., Noorthoorn, E., van Buuren, S., & de Jongh, A. (2011). A randomised comparison of cognitive behavioural therapy (CBT) and eye movement desensitisation and reprocessing (EMDR) in disaster exposed children. *European Journal of Psychotraumatology, 2*, 5694–doi: 10.3402/ejpt.v2i0.5694

Dell, P. (2006). The Multidimensional Inventory of Dissociation (MID): A comprehensive measure of pathological dissociation. *Journal of Trauma and Dissociation, 7*(2), 77–106.

Dell, P., & Eisenhower, J. W. (1990). Adolescent multiple personality disorder: A preliminary study of eleven cases. *Journal of the American Academy of Child and Adolescent Psychiatry, 29*, 359–366.

Dell, P., & O'Neil, J. (Eds.). (2009). *Dissociation and the dissociative disorders: DSM V and beyond.* New York, NY: Routledge.

DesLauriers, A. (1962). *The experience of reality in childhood schizophrenia.* Monograph Series on Schizophrenia, No. 6. New York, NY: International Universities Press.

Dutra, L., Bianchi, I., Lyons-Ruth, C., & Siegel, D. (2009). The relational context of dissociative phenomena. In P. F. Dell & J. A. O'Neil (Eds.), *Dissociation and the dissociative disorders: DSM-V and Beyond* (pp. 83–92). New York, NY: Routledge.

Dworkin, M. (2005). *EMDR and the relational imperative.* New York, NY: Routledge.

Eckers, D. (2010). The method of constant installation of present orientation and safety (CIPOS) for children. In M. Luber (Ed.), *Eye movement desensitization and reprocessing (EMDR) scripted protocols: Special populations* (pp. 51–58). New York, NY: Springer.

Ellenberger, H. (1970). *Discovery of the unconscious.* New York, NY: Basic Books.

Erikson, E. H. (1968). *Identity: Youth and crisis.* New York, NY: Norton.

Evers- Szostak, M., & Sanders, S. (1992). The children's perceptual alteration scale (CAPS): A measure of children's dissociation. *Dissociation, 5,* 91–97.

Fagan, J., & McMahon, P. P. (1984). Incipient multiple personality in children. *Journal of Nervous & Mental Disease, 172,* 26–36.

Fernandez, I. (2007). EMDR as treatment of post-traumatic reactions: A field study on child victims of an earthquake. *Educational and Child Psychology. Special Issue: Therapy, 24,* 65–72.

Fernandez, I., Gallinari, E., & Lorenzetti, A. (2004). A school-based EMDR intervention for children who witnessed the Pirelli building airplane crash in Milan, Italy. *Journal of Brief Therapy, 2,* 129–136.

Fisher, A., Murray, E., & Bundy, A. (1991). *Sensory integration: Theory and practice.* Philadelphia, PA: Davis.

Fisher, J. (2000, November 12). *Adapting EMDR techniques in the treatment of dysregulated or dissociative patients.* Paper presented at the International Society for the Study of Dissociation Annual Meeting, San Antonio, Texas.

Flavell, J. H. (1979). Metacognition and cognitive monitoring: A new area of cognitive-developmental inquiry. *American Psychologist, 34,* 906–911.

Fonagy, P., & Target, M. (1997). Attachment and reflective function: Their role in self-organization. *Development and Psychopathology, 9,* 679–700.

Fonagy, P., Gergely, G., Jurist, E. J., & Target, M. (2002). *Affect regulation, mentalization, and the development of the self.* New York, NY: Other Press.

Fonagy, P., Steele, H., & Steele, M. (1991). Maternal representations of attachment during pregnancy predict the organisation of infant-mother attachment at one year. *Child Development, 62,* 891–905.

Forbes, H. T., & Post, B. B. (2006). *Beyond consequences, logic, and control: A love bases approach to helping children with severe behaviors.* Doulder, CO: Beyond Consequences Institute.

Forbes, H. T. (2009). *Dare to love: The art of merging science and love into parenting children with difficult behaviors.* Boulder, CO: Beyond Consequences Institute, LLC.

Ford, J. D., & Courtois, C. A. (2009). Defining and understanding complex trauma and complex traumatic stress disorders. In C. A. Courtois & J. D. Ford (Eds.), *Treating complex traumatic stress disorders: An evidence-based guide* (pp. 13–30). New York, NY: The Guilford Press.

Fromm, E. (1965). Hypnoanalysis: Theory and two case excerpts. *Psychotherapy: Theory, Research, and Practice, 2,* 127–133.

Frost, J., Silberg, J., & McIntee, J. (1996, November). *Imaginary friends in normal and traumatized children.* Paper presented at the 13th meeting of the International Society for the Study of Dissociation, San Francisco, CA.

George, C., & Solomon, J. (2008). The caregiving system: A behavioral system approach to parenting. In J. Cassidy & P. R. Shaver (Eds.), *Handbook of attachment: Theory, research, and clinical application* (3rd ed., pp. 3–22). New York, NY: The Guilford press.

Gomez, A. M. (2006). *Creative approaches to motivate, prepare, and guide children to use EMDR.* Paper presented at the XI annual EMDR International Association conference. Philadelphia, PA.

Gomez, A. M. (2007a). *Dark, bad...day go away: A book for children about trauma and EMDR.* Phoenix, AZ: Author.

Gomez, A. M. (2007b). *Creative ways of administering the EMDR protocol with children.* Paper presented at the XII annual EMDR International Association conference. Dallas, TX.

Gomez, A. M. (2008a). *Beyond PTSD: Treating depression in children and Adolescents using EMDR.* Preconference workshop presented at the XIII annual EMDR International Association conference. Phoenix, AZ.

Gomez, A. M. (2008b). *Step by step: Making EMDR developmentally appropriate for children and adolescents.* Workshop co-sponsored by the EMDR Institute. San Diego, CA.

Gomez, A. M. (2009a). *The thought kit for kids.* Phoenix, AZ: Author.

Gomez, A. M. (2009b). *Complex trauma attachment and dissociative symptoms: Treating children with pervasive emotion dysregulation using EMDR and adjunctive approaches*. Workshop co-sponsored by the EMDR Institute. Seattle, WA.

Gomez, A. M. (2010a). *Treating children with pervasive emotion dysregulation using EMDR and adjunctive approaches*. Paper presented at the XV annual EMDR International Association conference. Minneapolis, MN.

Gomez, A. M. (2010b). Using olfactory stimulation with children to cue the safe or happy place. In M. Luber (Ed.), *Eye movement desensitization and reprocessing (EMDR) scripted protocols: Special populations* (pp. 9–18). New York, NY: Springer publishing.

Gomez, A. M. (2010c). Using olfactory stimulation with children to cue resource development and installation (RDI). In M. Luber (Ed.), *Eye Movement Desensitization and reprocessing (EMDR) scripted protocols: Special populations* (pp. 19–29). New York, NY: Springer publishing.

Gomez, A. M. (2011). *Treating children with pervasive emotion dysregulation using EMDR and adjunctive approaches*. Paper presented at the XVI annual EMDR International Association conference. Anaheim, CA.

Gomez, A. M., & Paulsen, S. (In press). The different colors of me: My first book about dissociation. Phoenix, AZ: Author

Goodyear-Brown, P. (2010). *Play therapy with traumatized children: A prescriptive approach*. Hoboken, NJ: John Wiley & Sons, Inc.

Greenwald, R. (1999). *Eye movement desensitization and reprocessing (EMDR) in child and adolescent psychotherapy*. Northvale, NJ: Jason Aronson Press.

Harris, J. (2005). The increased diagnosis of "Juvenile Bipolar Disorder": What are we treating?. *Child & Adolescent Psychiatry, 56*(5), 529–531.

Hensel, T. (2009). EMDR with children and adolescents after single-incident trauma an intervention study. *Journal of EMDR Practice and Research, 3*, 2–9.

Herman, J. (1992). *Trauma and recovery*. New York, NY: Basic Books.

Hesse, E. (1999). The adult attachment interview: Historical and current perspectives. In J. Cassidy & P. R. Shaver (Eds.), *Handbook of attachment: Theory, research and clinical applications* (pp. 395–433*)*. New York, NY: Guilford Press.

Hesse, E. (2008). The adult attachment interview: Protocol, method of analysis, and empirical studies. In J. Cassidy & P. R. Shaver (Eds.), *Handbook of attachment: Theory, research, and clinical application* (3rd ed., pp. 552–598). New York, NY: The Guilford press.

Hesse, E., & Main, M. (1999). Second-generation effects of unresolved trauma in non-maltreating parents: Dissociated, frightened, and threatening parental behavior. *Psychanalytic inquiry, 19*, 481–540.

Hesse, E., & Main, M. (2000). Disorganized infant, child, and adult attachment: Collapse in behavioral and attentional strategies. *Journal of the American Psychological Association, 48*, 1097–1127.

Hesse, E., & Main, M. (2006). Frightened, threatening, and dissociative parental behavior: Theory and associations with parental adult attachment interview status and infant disorganization. *Development and Psychopathology, 18*, 309–343.

Holmes, T. (2007). *Parts work: An illustrated guide to your inner Life*. Kalamazoo, MI: Winged Heart Press.

Homeyer, L. E., & Sweeney, D. S. (2011). *Santray therapy: A practical manual* (2nd ed.). New York, NY: Routledge.

Hornstein, N. L., & Putnam, F. W. (1992). Clinical phenomenology of child and adolescent dissociative disorders. *Journal of the American Academy of Child and Adolescent Psychiatry, 31*, 1077–1085. Retrieved from http://isst-d.org/education/faq-teachers.htm

Hulette, A. C., Fisher, P. A., Kim, H. K., Ganger, W., & Landsverk, J. L. (2008). Dissociation in foster preschoolers: A replication and assessment study. *Journal of Trauma and Dissociation, 9*, 173–190.

Hulette, A. C., Freyd, J. J., Pears, K. C., Kim, H. K., Fisher, P. A., & Becker-Blease, K. A. (2008). Dissociation and post-traumatic symptomatology in maltreated preschool children. *Journal of Child and Adolescent Trauma, 1*, 93–108.

Hyun, M., Friedman, S., & Dunner, D. (2000). Relationship of childhood physical and sexual abuse in adult bipolar disorder. *Bipolar Disorders, 2*, 131–135.

Jaberghaderi, N., Greenwald, R., Rubin, A., Dolatabadim S., & Zand, S. O. (2004). A comparison of CBT and EMDR for sexually abused Iranian girls. *Clinical Psychology and Psychotherapy, 11*, 358–368.

Jacobson, E. (1938). *Progressive relaxation*. Chicago, IL: University of Chicago Press.

Janet, P. (1898). *Névroses et idées fixes*. Paris, France: Felix Alcan.

Janet, P. (1907). *The major symptoms of hysteria: Fifteen lectures given in the medical school of harvard university*. London, UK: Macmillan & Co.

Jarero, I., Artigas, L., & Lopez-Lena, M. (2008). The EMDR integrative group treatment protocol: Application with child victims of mass disaster. *Journal of EMDR Practice and Research, 2*, 97–105.

Jarero, I., Artigas, L., Mauer, M., Alcala, N., & Lupez, T. (1999). *EMDR integrative group treatment protocol and the butterfly hug*. Paper presented at annual meeting of the International Society for Traumatic Stress Studies, Miami, FL.

Kandel, E. R. (2006). *In search of memory: The emergence of a new science of mind*. New York, NY: W.W. Norton & Company.

Kaplowa, J., Hallb, E., Koenenc, K., Dodged, K., & Amaya-Jacksone, L. (2008). Dissociation predicts later attention problems in sexually abused children. *Child Abuse Neglect, 32*(2), 261–275.

Kemp, M., Drummond, P., & McDermott, B. (2010). A wait-list controlled pilot study of eye movement desensitization and reprocessing (EMDR) for children with post-traumatic stress disorder (PTSD) symptoms from motor vehicle accidents. *Clinical Child Psychology and Psychiatry, 15*, 5–25.

Kisiel, C., & Lyons, J. (2001). Dissociation as a mediator of psychopathology among sexually abused children and adolescents. *American Journal of Psychiatry, 158*, 1034–1039.

Kitchur, M. (2005). The Strategic Developmental Model for EMDR. In R. Shapiro (Ed.), *EMDR solutions: Pathways to healing* (pp. 8–56). New York, NY: W.W. Norton & Company.

Klaff, F. (2005). *Practical EMDR with children and adolescents: An integrative family systems approach*. Paper presented at the X EMDR International Association conference. Seattle, WA.

Kluft, R. P. (1984). Multiple personality disorder in childhood. *Psychiatric Clinics of North American, 7*, 121–134.

Kluft, R. P. (1987a). First rank symptoms as a diagnostic clue to multiple personality disorder. *American Journal of psychiatry, 144*, 293–298.

Kluft, R. P. (1987b). The parental fitness of mothers with multiple personality disorder. *Child Abuse and Neglect, 2*, 273–280.

Kluft. R. P. (1985). Hypnotherapy of childhood multiple personality disorder. *American Journal of Clinical Hypnosis, 27*, 201–210.

Knipe, J. (2010). The method of constant installation of present orientation and safety (CIPOS). In M. Luber (Ed.), *Eye movement desensitization and reprocessing (EMDR) scripted protocols: Special populations* (pp. 235–241). New York, NY: Springer Publishing.

Koren-Karie, N., Oppenheim, D., Dolev, S., Sher, S., & Etziom-Carasso, A. (2002). Mother's insightfulness regarding their infants' internal experience: Relations with maternal sensitivity and infant attachment. *Developmental Psychology, 38*, 534–542.

Korn, D. L., & Leeds, A. M. (2002). Preliminary evidence of efficacy of EMDR resource development and installation in the stabilization phase of treatment of complex posttraumatic stress disorder. *Journal of Clinical Psychology, 58*(12), 1465–1487.

Kurtz, R. (1990). *Body-centered psychotherapy: The hakomi method*. Mendicino, CA: LifeRhythm.

Lanius, U.F. (2005). EMDR with Dissociative Clients: Adjunctive Use of Opioid Antagonists. In R. Shapiro (Ed). *EMDR Solutions: Pathways to Healing*. New York: W.W. Norton.

Lanius, R. A., Blum, R., Lanius, U., & Pain, C. (2006). A review of neuroimaging studies of hyperarousal and dissociation in PTSD: Heterogeneity of response to symptom provocation. *Journal of Psychiatric Research, 40*(8), 709–729.

Lanius, R. A., Williamson, P. C., Boksman, K., Densmore, M., Gupta, M., Neufeld, R. W.,…Menon, R. S. (2002). Brain activation during script-driven imagery induced dissociative responses in PTSD: A functional magnetic resonance imaging investigation. *Biological Psychiatry, 52*, 305–311.

Le Doux, J. (2002). *Synaptic self: How our brains become who we are.* New York, NY: Viking.

LeDoux, J. (1996). *The emotional brain: The mysterious underpinnings of emotional life.* New York, NY: Simon & Schuster.

Leeds, A. M. (2009). *A guide to the standard EMDR protocols for clinicians, supervisors, and consultants.* New York, NY: Springer.

Levine, P. A. & Frederick, A. (1997). *Waking the tiger: Healing trauma.* Berkeley, CA: North Atlantic Books.

Levine, P. A. (2010). *In an unspoken voice: How the body releases trauma and restores goodness.* Berkeley, CA: North Atlantic Books.

Levine, P. A., & Kline, M. (2007). *Trauma through a child's eyes: Awakening the ordinary miracle of healing.* Berkeley, CA: North Atlantic Books.

Levitan, R. D., Parikh, S. V., Lesage, A. D., Hegadoren, K. M., Adams, M., Kennedy, S. H., & Goering, P. N. (1998). Major depression in individuals with a history of childhood physical or sexual abuse: Relationship to neurovegetative features, mania, and gender. *American Journal of Psychiatry, 155*, 1746–1752.

Levy, B. (2009, October). *Bipolar disorder and dissociative identity disorder: A pluralistic approach to diagnosis and treatment.* Paper presented at the New England College Health Association and New York State College Health.

Lichtenstein, L. (Executive Producer). 2005. *The bipolar child. Infinite Mind.* New York, NY: National Public Broadcasting.

Liotti, G. (1992). Disorganized/disoriented attachment in the etiology of the dissociative disorders. *Dissociation, 5*, 196–204.

Liotti, G. (2006). A model of dissociation based on attachment theory and research. *Journal of Trauma & Dissociation, 7*(4), 55–73.

Liotti, G. (2009). Attachment and Dissociation. In P. F. Dell, J. A. O'Neil (Eds.) *Dissociation and the dissociative disorders: DSM-V and beyond* (pp. 53–65). New York, NY: Routledge.

London, S. (2004). Teaching meditation to children and beginners. *Insight Journal, 22*, 24–29.

Lovett, J. (1999). *Small wonders: Healing trauma with EMDR.* New York, NY: The Free press.

Lyon-Ruth, K., & Jacobvitz, D. (2008). Attachment disorganization: Genetic factors, parenting context, and developmental transformation form infancy to adulthood. In J. Cassidy & P. R. Shaver (Eds.), *Handbook of attachment: Theory, research, and clinical application* (pp. 666–697, 3rd ed.). New York, NY: The Guilford press.

Lyons-Ruth, K., & Jacobvitz, D. (1999). Attachment disorganization: Unresolved loss, relational violence and lapses in behavioral and attentional strategies. In J. Cassidy & P. R. Saver (Eds.), *Handbook of attachment* (pp. 520–554). New York, NY: Guilford Press.

MacCulloch, M. J., & Feldman, P. (1996). Eye movement desensitization treatment utilizes the positive visceral element of the investigatory reflex to inhibit the memories of post-traumatic stress disorder: A theoretical analysis. *British Journal of Psychiatry, 169*, 571–579.

Macfie, J., Ciccehtti, D., & Toth, S. (2001). The development of dissociation in maltreated preschool-aged children. *Development and Psychopathology, 13*, 233–254.

MacLean, P. D. (1985). Brain evolution relating to family, play, and the separation call. In *Archives of General Psychiatry, 42*(4), 405–417.

MacLean, P. D. (1990). *The triune brain in evolution.* New York, NY: Plenum Press.

Mahler, P., Pine, M. M., & Bergman, A. (1975). *The psychological birth of the human infant.* New York, NY: Basic Books.

Main, M. (1991). Metacognitive knowledge, metacognitive monitoring, and singular (coherent) vs. multiple (incoherent) models of attachment: Findings and directions for future research. In C.M. Parkes, J. Stevenson-Hinde, & P. Marris (Eds.) *Attachment across the life cycle* (pp. 127–159). London, UK: Routledge.

Main, M. (1995). Recent studies in attachment: Overview with selected implications for clinical work. In S. Goldberg, R. Muir, & J. Kerr (Eds.), *Attachment theory: Social, developmental, and clinical perspectives* (pp. 407–475). Hillsdale, NJ: Analytic press.

Main, M., & Solomon, J. (1986). Discovery of an insecure disorganized/disoriented attachment pattern: Procedures, findings and implications for the classification of behavior. In T. B. Brazelton & M. W. Yogman (Eds.), *Affective development in infancy* (pp. 95–124). Norwood, NJ: Ablex.

Main, M., Hesse, E., & Goldwyn, R. (2008). Studying differences in language usage in recounting attachment history: An introduction to the AAI. In H. Steele & M. Steele (Eds.), *Clinical applications of the adults attachment interview* (pp. 31–68). New York, NY: The Guilford Press.

Malinosky-Rummel, R. R., & Hoier, T. S. (1991). Validating measures of dissociation. *Behavior Assessment, 13*, 341–357.

Mann, B. J., & Sanders, S. (1994). Child dissociation and the family context. *Journal of Abnormal Child Psychology, 22*(3), 373–388.

Marschak, M. (1960). A method for evaluating child-parent interactions under controlled conditions. *The Journal of Genetic Psychology, 1960, 97*, 3–22.

Marschak, M. (1980). *Parent-child interaction and youth rebellion.* New York, NY: Gardner Press.

Maxfield, L., Melnyk, W. T., & Hayman, C. A. G. (2008). A working memory explanation for the effects of eye movements in EMDR. *Journal of EMDR Practice and Research, 2*, 247–261.

McCallum, K. E., Lock, J., Kulla, M., & Rorty, M., & Wetzel,R. (1992). Dissociative symptoms and disorders in patients with eating disorders. *Dissociation, 5*(4), 227–235.

McElroy, L. P. (1992). Early indicators of pathological dissociation in sexually abused children. *Child Abuse & Neglect, 16*, 833–842.

McGilchrist, I. (2009). *The master and his emissary.* New Haven, CT: Yale University Press.

Meins, E., Fernyhough, C., Fradley, E., & Tuckey, M. (2001). Rethinking maternal sensitivity: Mothers' comments on infants' mental processes predicts security of attachment at 12 months. *Journal of Child Psychology and Psychiatry, 42*, 637–648.

Minton, K. (2009, December 17). *Somatic interventions for enhancing EMDR effectiveness.* Paper presented at seminar in Vancouver, Canada.

Minuchin, S. (1974). *Families and family therapy.* Cambridge, MA: Harvard University Press.

Moreno, C., Gonzalo, L., Blanco, C., Jiang, H., Schmidt, A. B., & Olfson, M. (2007). National trends in the outpatient diagnosis and treatment of bipolar disorder in youth. *Archives of General Psychiatry, 64*, 1032–1039.

Moskowitz, A. (2011). Schizophrenia, trauma, dissociation, and scientific revolutions. *Journal of Trauma & Dissociation, 12*(4), 347–357.

Mueser, K. T., Goodman, L. B., Trombetta, S. L., Rosenberg, D., Osher, C., Vidaver, R., & Auciello, P. (1998). Trauma and posttraumatic stress disorder in severe mental illness. *Journal of Consulting Clinical Psychology, 66*(3), 493–499.

National Institute Mental Health. (2007). *Rates of bipolar diagnosis in youth rapidly climbing, treatment patterns similar to adults.* Retrieved from www.nimh.nih.gov/science-news/2007/rates-of-bipolar-diagnosis-in-youth-rapidly-climbing-treatment-patterns-similar-to-adults.shtml

Nelson, C. A. (2007). What would Superman do? In L. C. Rubin (Ed.), *Using superheroes in counseling and play therapy* (pp. 49–67). New York, NY: Springer publishing.

Nijenhuis, E. R. S. & van der Hart, O. (1999). Somatoform Dissociative Phenomena: A Janetian Perspective. In J.Goodwin & R. Attias (Eds.), *Splintered reflections: Images of the body in trauma.* Basic Books, Inc.

Nijenhuis, E. R. S., & van der Hart, O. (2011). Dissociation in trauma: A new definition and comparison with previous formulations. *Journal of Trauma & Dissociation, 12*(4), 416–445.

Noyes, R., & Kletti, R. (1977). Depersonalization in response to life-threatening danger. *Psychiatry, 18*, 375–384.

Ogden, P. (1995). *The use of somatics with the sexually abused.* Paper presented at the Proceedings of the International Somatics Congress, San Francisco, California.

Ogden, P. (1997). *Inner body sensation. Part one.* In E. G. Hanna (Ed.), *Somatics*, XI(2). 40–43.

Ogden, P. (1998). *Inner Body Sensation. Part two.* In E G. Hanna (Ed.), *Somatics*, XI(3), 42–49.

Ogden, P. (2007). *Beneath the words: A clinical map for using mindfulness of the body and the organization of experience in trauma treatment.* Paper presented at Mindfulness and Psychotherapy Conference. Los Angeles, CA: UCLA/Lifespan Learning Institute.

Ogden, P. K. (2009). Emotion, mindfulness, and movement: Expanding the regulatory boundaries of the window of affect tolerance. In D. Fosha, D. J. Siegel, M. Solomon (Eds.), *The healing power of emotion: Affective neuroscience, development & clinical practice* (pp. 204–231). New York, NY: W.W. Norton & Company.

Ogden, P. (2011). *The role of the body in forecasting the future.* Paper presented at the Proceedings of the Affect Regulation Convened: Implicit Communication and Therapeutic Change. New York, NY.

Ogden, P. K., Minton, K., & Pain, C. (2006). *Trauma and the body: A sensorimotor approach to psychotherapy.* New York, NY: Norton.

Ogden, P. & Fisher, J. (in press). *The body as resource: Sensorimotor psychotherapy interventions for the treatment of trauma.* New York: W. W. Norton.

Ogden, P., & Goldstein, B. (in press). *New directions in child and adolescent treatment: A sensorimotor psychotherapy approach.* New York, NY: W.W. Norton & Company.

Ogden, P., & Minton, K. (2000). Sensorimotor psychotherapy: One method for processing traumatic memory. In *Traumatology, 3*(3), 1–20.

Ogden, P., & Peters, A. (1990). Translating the body's language. *Hakomi Forum, 8,* 31–34.

Ogden, P., Goldstein, B. & Fisher, J. (in press) A sensorimotor psychotherapy perspective on the treatment of children and adolescents in R. Longe, J. Bergman, K. Creeden, & D. Prescott (Eds.) *Current Perspectives & Applications in Neurobiology: Working with Young Persons who are Victims and Perpetrators of Sexual Abuse.* Fitchberg, MA: Neari Press.

Ogden, P., Minton, K., & Pain, C. (2006). *Trauma and the body: A sensorimotor approach to psychotherapy.* New York, NY: Norton.

O'Shea, K. (2009). The EMDR early trauma protocol. In R. Shapiro (Ed.), *EMDR solutions II: For depression, eating disorders, performance, and more* (pp. 313–334). New York, NY: W.W. Norton & Company.

Panksepp, J. (1998). *Affective neuroscience: The foundations of human and animal emotions.* New York, NY: Oxford University Press.

Panksepp, J. (2009). Brain emotional systems and qualities of mental life: From animal models of affect to implications for psychotherapeutics. In D. Fosha, D. J. Siegel, & M. Solomon (Eds.), *The healing power of emotion: Affective neuroscience, development & clinical practice* (pp. 1–26). New York, NY: W.W. Norton & Company.

Papolos, D., & Papolos, J. (2000). *The bipolar child: The definitive and reassuring guide to childhood's most misunderstood disorder.* New York, NY: Broadway Books.

Parry, P. I., & Levin, E. C. (2012). Pediatric bipolar disorder in an era of "mindless psychiatry." *Journal of Trauma & Dissociation, 13*(1), 51–68. doi: 10.1080/15299732.2011.597826

Paulsen, S. (2009). *Looking through the eyes of trauma and dissociation: An illustrated guide for EMDR therapist and clients.* Bainbridge Island: the Bainbridge Institute for Integrative Psychology.

Paulsen, S., & Lanius, U. (2009). Towards and embodied self: Integrating EMDR with somatic and ego state interventions. In R. Shapiro (Ed.), *EMDR Solutions II: For depression, eating disorders, performance, and more* (pp. 335–388). New York, NY: W.W. Norton & Company.

Pellegrini, A. D. (2009). *The role of play in human development.* New York, NY: Oxford University Press.

Perry, B. D, (2009). Examining child maltreatment through a neurodevelopmental lens: Clinical Applications of the Neurosequential Model of Therapeutics. *Journal of Loss and Trauma, 14,* 240–255. doi: 10.1080/15325020903004350

Perry, B. D. (2006). The neurosequential model of therapeutics: Applying principles of neurodevelopment to clinical work with maltreated and traumatized children. In N. B. Webb (Ed.), *Working with traumatized youth in child welfare.* New York, NY: Guildford Press.

Perry, B. D., & Hambrick, E. (2008). The neurosequential model of therapeutics. *Reclaiming Children and Youth: The Journal of Strength-Based Interventions, 17,* 38–43.

Perry, B., & Szalavitz, M. (2006). *The boy who was raised as a dog and other stories from a child psychiatrist's notebook.* New York, NY: Basic Books.

Peterson, G. (1991). Children coping with trauma: Diagnosis of dissociation identity disorder. *Dissociation, 4,* 152–164.

Peterson, G., & Boat, B. (1997). Concerns and issues in treating children of parents diagnosed with dissociative identity disorder. *Journal of Child sexual Abuse, 6*(3), 1–13.

Peterson, G., & Putnam, F. W. (1994). Further validation of the child dissociation checklist. *Dissociation, 7,* 204–211.

Piaget, J. (1954). *The construction of reality in the child.* New York, NY: Ballentine.

Porges, S. W. (1995). Orienting in a defensive world: Mammalian modifications of our evolutionary heritage: A polivagal theory. *Psychophysiology, 32,* 301–318.

Porges, S. W. (2009). Reciprocal influences between body and brain in the perception and expression of affect: A polyvagal perspective. In D. Fosha, D. J. Siegel, & M. Solomon (Eds.), *The healing power of emotion: Affective neuroscience, development & clinical practice* (pp. 27–54). New York, NY: W.W. Norton & Company.

Porges, S. W. (2011). *The polyvagal theory: Neurophysiological foundations of emotions, attachment, communication, self-regulation.* New York, NY: W.W. Norton & Company.

Post, R., Weiss, S., Smith, M., Li, H., & McCann, U. (1997). Kindling versus quenching: Implications for the evolution and treatment of posttraumatic stress disorder. In R. Yehuda & A. C. McFarlane (Eds.), *Psychobiology of posttraumatic stress disorder* (pp. 285–295). New York, NY: New York Academy of Sciences.

Prochaska, J. O., & Norcross, J. C. (2010). *Systems of psychotherapy: A transtheoretical analysis.* Belmont, CA: Brooks/Cole.

Putnam, F. W. (1997). *Dissociation in children and adolescents: A developmental perspective.* New York, NY: Guilford.

Putnam, F. W., & Trickett P. K. (1993). Child sexual abuse: A model of chronic trauma. *Psychiatry, 56,* 82–95.

Putnam, F. W., Hornstein, N., & Peterson, G. (1996). Clinical phenomenology of child and adolescent dissociative disorders: Gender and age effects. *Child and Adolescent Psychiatric Clinics of North America, 5,* 351–360.

Putnam, F., Helmers, K., & Trickett, P. (1993). Development, reliability, and validity of a child dissociation scale. *Child Abuse & Neglect, 17*(6), 731–741.

Ribchester, T., Yule, W., & Duncan, A. (2010). EMDR for childhood PTSD after road traffic accidents: Attentional, memory, and attributional processes. *Journal of EMDR Practice and Research, 4*(4), 138–147.

Riley, R. L., & Mead, J. (1988). The development of symptoms of multiple personality in a child of three. *Dissociation,1,* 41–46.

Rodenburg, R., Benjamin, A., de Roos, C., Meijer, A. M., & Stams, G. J. (2009). Efficacy of EMDR in children: A meta-analysis. *Clinical Psychology Review, 29,* 599–606.

Rogers, S., & Silver, S. M. (2002). Is EMDR an exposure therapy? A review of trauma protocols. *Journal of Clinical Psychology, 58,* 43–59.

Rosenbaum, M. (1980). The role of the term schizophrenia in the decline of diagnoses of multiple personality. *Archives of General Psychiatry, 37,* 1383–1385.

Ross, C. A., Joshi, S., & Currie, R. P. (1990). Dissociative experiences in the general population. *American Journal of Psychiatry, 147,* 1547–1552.

Ross, C. A., Miller, S. D., Reagor, P., Bjronson, L., Fraser, G., & Anderson, G. (1990). Schneiderian symptoms in multiple personality disorder and schizophrenia. *Comprehensive Psychiatry, 31,* 111–118.

Ross, C. A., Norton, G. R., & Wozney, K. (1989). Multiple personality disorder: An analysis of 23 cases. *Canadian Journal of Psychiatry, 34,* 413–418.

Rubin, P. B., Lendner, D., & Mroz Miller, J. (2010). Theraplay for children with histories of complex trauma. In P. B. Booth & A. M. Jernberg, *Theraplay: Helping parents and children build better relationships through attachment-based play.* San Francisco, CA: John Wiley & Sons.

Sack, M., Lempa, W., Steinmetz, A., Lamprecht, F., & Hofmann, A. (2008). Alterations in autonomic tone during trauma exposure using Eye Movement Desensitization. *Journal of Anxiety Disorders, 22,* 1264–1271.

Sanders, S. (1986). The perceptual alteration scale: A scale measuring dissociation. *American Journal of Clinical Hypnosis, 29,* 95–192.

Sar, V., & Ozturk, E. (2009). Psychotic presentations of dissociative identity disorder. In P. Dell & J. O'Neil (Eds.), *Dissociation and the dissociative disorders: DSM V and beyond* (pp. 535–545). New York, NY: Routledge.

Satir, V. (1983). *Conjoint family therapy.* Palo Alto, CA: Science and Behavior Books.

Schore, A. (1994). *Affect regulation and the origin of the self: The neurobiology of emotional development.* Hillsdale, NJ: Lawrence Erlbaum Associates.

Schore, A. (2001). The effects of early relational trauma on right brain development, affect regulation, and infant mental health. *Infant Mental Health Journal, 22,* 201–269.

Schore, A. (2010). The right brain implicit self: A central mechanism of the psychotherapy change process. In J. Pertucelli (Ed.), *Knowing, not-knowing and sort-of-knowing: Psychoanalysis and the experience of uncertainty* (pp. 177–202). Paper originally presented at the annual meeting of Division 39 (Psychoanalysis) of the American Psychological Association, spring 2008. London, UK: Karnac Books.

Schore, A. (2011). The right brain implicit self lies at the core of psychoanalysis. *Psychoanalytic dialogues, 21,* 75–100.

Schore, A. N. (2003a). *Affect dysregulation and disorders of the self* (1st ed.) New York, NY: W.W. Norton & Company.

Schore, A. N. (2003b). *Affect regulation and the repair of the self* (1st ed.) New York, NY: W.W. Norton & Company.

Schore, A. N. (2009). Attachment trauma and the developing right brain: Origins of pathological dissociation. In P. F. Dell & J. A. O'Neil (Eds.), *Dissociation and the dissociative disorders: DSM-V and beyond* (pp. 107–141). New York, NY: Routledge.

Schore, A. N. (2010). Relational trauma and the developing right brain: The neurobiology of broken attachment bonds. In T. Baradon (Ed.), *Relational trauma in infancy: Psychoanalytic, attachment and neuropsychological contributions to parent-infant psychotherapy* (pp. 19–47). London, UK: Routledge.

Schubert, S. J., Lee, C. W., & Drummond, P. D. (2011). The efficacy and psychophysiological correlates of dual-attention tasks in eye movement desensitization and reprocessing (EMDR). *Journal of Anxiety Disorders, 25*(1), 1–11.

Schwartz, R. C. (1995). *Internal family systems therapy.* New York, NY: The Guildford Press.

Schwartz, R. C., Schwartz, M. F., & Galperin, L. (2009). Internal family systems therapy. In C. A. Courtois & J. D. Ford (Eds.), *Treating complex traumatic stress disorders: An evidence-based guide* (pp. 353–370). New York, NY: The Guilford Press.

Seidler, G. H., & Wagner, F. E. (2006). Comparing the efficacy of EMDR and trauma-focused cognitive-behavioral therapy in the treatment of PTSD: A meta-analytic study. *Psychological Medicine, 36,* 1515–1522.

Shapiro, E., & Laub, B. (2008). Early EMDR intervention (EEI): A summary, a theoretical model, and the recent traumatic episode protocol (R-TEP). *Journal of EMDR Practice and Research, 2*(2), 79–96.

Shapiro, F. (1995). *Eye movement desensitization and reprocessing: Basic principles, protocols and procedures.* New York, NY: Guilford Press.

Shapiro, F. (2001). *Eye movement desensitization and reprocessing. Basic principles, protocols and procedures* (2nd ed.) New York, NY: Guilford Press.

Shapiro, F. (2005). *Eye movement desensitization and reprocessing (EMDR) training manual.* Watsonville, CA: EMDR Institute.

Shapiro, F. (2005). *Eye movement desensitization and reprocessing (EMDR) training manual.* Watsonville, CA: EMDR Institute.

Shapiro, F. (2007). EMDR, adaptive information processing, and case conceptualization. *Journal of EMDR Practice and Research, 1,* 68–87.

Shapiro, F. (2010). *Eye movement desensitization and reprocessing (EMDR) training manual.* Watsonville, CA: EMDR Institute.

Shapiro, F. (2012). *Getting past your past: Take control of your life with self-help techniques from EMDR therapy.* New York, NY: Rodale.

Shapiro, F. (in press). Redefining trauma and its hidden connections: Identifying and reprocessing the experiential contributors to a wide variety of disorders. In M. Solomon & D. S. Siegel (Eds.), *Healing moments in psychotherapy: Mindful awareness, neural integration, and therapeutic presence.* New York, NY: W.W. Norton.

Shapiro, F., Kaslow, F., & Maxfield, L. (2007). *Handbook of EMDR and family therapy processes.* Hoboken, NJ,: John Wiley & Sons.

Shimizu, M., & Sakamoto, S. (1986). Depersonalization in early adolescence. *Japanese Journal of Psychiatry and Neurology, 40,* 4, 603–608.

Shirar, L. (1996). *Dissociative children.* New York, NY: W. W. Norton.

Siegel, D. J. (1999). *The developing mind: How relationships and the brain interact and shape who we are.* New York, NY: The Guilford Press.

Siegel, D. J.(2007). *The Mindful Brain: Reflection and attunement in the cultivation of well-being.* New York: W. W. Norton.

Siegel, D. J. (2010). *Mindsight: The new science of personal transformation.* New York, NY: Bantam Books Trade Paperbacks.

Siegel, D. J. (speaker). (2008). *The neurobiology of we: How relationships, the mind, and the brain interact to shape who we are.* [Audio Recordings]. Louisville, CO: Sounds True.

Siegel, D. J., & Bryson, T. B. (2011). *The whole brain child: 12 revolutionary strategies to nurture your child's developing mind.* New York, NY: Delacorte Press.

Siegel, D. J., & Hartzell, M. (2003). *Parenting from the inside out: How a deeper self-understanding can help you raise children who thrive.* New York, NY: Tarcher & Putnam.

Silberg, J. (1998). Interviewing strategies for assessing dissociative disorders in children and adolescents. In J. Silberg (Ed.), *The dissociative child* (2nd ed., pp. 47–58). Lutherville, MD: Sidran Press.

Silberg, J. (2000). Fifteen years of dissociation in maltreated children: Where do we go from here? *Child Maltreatment, 5,* 119–136.

Silberg, J. (2001). An optimistic look at childhood dissociation. *ISSTD News, 19*(2), 1.

Silberg, J. (2012). *The child survivor.* New York, NY: Routledge Press.

Silberg, J. (Ed.), (1998). *The dissociative child* (2nd ed.). Lutherville, MD: Sidran Press.

Silberg, J. L. (Ed) (1996/1998). *The dissociative child: Diagnosis, treatment and management.* Lutherville, MD: Sidran Press.

Silberg, J. L., & Dallam, S. (2009). Dissociation in children and adolescents: At the crossroads. In P. F. Dell & J. A. O'Neil (Eds.), *Dissociation and the dissociative disorders: DSM-V and beyond* (pp. 67–81). New York, NY: Routledge.

Sim, L., Friedrich, W., Hobart Davies, W., Trentham, B. Lengua, L., & Pithers, W. (2005). The child behavior checklist as an indicator of posttraumatic stress disorder and dissociation in normative, psychiatric, and sexually abused children. *Journal of Traumatic Stress, 18*(6), 697–705.

Simeon, D., Guralnik, O., Schmeidler, J., Sirof, B., & Knutelska, M. (2001). The role of childhood interpersonal trauma in depersonalization disorder. *American Journal of Psychiatry 158,* 1027–1033.

Sleed, M., & Fonagy, P. (2010). Understanding disruptions in the parent-infant relationship: Do actions speak louder than words? In T. Baradon (Ed.), *Relational trauma in infancy: Psychoanalytic, attachment and neuropsychological contributions to parent-infant psychotherapy* (pp. 136–162). London, UK: Routledge.

Soberman, G. B., Greenwald, R., & Rule, D. L. (2002). A controlled study of eye movement desensitization and reprocessing (EMDR) for boys with conduct problems. *Journal of Aggression, Maltreatment, and Trauma, 6,* 217–236.

Solomon, J., & George, C. (Eds.). (1999). *Attachment disorganization.* New York, NY: Guilford Press.

Sroufe, L. A., & Ward, M. J. (1980). Seductive behavior of mothers of toddlers: Occurrence, correlates, and family origins. *Child Development, 51,* 1222–1229.

Sroufe, L. A., Egeland, B., Carlson, E., & Collins, W. A. (2005). *The development of the person: The Minnesota Study of risk and adaptation from birth to adulthood.* New York, NY: Guilford Press.

Steele, H., & Steele, M. (2008). The clinical uses of the adult attachment interview. In H. Steele & M. Steele (Eds.), *Clinical applications of the adults attachment interview* (pp. 3–30). New York, NY: The Guilford Press.

Steele, K., Dorahy, M. J., van der Hart, O., & Nijenhuis, E. R. S. (2009). Dissociation versus alterations in consciousness: Related but different concepts. In P. Dell & J. O'Neil (Eds.), *Dissociation and the dissociative disorders: DSM V and beyond* (pp. 155–169). New York, NY: Routledge.

Steele, M., Steele, H., & Murphy, A. (2010). The adult attachment interview and relational trauma: Implications for parent-child psychotherapy. In H. Steele & M. Steele (Eds.), *Clinical applications of the adults attachment interview* (pp. 3–30). New York, NY: The Guilford Press.

Steele, W., & Raider, M. (2001). *Structured sensory interventions for traumatized children, adolescents and parents: Strategies to alleviate trauma.* Lewiston, NY: The Edwin Mellen press.

Stein, M. B., Koverola, C., Hanna, C., Torchia, M. G., & McClarty, B. (1997). Hippocampal volume in women victimized by childhood sexual abuse. *Psychological Medicine, 27,* 951–959.

Steinberg, M. (1994). *Interviewer's guide to the structured clinical interview for DSM-IV dissociative disorders* (Rev. ed.). Washington, DC: American Psychiatric Press.

Steinberg, M. (1995). *Handbook for the assessment of dissociation: A clinical guide.* Washington, DC: American Psychiatric Press.

Stern, D. N. (1985). *The interpersonal world of the infant: A view from psychoanalysis and developmental psychology.* New York, NY: Basic Books, Inc.

Stickgold, R. (2002). EMDR: A putative neurobiological mechanism of action. *Journal of Clinical Psychology, 58,* 61–75.

Stickgold, R. (2008). Sleep-dependent memory processing. *Journal of EMDR Practice and Research, 2*(4), 2, 289–299.

Stien, P., & Kendall, J. (2004). *Complex PTSD in children: Brain and behavior. Psychological trauma & the developing brain neurologically based interventions for troubled children.* New York, NY: Haworth Press.

Stolbach, B. C. (1997). The children's dissociative experiences scale and posttraumatic symptom inventory: Rationale, development, and validation of a self-report measure. *Dissertation Abstracts International, 58*(3), 1548B.

Stolbach, B. C. (2005). Psychotherapy of a dissociative 8-year-old boy burned at age 3. *Psychiatric Annals, 35,* 685–694.

Teicher, M. H, Samson, J. A., Polcari, A., & C. E. McGreenery. (2006). Sticks, stones, and hurtful words: Relative effects of various forms of childhood maltreatment. *American Journal of Psychiatry, 163,* 993–1000.

Terr, L. C. (1991). Childhood trauma: An outline and overview. *American Journal of Psychiatry, 148,* 10–20.

Tinker, R. H., & Wilson, S. A. (1999). *Through the eyes of a child: EMDR with children.* New York, NY: W. W. Norton.

Trevarthen, C. (1989). Development of early social interactions and the affective regulation of brain growth. In C. von Euler, H. Fossberg, & H. Lagercrantz (Eds.), *Neurobiology of early infant behavior.* Wenner-Gren Center International Symposium Series, Vol. 55. New York, NY: Stockton Press.

Tronick, E. (2007). *The neurobehavioral and social-emotional development of infants and children.* New York, NY: W.W. Norton & Company.

Twombly, J. H., & Schwartz, R. C. (2008). The integration of internal family systems model and EMDR. In C. Forgash & M. Copeley (Eds.), *Healing the heart of trauma and dissociation with EMDR and ego state therapy* (pp. 295–311). New York, NY: Springer publishing.

van der Hart, O., Nijenhuis, E., Steele, K., & Brown, D. (2004). Trauma-related dissociation: conceptual clarity lost and found. *The Australian and New Zealand Journal of Psychiatry, 38,* 906–914.

van der Hart, O., Nijenhuis, E. R. S., & Steel, K. (2006). *The haunted self: Structural dissociation and the treatment of chronic traumatization.* New York, NY: W.W. Norton.

van der Kolk, B. A. (1996). Trauma and memory. In B. A. van der Kolk, A. C. McFarlane, & L. Weisaeth (Eds.), *Traumatic stress:The effects of overwhelming experience on the mind, body, and society* (pp. 279–302). New York, NY: Guildford Press.

van der Kolk, B. A. (2005). Developmental trauma disorder. *Psychiatric Annals, 35*(5), 401–408.

van der Kolk, B. A., & McFarlane, A. (1996). The black hole of trauma. In B. A. van der Kolk, B. A. McFarlane, & L. Weisaeth (Eds.), *Traumatic stress: The effects of overwhelming experience on mind, body, and society* (pp. 3–23). New York, NY: The Guilford press.

van der Kolk, B. A., McFarlane, A., & Weisaeth, L. (1996). *Traumatic stress: The effects of overwhelming experience on mind, body and society.* New York: Guilford Press.

van der Kolk, B., Pynoos, R. S., Cicchetti, D., Cloitre, M., D'Andrea, W., Ford, J. D., … Teicher, M. (2009, February 2). *Proposal to a developmental trauma disorder diagnosis for children and adolescents in DSMV.* Retrieved from www.traumacenter.org/announcements/DTD_papers_Oct_09.pdf

van der Kolk, B., van der Hart, O., & Marmar, C. (1996). Dissociation and information processing in posttraumatic stress disorder. In B. van der Kolk, A. McFarlane, & L. Weisaeth (Eds.), *Traumatic stress: The effects of overwhelming experience on mind, body and society* (pp. 303–327). New York, NY: Guilford Press.

Vermetten, E., Schmahl, C., Lindner, S., Loewenstein, R. J., & Bremner, J. D. (2006). Hippocampal and amygdalar volumes in dissociative identity disorder. *American Journal of Psychiatry, 163*, 1–8.

Vincent, M., & Pickering, M. R. (1988). Multiple personality disorder in childhood. *Canadian Journal of Psychiatry, 33*, 524–529.

Wadaa, N. N., Zaharim, N. M., & Alqashan, H. F. (2010). The use of EMDR in treatment of traumatized Iraqi children. *Digest of Middle East Studies, 19*, 26–36.

Wanders, F., Serra, M., & de Jongh, A. (2008). EMDR versus CBT for children with self-esteem and behavioral problems: A randomized controlled trial. *Journal of EMDR Practice and Research, 2*, 180–189.

Waters, F. S. (1996, November). *Quadri-theoretical model for the treatment of children with dissociation.* Paper presented at the meeting of the International Society for the Study of Dissociation, San Francisco, CA.

Waters, F. S. (2005a). When treatment fails with traumatized children…Why? *Journal of Trauma & Dissociation, 6*(1), 1–8.

Waters, F. S. (2005b). Recognizing dissociation in preschool children. *ISSTD News, 23*(4), 1–2, 4–5.

Waters, F. S. (2005c). Atypical DID adolescent case. *ISSTD News, 23*(3), 1–2, 4–5.

Waters, F. S. (2011). Ryan (8 to 10 years old) connecting with the body. In S. Wieland, (Ed.), *Dissociation in traumatized children & adolescents: Theory and clinical interventions* (pp. 141–195). New York, NY: Routledge.

Waters, F. S. (Executive Producer of ISSTD) (2007). *Trauma and dissociation in children. I: Behavioral impacts, II: Issues for interviewing, III: Guidelines for prosecutors.* Nevada City, CA: Cavalcade Productions.

Waters, F. S., Laddis, A., Soderstrom, B., Yehuda, N. (2007, November). *Differential diagnostic issues in dissociative and bipolar disorders in children & adults.* In F. S. Waters (Chair). Symposium conducted at the meeting of the 24th International Society for the Study of Trauma and Dissociation, Philadelphia, PA.

Waters, F. W., & Silberg, J. (1998). Therapeutic phases in the treatment of dissociative children. In J. L. Silberg (Ed.), *The dissociative child: Diagnosis, treatment, and management* (2nd ed., pp. 135–156). Lutherville, MD: The Sidran Press.

Watkins, J., & Watkins, H. (1997). *Ego states: Theory and therapy.* New York, NY: W.W. Norton and Company.

Weiss, M., Sutton, P. J., & Utecht, A. J. (1985). Multiple personality in a 10-year-old girl. *Journal of the American Academy of Child & Adolescent Psychiatry, 24*, 495–501.

Welch, M. (1988). *The holding time.* New York, NY: Fireside.

Wesselmann, D. (2007). *Overcoming obstacles to healthy bonds: Treating parent-child attachments with EMDR.* Paper presented at the XII annual EMDR International Association conference. Dallas, TX.

Wesselmann, D. (2010). *Facilitating the journey from fear to love: Using EMDR to treat insecure and disordered attachments in children and adults.* Paper presented at the XV annual EMDR International Association conference. Minneapolis, MN.

Wexler, B. E., Lyons, L., Lyons, H., & Mazure, C. M. (1997). Physical and sexual abuse during childhood and development of psychiatric illness during adulthood. *Journal of Nervous Mental Disorder, 185,* 522–524.

Whitfield, C. L., Shanta, R., Dube, S. R., Felitti, V. J., & Anda, R. (2005). Adverse childhood experiences and hallucinations. *Child Abuse & Neglect, 29,* 797–810.

Wieland, S. (2011). Dissociation in children and adolescents: What it is, how it presents, and how we can understand It. In S. Wieland (Ed.), *Dissociation in traumatized children and adolescents: Theory and clinical interventions* (pp. 1–27). New York, NY: Routledge.

Wieland, S. (Ed.). (2011). *Dissociation in traumatized children & adolescents: Theory and clinical interventions.* New York, NY: Routledge.

Yeager, C. A., & Lewis, D. O. (1996). The intergenerational transmission of violence and dissociation. *Child & Adolescent Psychiatric Clinics of North America, 5*(2), 393–430.

Zaghrout-Hodali, M., Alissa, F., & Dodgson, P. W. (2008). Building resilience and dismantling fear: EMDR group protocol with children in an area of ongoing trauma. *Journal of EMDR Practice and Research, 2,* 106–113.

Index